FIBER TO FABRIC

M. DAVID POTTER

Associate Professor in Business
San Francisco State College

BERNARD P. CORBMAN

Retail Distribution Department
New York City Community College
of Applied Arts and Sciences
Brooklyn, New York

SECOND EDITION

New York
Chicago
San Francisco
Dallas
Toronto
London

GREGG PUBLISHING DIVISION
McGraw-Hill Book Company, Inc.

PUBLISHED BY GREGG PUBLISHING DIVISION
McGraw-Hill Book Company, Inc.

Printed in the United States of America

PREFACE

PURPOSE

This book has been prepared to fulfill three purposes. One of these is to meet vocational needs for students expecting to enter into such business careers as retailing and to aid those already in the field. Another objective is to satisfy the needs of consumers. A third objective is to provide teachers with a basic, complete textile book that will satisfy the requirements of most teachers of a basic course in textiles. In fact, this text is easily adaptable for a methods course for teachers of textiles.

PLAN

For those who intend to enter areas of business that deal in textiles or textile products, this book provides all the basic information they may need. Its presentation does not require of the reader any prior knowledge of textiles; nor does it try to overwhelm the student with complicated technical descriptions. Rather, the information is presented in a clear, simplified manner. There is an abundance of diagrams and photographs to help make the written material even more meaningful.

For those now working with textiles or textile products, the information here is so organized as to make it possible for them to find easily whatever information they seek, whether it be properties of fibers, descriptions of fabrics, new finishes, new fibers, or the like. They need not read through a great many pages making constant cross references to find what they want.

The consumer is also given a great deal of consideration in the treatment of the general topic of textiles. He is told how to identify fibers and fabrics. The differential qualities of *all* fibers, including natural, man-made, and synthetic, are fully explained. Adequate consideration is given to the weaving and finishing of fabrics. Information is provided to assist the consumer in determining how well a particular fabric will serve his purposes through a discussion of the properties of the fibers and their blends into various fabrics. Also of particular interest to the consumer are specific facts to be considered when purchasing such items as sheets, towels, hosiery, and rugs. Consideration is also given to the care of fabrics and clothing as well as a chapter on stain removal.

TEACHABILITY

Present and future teachers of elementary textiles will find that this text presents the subject in a very teachable manner. The text is replete with visual material. Each chapter has projects and questions that provide a basis for review and further investigation. Beginning with the examination of the structure and appearance of all the fibers, there follow a discussion and comparison of the important properties of the fibers. Identification of these fibers is the next logical step. Using cotton fiber as an example, consideration is given to the spinning of fiber into yarn and weaving the yarn into fabric. The discussion continues with consideration of the latest finishing processes— dyeing, printing, and so on. The text then devotes separate chapters to discussions of each of the seventeen fibers: their production, their processing from fiber to fabric, their finishing, their blending, judging the fabrics, and glossary of fabrics. Merchandise information is provided both for motivation and as a source of pertinent consumer education information.

IMPROVEMENTS IN THIS EDITION

This second edition offers much new material. Improved methods of manufacture and finishing of older fibers and fabrics are discussed. New fibers discussed are acetate, nylon, Orlon, Acrilan, Dynel, X-51, Dacron, Vicara, Vinyon N, saran, and Fiberglas. The information includes previously unpublished data. It also contains discussions of the advantages and disadvantages of fabrics made from blends, such as Nylon-acetate, Orlon-wool, and the like.

One chapter is devoted to a thorough comparison of all the fibers with each other. This includes such practical data as the relative strength, warmth, absorbency, washability, resistance to mildew, and so on, of the natural, man-made, and synthetic fibers. A summary chart of these data is also included.

The revision includes more complete data on such merchandise as sheets and towels. The chapter on hosiery has also been rewritten and provides the latest information on women's nylon hosiery, its manufacture, critical analysis of proper hosiery construction and fitting, and size charts.

ACKNOWLEDGMENTS

Acknowledgments are due the following:

C. W. Bendigo, American Cyanamid Company; Ruth Leigh, Cannon Mills, Inc.; R. W. Kennedy, Carbide and Carbon Chemicals Company; J. L. Bixby, The Chemstrand Corporation; Dr. Claudius T. Murchison, President of Cotton Textile

Institute, Inc.; G. E. Ferris, Deere & Company; W. H. Radebaugh, E. I. du Pont de Nemours & Company; Dr. William E. Coughlin, Director of Textile Laboratories of Good Housekeeping Institute; Doris Kimball, *Hosiery and Underwear Review*; L. A. Beers, President of the Institute of Carpet Manufacturers of America; Harry S. Radcliffe, Secretary of the Linen Trade Association; R. C. Ball, Secretary of the National Association of Hosiery Manufacturers; Irene L. Blunt, Secretary of the National Federation of Textiles; S. Stambaugh and J. W. Dougherty, Owens-Corning Fiberglas Corporation; H. S. Ortgies, The Saran Yarns Company; W. J. Martin and D. A. Spencer, United States Department of Agriculture; J. H. Jordan and J. H. Karrh, Virginia Carolina Chemical Company; W. Jaeger, The Wool Bureau, Inc.; S. C. Carse, President of York Street Flax Spinning Company.

M. DAVID POTTER
BERNARD P. CORBMAN

CONTENTS

1 | TEXTILE FIBERS

Under the Microscope

Some knowledge of textile fibers is necessary to everyone because textiles have such an important bearing on our daily lives. From earliest times, man has used woven fabrics for covering, warmth, personal adornment, and even to display personal wealth. Fabrics both useful and beautiful have been used as draperies in primitive thatched hut and in cold stone palace to provide warmth as well as decoration.

Today, fabrics are still used for these two main purposes. Everyone is an ultimate consumer of textile materials. He uses textiles in some form even if he is not the direct purchaser. Included among consumers are merchandisers of many types, from the wholesale textile manufacturer and merchant to the retail store sales force. Many of the industries—for example, the automobile industry—are important consumers of textiles in various forms. Other consumers are homemakers, dressmakers, interior decorators, and retail store customers, as well as students who are studying for these and various other occupations and professions in which a knowledge of textiles is of major importance.

The merchant, particularly, and all those who work for him must be thoroughly familiar with the merchandise they are handling if they wish to be successful in the mercantile field. Only thorough knowledge will prevent the mistakes that are too often made in buying and selling.

Reasons for Studying Textiles. A study of textiles will show, for example, why certain fabrics are more durable and therefore more serviceable for specific purposes. It will explain why certain fabrics make cool wearing apparel as well as give an impression of coolness when used as decoration. The quality of cleanliness, also, may be estimated before purchasing, when that is an important factor.

Complete knowledge of textiles will facilitate an intelligent appraisal of standards and brands of merchandise and will develop the ability to distinguish quality in fabrics and, in turn, to appreciate the proper uses for the different qualities. As a result, the consumer merchant and the consumer customer will know how to buy and what to buy, and salespeople will know how to render good service to those consumers who have not had the advantage of a formal course in textiles.

In the study of textiles, the initial interest of the student will become an absorbing one when he discovers the natural fascination of fabrics and their cultural associations, particularly when factual study is supplemented by the handling of actual textile materials. The subject will seem worth while to the student when he becomes familiar with illustrative specimens and fabrics, and handles and compares the raw materials of which fabrics are made as well as the finished consumers' goods.

Sequence of Fabric Construction. In beginning the study of textiles, the student should have in his hand a sample of a *woven fabric*. He should examine the sample closely. He should note that it is constructed by interlacing sets of yarns that run lengthwise and crosswise. It is from the interlacing, or weaving, of yarns that textile materials are made. A close examination of any one of these yarns will reveal the fibrous substance from which the yarn is made. Such yarns comprise a multitude of fibers or filaments that have been separated, made parallel, overlapped, and twisted together by various processes.

There is a logical development of raw material into finished consumers' goods. Though the student may hold in his hand a woven fabric as the consumer sees it, and as it appears when ready for mercantile use, he must study textile materials in the interesting sequence of "fiber to yarn to fabric" to understand the construction and ultimate qualities of the fabrics with which he will become familiar.

The steps in the manufacture of fabrics, from raw material to finished goods, may be summarized thus:

1. Fiber, which is spun (or twisted) into yarn or directly felted into fabric.
2. Yarn, which is woven or knitted or braided into fabric.
3. Fabric, which by various finishing processes becomes finished consumers' goods.

The scope of this development from raw material into finished consumers' goods is also indicated by the following sketch, which should help the student to visualize the entire field of textile manufacture—from fiber to yarn to fabric to finished goods.

FIBER   YARN   FABRIC   FINISHED
                                                        GOODS
|___SPINNING_____| |_WEAVING_| |_FINISHING_____|
|___FELTING_____| |_KNITTING_| PROCESSES

Kinds of Fibers.

The textile industry uses many different kinds of fibers as its raw materials. Some of these fibers were known and used by mankind in the earlier years of civilization as well as in modern times. Other fibers have become important in recent years. New man-made and synthetic fibers are being produced and tested daily. Some fibers have assumed importance from time to time because of a specific quality, such as low cost production, which is always a factor in the business world.

In this text, seventeen fibers are classified into three general groups: natural, man-made, and synthetic. The first, and original, group consists of the *natural fibers,* some produced by plants, others by animals, which have been known and used for thousands of years.

The second group consists of the *man-made fibers,* so called because man has taken natural materials, such as cellulose and protein (cotton linters, wood pulp, corn), and transformed their form and certain other characteristics into long and short fibers as desired.

The third group consists of *synthetic fibers,* which are so named because they do not occur in nature in any manner whatsoever. Man has taken separate chemical elements, such as carbon, oxygen, hydrogen, and others, and synthesized them into new textile fibers with many characteristics that were lacking in the natural and man-made fibers.

(In this text, we have differentiated between man-made and synthetic fibers to help the student understand the differences between the new fibers and the reasons for their various characteristics. But in many other publications, the student will notice that the two terms, man-made and synthetic, are used interchangeably.)

These three general groups and their sources of classification are shown on page 4.

	Fibers	Sources or Classification
Natural fibers:	Cotton	Cotton plant (cellulose)
	Linen	Flax plant (cellulose)
	Wool	Sheep (protein)
	Silk	Silkworm (protein)
Man-made fibers:	Viscose rayon	Cotton plant (cellulose)
	Cuprammonium rayon	Cotton plant (cellulose)
	Acetate	Tree (cellulose)
	Vicara	Corn (protein)
Synthetic fibers:	Nylon	Polyamide
	Orlon	Acrylic
	Acrilan	Acrylic
	Dynel	Acrylic
	X-51	Acrylic
	Dacron	Polyester
	Vinyon N	Vinyl resin
	Saran	Vinylidene chloride
	Fiberglas	Glass

Additional animal fibers—such as camel's hair, mohair, cashmere, alpaca, llama, and vicuna—as well as certain vegetable and mineral fibers, also lend themselves to various uses in the textile industry.

Composition and Structure of Fibers. Each textile fiber has its own distinctive structural markings that, under a microscope with a magnification of at least 100, supply an absolute identification of the fiber. Certain general observations also make it possible sometimes to identify fibers without the use of a microscope. These differences in structure determine the various characteristics of the different fibers and explain why some fibers are to be preferred to others for certain uses. All illustrations in this chapter show both the cross-section and longitudinal views of the various fibers as seen under a microscope.

• *Cotton.* Unlike other fibers obtained from plants, the cotton fiber is a single elongated cell. Under the microscope, it resembles a collapsed, spirally twisted tube with a rough surface. The thin cell wall of the fiber has from 200 to 400 turns of natural twist, or convolutions, to the inch. The fiber appears flat, twisted, and ribbonlike, with a wide inner canal (the lumen) and a granular effect. Chemically, the fiber contains about 90 per cent cellulose and about 6 per cent moisture; the remainder consists of natural impurities.

Cotton   Mercerized Cotton

The outer surface of the fiber is covered with a protective waxlike coating, which gives the fiber a somewhat adhesive quality.

Because of the natural twist in cotton fiber, the fibers may be easily spun into yarn. Some cotton fibers, however, look different under the microscope and do not have this natural twist. Such fibers have been subjected to the commercially important process of mercerization. (See Chapter 6.)

By this process of mercerization, the naturally flat, twisted cotton fiber swells and becomes straight, smooth, and round. The straightness of the fiber causes light to be reflected on the smooth surface and produces a lustrous effect that is commercially valuable. The resultant fabric is called *mercerized cotton.*

• *Flax.* Under the microscope, the flax fiber shows hairlike cylindrical filaments with fine pointed ends. The filaments are cemented together at intervals in the form of markings, or nodes, by a gummy substance called *pectin.* The long flax filaments contain a lumen, or inner canal, which shows as a narrow line. The fiber resembles a straight, smooth bamboo stick, with

Illustrations this page courtesy U.S. Testing Co.; U.S. Dept. of Agriculture.

Flax

its joints producing a slight natural unevenness that cannot be eliminated. Chemically, the flax fiber is composed of about 70 per cent cellulose and about 25 per cent pectin; the remainder consists of woody tissue and ash.

From such fibers, linen yarns are produced that, to the naked eye, appear smooth, straight, compact, and lustrous. Linen fibers are more brittle than cotton fibers.

• *Wool*. Wool fiber is irregular and roughly cylindrical, tapered at the end, and multicellular in structure. Under the microscope, a cross section shows three fundamental layers. The epidermis, or outer layer, consists of scales or flattened plates, ranging from 1,000 to 4,000 to an inch. These scales give the fiber its cohesive quality. They vary in type, from those having straight edges to those having marked wavy serrations. The finer, softer, warmer fibers have the more numerous straight-edged scales. The thicker, coarser, less warm fibers have the fewer, rougher scales.

The second layer, the cortex, is the main fiber body, which gives strength and elasticity to the fiber. The cortex consists of intermediate cells that hold the color pigment.

The innermost layer is the medulla, which consists of large air-filled cells. The medulla is discernible only in coarse and medium wools and only under high magnification. It is the central canal, varying in appearance from a narrow to a broad line or from a continuous to an interrupted line. Some wool fibers that have no cortical layer are compensated with a larger proportion of medullary cells; this fact lessens the affinity for dyes, because the medulla has more fat than has the rest of the fiber. The finer wools, having no medulla, absorb dyes more readily.

Two striking characteristics of wool fiber are its susceptibility to heat and its felting property, which is caused by the horny epidermal scales. Because of this felting property, only pressure, heat, and moisture are required to make wool fibers into the type of fabric called *felt*.

Chemically, wool is the only natural fiber that contains sulphur. It is composed of the following basic elements in these approximate proportions: carbon, 49 per cent; oxygen, 24 per cent; nitrogen, 16 per cent; hy-

Wool

Courtesy Am. Woolen Co.; U.S. Testing Co.

Courtesy U.S. Testing Co.; U.S. Dept. of Agri.

Silk   Wild, or Tussah, Silk

drogen, 7 per cent; sulphur, 4 per cent. These elements combine to form a protein known as *keratin*.

• *Silk*. The raw silk fiber as it comes from the cultivated cocoon is called the *bave*. Under the microscope this bave appears somewhat elliptical and is composed of the *fibroin*, which consists of two filaments, each of which is called a *brin*, held together by a gummy substance known as *sericin*. This sericin gives the bave a rather uneven surface. As the sericin is removed by hot water, the two filaments appear clearly as fine, lustrous, uniform, transparent rods.

Wild silk, or tussah silk, may be distinguished from cultivated silk by its coarse thick form, which appears flattened. Cultivated silk is a narrow fiber with no markings. Wild silk is a broad fiber with fine, wavy longitudinal lines running across its surface, giving it a dark hue under the microscope.

Chemically, the silk fibroin and sericin are composed of approximately 95 per cent protein and about 5 per cent wax, fat, salts, and ash.

• *Rayon* is a man-made fiber derived from cellulose, an inert, formless white substance found in the cell walls of all plant life. There are three varieties of rayon: viscose, cuprammonium, and nitrocellulose.

Nitrocellulose, the third kind of rayon, is not manufactured to any great extent because of the high cost of the chemicals. In the history of man-made fibers, however, nitrocellulose rayon is important because it was the first to be produced.

In general, rayon fiber is easily recognized under the microscope by its glasslike luster and uniform diameter. (The appearance of fine pepperlike particles on a cross-section view is an indication that the rayon has been delustered.) The rayon filaments differ according to the process used in their manufacture.

Viscose, under the microscope, shows many threadlike longitudinal lines that are spiral and somewhat glossy. A cross-section view shows a serrated edge.

Cuprammonium shows no markings. It is fine and glossy and resembles silk more closely than other fibers. The cross-section appearance is small and nearly round.

• *Acetate* is a compound of cellulose that possesses different qualities from those of viscose rayon. The fibers are fine and have line markings. They are less lustrous than the fibers of viscose or cuprammonium rayon and sometimes show a central groove under the microscope. The cross-section appearance is bulbous, with indentations. The resultant fabric is called acetate or cellulose acetate.

Illustrations this page courtesy U.S. Testing Co.

• *Nylon* is a synthetic known chemically as a polyamide. The fibers are very fine, round, smooth, and translucent. They can be highly lustrous, semidull, or dull, depending on the amount of luster desired.

Orlon (staple)

• *Orlon* is a synthetic known chemically as an acrylic. The fiber can be produced in both continuous filament and staple (short) forms. The properties of the fiber in the two forms are different in certain respects. The cross-section shape of Orlon acrylic fiber is dog-bone. The longitudinal shape is somewhat flat and smooth. The fiber can be lustrous or dull as desired.

(Continuous filament and staple forms of fibers are explained in the next chapter.)

Illustrations this page courtesy E. I. du Pont de Nemours & Co.

Orlon (continuous filament)

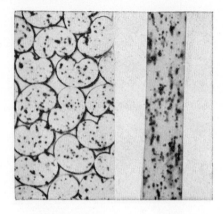

• *Acrilan* is another acrylic. The fiber is produced in staple form only. Its microscopic appearance is very much like that of Orlon. Acrilan has a semidull, cream-colored appearance.

Courtesy The Chemstrand Corp.

• *Dynel* is partly an acrylic and partly a vinyl chloride. It is produced in staple form only. The fibers are flat and somewhat smooth, but they are artificially crimped.

Courtesy Carbide & Carbon Chem. Co.

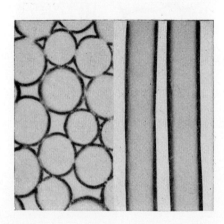

• *X–51* is a wholly acrylic fiber. It is produced in both continuous filament and staple forms. The filament and staple fibers have different properties in certain respects. The fibers are round, smooth, and semidull. (Also registered under trade names of Creslan and Cyania.)

Courtesy American Cyanamid Co.

• *Dacron* is a synthetic fiber known chemically as a polyester. The fiber is straight, smooth, and almost perfectly round. It has a characteristic speckled appearance that is visible both in the longitudinal and cross-section views.

Courtesy E. I. du Pont de Nemours & Co.

• *Vicara* is a man-made fiber. It is produced from zein, a corn protein. The fiber is somewhat round and smooth. It is always cut into staple of 0.5 to 6 inches in length.

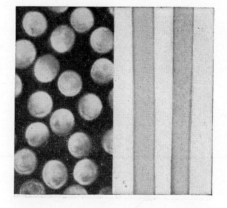

Courtesy Virginia Carolina Chem. Corp.

• *Vinyon N* is a synthetic known chemically as a vinyl resin. The fibers are extremely fine, some being produced as fine as 0.35 denier. The fiber is dog-bone shaped in the cross-section view. The longitudinal view is somewhat flat, straight, and smooth.

Courtesy Carbide & Carbon Chem. Co.

• *Saran* is a synthetic known chemically as a vinylidene chloride. The fiber is smooth, round, and translucent.

Courtesy Saran Yarns Co.

• *Fiberglas* is made of glass. The fiber is smooth, round, translucent, highly lustrous, and quite flexible.

Courtesy Owens-Corning Fiberglas Corp.

2 | TEXTILE FIBERS

Comparative Qualities

To identify any fiber and make a satisfactory choice of the textile desired for a particular use, the consumer must understand the separate properties of each of the fibers. This knowledge will increase the consumer's use of the finished goods. The commercial value of any fiber depends largely on the extent to which it possesses certain properties or qualities. Some of the most important properties are tensile strength, elasticity, fineness, cohesiveness, and sufficient length—all of which facilitate the process of spinning into yarn. Fibers also must have some degree of porosity to permit the absorption of bleaching and dyeing liquids. These various properties are studied in the following order.

1. Length
2. Luster
3. Strength
4. Elasticity
5. Heat conductivity
6. Absorbency
7. Cleanliness and washability
8. Reaction to bleaches
9. Reaction to heat
10. Effect of mildew
11. Effect of light and outdoor exposure
12. Reaction to alkalies and acids
13. Affinity for dyes

Length of Fiber. When fibers are spun into yarn, they are made to lie parallel, and are drawn out and twisted to form a continuous yarn. If the fibers are long, there will be fewer ends in the twisted yarn. Fewer surface

The longer fibers produce the smoother yarns; the shorter fibers cause more surface ends.

ends result in a smoother fabric, which naturally has less attraction for dirt particles. The smooth surface also helps to give an attractive luster to the finished cloth. Short fibers cause more surface ends and more points of potential separation, thus making a relatively weaker fabric.

The length of the fiber, termed *length of staple,* is therefore of fundamental importance in textiles. This fact has given rise to the expression, "The longer the fiber, the stronger the yarn." This statement, however, is true only when fibers within a single group are compared; for example, two or more wool fibers or two or more cotton fibers. A comparison of wool with cotton reveals that the wool fiber, although longer than the cotton fiber, is not stronger.

Long-staple yarns within each group of fibers produce stronger, smoother, more serviceable fabrics that cost more than the less durable fabrics made from short-staple yarns. In wool, for example, the short-staple fiber is used in the manufacture of woolens, and the longer staple is reserved for worsteds. Worsteds are considered more serviceable. A similar distinction is found in every textile fiber.

The sequence of fibers according to comparative length of staple is as follows:

1. All the man-made and synthetic fibers may be made as long or as short as desired. The length of the fiber is dependent on its ultimate use. The long filament is known in the textile industry as continuous filament fiber and is used to produce smooth-surfaced fabrics with no loose ends. The short filament is called staple or spun fiber and is used for soft, fuzzy fabrics.

Dynel, Acrilan, and Vicara are the only man-made or synthetic fibers that are produced as staple fibers only.

2. *Silk.* Raw silk fiber from cultivated cocoons is the longest of natural fibers. It consists of a continuous fiber that varies in length from 1,200 to 4,000 feet. It produces a smooth, lustrous fabric.

3. *Linen.* The flax fiber is longer than the cotton fiber and the wool fiber, ranging from 12 to 20 inches. This length accounts for the absence of lint in linen fabrics.

4. *Wool.* The length of the average woolen staple varies from 1 to 3 inches. Worsted yarns are made from staple fibers that are from 3 to 8 inches in length.

5. *Cotton.* Cotton fiber is the shortest of all fibers, varying from $\frac{1}{2}$ inch to $2\frac{1}{2}$ inches. The bulk of the domestic cotton crop ranges from $\frac{3}{4}$ inch to $1\frac{1}{2}$ inches in length.

Luster of Fibers. Luster is produced by the reflection of light from a smooth surface. A lustrous effect in fabrics adds to their attractiveness, and in some cases may be absolutely necessary, depending on the purpose of the fabric. On the other hand, luster may not be desired, as in napped or crepe surfaces. But an appropriate lustrous effect is a generally desired quality.

Degrees of luster are obtained in several ways. The use of long-staple yarns produces a smooth surface, which will have a natural luster. The use of caustic soda in the mercerizing process is a chemical method of producing luster. The satin weave and certain finishing processes also are used for this purpose.

The luster of a fiber has an important effect on its ultimate use. A fabric such as satin is expected to have a high luster and therefore should be made of a highly lustrous fiber, while a fabric such as flannel is expected to be dull and therefore should be made of a dull fiber.

The sequence of fibers according to luster is as follows:

1. *Rayon, acetate, nylon, Orlon, Dacron, Fiberglas.* These fibers could have a very high luster. In man-made and synthetic fibers, however, luster can be controlled to a great extent.

2. *Silk.* The luster of silk is dependent on the amount of surrounding sericin, or gum, that is removed from the surface of the filaments. The degree of luster is generally high.

3. *Linen.* The luster of the flax fiber is apparent at all times. This characteristic is helpful in identifying the fiber.

4. *Vinyon N* and *saran.* These fibers have a soft luster.

5. *Vicara, Acrilan, Dynel,* and *X-51.* These fibers are semidull. This property contributes to such uses as substituting for and blending with wool.

6. *Cotton.* Cotton generally does not have much natural luster. However, the degree of luster varies with the type of cotton: the better the quality of cotton, the higher the luster.

7. *Wool.* Wool has crimp and a serrated or scaly surface. The better quality of wool has a great amount of crimp and serrations, which, in turn, reduces the amount of luster possible. Therefore, a good quality of wool does not have natural luster. In fact, the better the quality of wool, the lower the luster. The converse of that is also true: the higher the luster of wool, the poorer the quality.

Some fibers that belong to the wool group show some degree of luster; these are the hair fibers, such as mohair, vicuna, camel's hair, alpaca, and cashmere.

Strength of Fibers. Fibers differ in their resistance to tearing apart when subjected to tension. The serviceability and durability of a fabric, therefore, cannot be determined by the length of staple alone. Tensile strength is a prime necessity in fibers if the resultant fabric is to stand the strain of wear.

The sequence of fibers according to tensile strength is as follows:

1. *Fiberglas.* This is by far the strongest of all the textile fibers. By way of comparison, it is about twice as strong as cotton and about five times as strong as wool. However, its use is still limited because it lacks many other properties important for consumer products.

2. *Nylon.* Nylon was originally called the miracle fiber because of its great strength. Although it loses about 10 per cent of its strength when wet, it still is stronger than other fibers when wet.

3. *Silk.* This fiber has long been known to be the strongest of the natural fibers. When the extremely small diameter of the silk fiber, which varies from .001 to .005 inch, is considered, silk is the strongest of all textile fibers. The breaking strength of raw silk is equivalent to nearly one-third of the breaking strength of the best iron wire of the same size.

4. *Linen.* The flax fiber is second in strength to silk and is especially durable. Linen gains strength when wet.

5. *Orlon.* This is one of the strongest of synthetic fibers. When wet, Orlon loses only about 7 to 10 per cent of its strength.

6. *Dacron.* Although ranked sixth in this list, Dacron is not a weak fiber. Actually, it is only slightly weaker than nylon. It loses less strength when wet than does Orlon. In fact, its loss in strength when wet is almost nil.

7. *Cotton.* This natural fiber has good strength. When wet, its strength may increase temporarily by as much as 30 per cent. Cotton may be permanently strengthened by mercerization.

8. *X-51.* This fiber comes in two forms: continuous filament and staple. The filament is the stronger of the two. The staple is slightly weaker than Acrilan and Dynel.

9. *Vinyon N.* This is a fairly strong fiber.

10. *Acrilan* and *Dynel.* These two fibers are equal in strength. They are two to three times as strong as wool, and since many of their other properties are similar to those of wool, both Acrilan and Dynel are considered very good for blending with and substituting for wool. These fibers are not weakened when wet.

11. *Saran.* The strength of saran has been demonstrated by a man standing on a suspended window screen made of this fiber. Since saran is virtually nonabsorbent, it is not weakened by water.

12. *Rayon.* Viscose and cuprammonium rayons are approximately equal in strength. The strength of rayon fiber is conditioned by its moisture content. When wet, rayon loses from 40 to 70 per cent of its natural strength, but this strength is completely regained when the fiber is dry. Rayon therefore is not considered a weak fiber because it is judged by its natural strength when dry, which is one-half to one-third that of silk.

13. *Wool.* Wool has the lowest tensile strength of the natural fibers. However, springiness and resilience actually increase its wearing strength above some of the other fibers. While wet, wool may lose temporarily as much as 25 per cent of its strength.

14. *Vicara.* Vicara, which looks and feels very much like wool, has a strength closely comparable to that of wool. When wet, Vicara loses about 50 per cent of its strength, but regains it when it dries.

15. *Acetate.* This is the weakest of the fibers. While wet, it may temporarily lose up to 45 per cent of its strength.

Elasticity of Fibers. Elasticity includes several factors. True elasticity requires that the fiber can be stretched and that it will tend to return to its original size. The less strain necessary to cause the fiber to stretch, the more elastic it is.

When a fiber is elastic, the yarn is springy; and the resultant fabric will be resilient. This resiliency causes the fabric to be wrinkle-resistant, the resistance varying according to the degree of elasticity inherent in the fiber. Since elastic fibers resist tearing, this quality of elasticity contributes to the strength of a fabric. It also permits materials to drape well on the human figure. Elasticity facilitates the spinning process because inelastic fibers break more easily than elastic fibers.

Fibers that are naturally inelastic, however, can be given a degree of elas-

Elastic fibers produce springy yarns, and the resultant fabric is resilient and wrinkle-resistant.

Comparative elasticity of silk and cotton may be tested by attaching silk and cotton yarns to a fixed object. Hold both yarns taut Pull slowly until each yarn breaks. Cotton breaks first, as it lacks elasticity. Silk breaks only after considerable stretching because of its natural elasticity.

ticity by reducing them to short staple. Short-staple yarns contribute softness to a fabric, helping to make the fabric somewhat crease-resistant; but some strength is sacrificed. A chemical finish can be used to obtain crease resistance. This method is preferable because it does not affect the strength of the fiber.

According to this broad definition of elasticity, it is difficult to establish an absolute range for the fibers. However, the following generalities may be considered adequate for the average consumer needs.

1. *Vicara.* Vicara can be stretched 40 per cent of its original length without breaking. It is also extremely resilient and wrinkle-resistant.

2. *Nylon.* Nylon is extremely elastic. It has an unusual ability to return to its original shape after a great deal of stretching. It does not wrinkle easily and is very resilient.

3. *Wool.* Wool is one of the most elastic fibers, certainly the most elastic of the natural fibers. It can be stretched about 30 per cent of its original length without breaking. It is known to be resilient. The better qualities do not wrinkle readily.

4. *Vinyon N.* Vinyon N has a high degree of stretchability and recovery.

5. *Saran.* This fiber behaves similarly to Vinyon N.

6. *Silk.* Silk is the second most elastic of the natural fibers. However, with too much strain, it will never recover to its original size. It has excellent resilience.

7. *Dynel.* Dynel is rather elastic and has excellent resilience.

8. *Dacron.* While Dacron is less elastic than the above fibers, it is known for its excellent resilience and wrinkle resistance.

9. *Acetate.* The elasticity of acetate is fairly good. It is also fairly wrinkle-resistant and resilient. Acetate fabrics can be processed to be even more wrinkle-resistant.

10. *Rayon.* Viscose and cuprammonium rayons have approximately equal properties in this category. Their elasticity is fair. They are not very wrinkle-resistant. To overcome this, viscose fabrics can be processed to impart a good degree of wrinkle resistance. Spun-rayon fabrics tend to be more naturally wrinkle-resistant because of their soft texture.

11. *Orlon* and *Acrilan.* These two fibers have approximately equal elasticity. They are about four times as elastic as cotton. Both are very resilient.

12. *X–51.* This fiber follows closely behind Orlon and Acrilan fibers in its elastic and resilient properties.

13. *Cotton.* Cotton has virtually no elasticity; therefore, fabrics made from cotton wrinkle easily. When a piece of cotton fabric is creased with the fingernail, the crease is retained; silk and wool are not so easily affected. Fingernail creasing may serve as a test, therefore, to distinguish silk and wool from cotton and linen. Cotton fabrics can be processed to be wrinkle-resistant.

14. *Linen.* Linen is the least elastic and resilient of the natural fibers. Linen fabrics wrinkle and crease easily; however, they too can be processed to improve their wrinkle resistance.

15. *Fiberglas.* Fiberglass is not elastic, but this does not imply that it is stiff. Fiberglas fabrics drape well.

Heat Conductivity of Fibers.

The quality of a fiber to conduct heat, or to act as a nonconductor of heat and therefore serve an insulative purpose, has great significance in textiles. The degree of heat conductivity determines whether fabrics are suitable for winter or for summer use.

In addition to the heat conductivity inherent in the fiber, the weaving, knitting, and finishing processes affect this quality. When a fabric is loosely constructed, for example, it has air spaces, which have an insulative property. The captive air pockets contained in a napped surface add warmth to a fabric.

The sequence of fibers according to heat conductivity is as follows:

1. *Linen.* The flax fiber is the best conductor of heat. Linen fabric is therefore most suitable for summer apparel, as it allows the heat of the body to escape easily and quickly.

2. *Cotton.* Cotton fiber is a good conductor of heat. Cotton fabrics are also suitable for summer clothing. The surface of the cloth has much to do with the degree of heat conductivity.

3. *Cuprammonium rayon.* In addition to the fact that cuprammonium rayon is inherently a good heat conductor, it also lends itself to sheer and therefore cool fabrics because the yarn can be made extremely fine in denier.

4. *Viscose rayon.* The primary reason that this fiber is not as cool as cuprammonium is the comparatively heavier yarn that is produced in its manufacture.

5. *Acetate.* Acetate is a poorer conductor of heat. Because it does not absorb much moisture, it has a tendency to feel warm and clammy on warm, humid days.

6. *Nylon.* Nylon fabrics seem to have the peculiar property of being cold in winter and warm in summer. Actually, this is dependent on whether filament or staple is used and on the construction of the fabric. The spun staple nylon has thousands of air pockets that act as an excellent insulator; therefore, the staple nylon fabrics will be warm. The warmth or coolness of the filament fabrics is dependent on the porosity of the weave and on the amount of moisture in the air and on the body, for nylon reacts to moisture in the same way as acetate does.

7. *Dacron.* Dacron is being promoted for men's summer suiting for several reasons, one of which seems to be its relative coolness for that purpose. It has outstanding wrinkle resistance and crease retention (wet or dry), good draping quality, and resistance to shrinking or stretching.

8. *X–51.* X–51 has high bulking power. This means that the fiber, particularly in staple form, would produce warmer fabrics than the preceding fibers. On the other hand, since extremely fine deniers can be produced in the filament form of X–51, it also is possible to obtain very sheer and therefore cool fabrics.

9. *Orlon, Acrilan,* and *Dynel.* These fibers are warm for two reasons: their chemical composition, which is principally acrylic, is a poor conductor; and the cross-section shape is dog-bone and therefore rather flat. As a result, these fibers have a good covering and bulking property, which provides warmth.

10. *Silk.* Silk is a natural protein fiber, and therefore a nonconductor of heat, and may be used for winter clothing. Some people consider silk to be good as a cool summer fabric. However, the coolness of a silk garment for summer wear is directly dependent on the lightness in weight and the sheerness of the fabric: the lighter and sheerer the silk fabric, the cooler; the heavier the silk fabric, the warmer.

11. *Vicara.* This fiber is warm because it is composed of a protein. In fact, its warmth is considered to be closely comparable to wool.

12. *Wool.* Wool is very warm for two reasons: it has a scaly surface that provides air pockets for insulation, and it is composed of a protein, which is a nonconductor of heat.

Fiberglas, Vinyon N, and *saran* have not been included in this sequence of heat conductivity because their properties are unique with regard to heat. While Fiberglas filaments conduct heat, the Fiberglas staple acts as an excellent insulator because of the thousands of air pockets it traps. For this reason, Fiberglas staple batting is used for insulating refrigerators, stoves, and houses.

Vinyon N and saran have very low melting points. Vinyon N softens at 170 degrees Fahrenheit; saran softens at 167 degrees Fahrenheit.

Absorbency of Fibers.   The quickness with which a fabric absorbs moisture and gives it up again in evaporation has an important bearing on health and comfort. Textile fibers vary in their natural absorptive capacity, but absorbency may be increased by fabric construction or by a finishing process. A loosely constructed fabric or one with a napped surface, for example, is more absorptive than a smooth-surfaced fabric.

1. *Wool.* Wool fibers absorb moisture quickly and hold a large amount, allowing it to evaporate slowly. In fact, wool can absorb up to 20 per cent of its weight in water without feeling damp, and 50 per cent of its weight in water without dripping. When wet, wool does not stick to the body and is ideal for outer wear on cold, damp days.

2. *Silk.* Silk fiber absorbs moisture readily and, like wool, can hold much water without feeling wet.

3. *Rayon.* The absorbency and drying qualities of both viscose and cuprammonium rayons are closely akin to those of silk.

4. *Vicara.* Of all the man-made and synthetic fibers that resemble and feel like wool, Vicara absorbs water more nearly like wool than any of the other fibers.

5. *Linen.* Linen absorbs moisture more quickly and dries more quickly than cotton. For this reason, coupled with its strength and hygienic characteristics, it is excellent for towels and handkerchiefs.

6. *Cotton.* Cotton absorbs water rather well, but does not dry very quickly.

7. *Acrilan.* Acrilan does not absorb as much moisture as cotton, but it dries more quickly.

8. *Acetate.* Acetate does not absorb much moisture: only 14 per cent of its weight at a 95 per cent relative humidity. Therefore, on warm humid days, the moisture clings to the surface of acetate, and it feels uncomfortable. Acetate clings to the body and feels warm and clammy. However, it dries quickly. In these respects it behaves much like nylon.

9. *Nylon.* Nylon absorbs about half as much moisture as acetate. It also feels very clammy and uncomfortable on warm, humid days. Filament nylon

garments dry very rapidly, often in one hour. Staple nylon yarn dries more slowly. Water droplets cling to the surfaces of the short pieces of nylon fiber, and have difficulty evaporating from within the central portion of the yarn. Garments made of spun nylon yarn may take as long as twenty-four hours to dry.

10. *Orlon.* Orlon absorbs very little moisture and dries quickly.

11. *X–51.* The properties of this fiber in filament and staple forms are not always the same. However, since this fiber is an acrylic, its water absorbency probably falls somewhere within the range of Orlon and Dacron.

12. *Dynel.* This fiber absorbs very little water and dries rapidly.

13. *Dacron.* Dacron absorbs a very small amount of water and dries very rapidly.

14. *Vinyon N.* The absorbency of Vinyon N is closely comparable to Dacron.

15. *Fiberglas* and *saran.* The most that can be stated for these two fibers is that their surfaces get wet.

Cleanliness and Washability of Fibers.

The consumer is interested in knowing what textiles are hygienic, how long a garment may be expected to remain clean, and whether it will require unusual care when laundering or dry cleaning is necessary. The fibers that show smooth surfaces under the microscope produce fabrics that are easy to launder; thus garments made of linen, silk, and rayon wash easily. A napped surface on any one of these materials makes it necessary to give the garment more care in washing.

The fact that a fiber does not absorb much water does not imply that the fiber is unhygienic. Actually, those fibers that do not absorb much water usually do not absorb dirt particles and have relatively smooth surfaces. The water then washes the dirt off the surface, and the fiber dries quickly.

The sequence of fibers according to comparative cleanliness is as follows:

1. *Fiberglas.* A fabric made of Fiberglas filament yarn may be washed clean by either rinsing in water or even wiping with a damp cloth. Neither dirt nor water affects Fiberglas because both remain on the surface.

2. *Saran.* Saran will get slightly dirtier than Fiberglas because dirt can get imbedded into its slightly softer surface. However, it does wash easily. The water should not be too hot.

3. *Dacron.* Dacron is a smooth-surfaced fiber that does not get dirty easily. It may be laundered with a soap or a detergent. Most stains wash out readily. Heat-set garments made of Dacron do not lose their shape or permanent creases after washing. These garments also dry very quickly and do not shrink.

4. *Nylon*. Nylon filament is also a smooth-surfaced fiber that does not get dirty easily. It may be easily laundered with a soap or a detergent. Fabrics made of nylon filament may be heat-set so that they will retain their shape and creases or pleats after washing. Staple nylon launders easily also, but takes longer to dry.

5. *Dynel*. Being dog-bone shaped rather than round, Dynel will get dirty a little more easily than the above fibers. However, it launders very easily, and most stains wash out easily. It does not shrink, and retains its shape and creases when heat-set. Dynel will not felt or pill when washed.

6. *Orlon, Acrilan, X–51*. These three fibers being acrylics wash very much like Dynel. Under ordinary conditions, they will not shrink, and will hold their shapes well.

7. *Vinyon N*. Also a clean fiber that washes in a soap or a detergent and, if heat-set, will hold its original shape and creases. Vinyon N will not shrink.

8. *Vicara*. Vicara is a round fiber, and therefore dirt does not cling easily. It washes very well, and does not shrink, felt, or pill. However, it cannot be permanently shaped by heat setting.

9. *Silk*. Silk makes a hygienic material because its smooth surface and absence of short fiber causes it to shed dust and to give up dirt readily. If handled properly, silk can be washed easily.

10. *Acetate*. Acetate is not as smooth as silk, but nevertheless is a clean fiber. It should be laundered with a mild soap in warm water. Acetate shrinks slightly.

11. *Rayon*. Although dirt particles may be easily removed from rayon fiber, care must be taken to avoid undue strain on the material when rayon garments are being washed. Rayon loses much of its strength when wet, but regains it entirely when dry. Rayon shrinks but may be processed so as to reduce the shrinkage to a residual amount of 2 per cent.

12. *Linen*. Because of the smooth surface of its fiber, linen gives up stains readily and affords little adhering surface for particles of dirt. Bacteria do not thrive on linen. Linen launders well; its softness is enhanced by repeated washings. Linen will shrink.

13. *Cotton*. The short cotton fiber produces a fabric with a relatively rougher surface than that of linen, silk, or rayon, and therefore soils easily. Nevertheless, cotton fabric is considered a hygienic material because it can be cleaned easily—it withstands rough handling and boiling temperature.

Cotton will shrink, but the shrinkage may be reduced to as much as 1 per cent by a preshrinking process such as Sanforizing.

14. *Wool.* The serrated surface of the outer scales of the epidermis of wool fiber attracts dust, bacteria, and dirt particles. Consequently, wool fabric requires frequent dry cleaning, or washing if the nature of the fabric permits it. Wool fabrics that have a high grease content must not be washed; they must be dry-cleaned. Wool fiber is softened by moisture and heat, and therefore the fabric shrinks easily; felting occurs when wool is washed improperly. A wool garment should not be rubbed or handled like a cotton one. However, there are preshrinking and shrinkproofing processes available for wool fabrics.

Reaction of Fibers to Bleaches. It is sometimes desired to bleach fabrics to get them whiter or to remove stains. However, before a bleach is used, it is necessary to know whether it will affect or damage the fabric. The fibers may be classified into two groups: those that can, and those that cannot be safely subjected to bleaches.

The fibers that may be safely bleached in ordinary household bleaches, such as sodium hypochlorite (Rose-X, Clorox, and the like) or hydrogen peroxide, are: *cotton, linen, Orlon, Dacron, Dynel, Vicara, Acrilan, Vinyon N, saran, Fiberglas, X–51.* Actually, with the exception of cotton and linen, these fibers generally retain their natural color and, furthermore, do not permanently stain easily.

Bleaches should not be used on *silk, rayon, acetate, nylon,* and *wool.* (Wool may be bleached with a mild solution of hydrogen peroxide.) White rayon and nylon do not discolor but remain naturally white.

Effect of Heat on Fibers. It is quite important to the consumer to know what effect heat has on textile fibers. For example, one needs to know whether a fiber is inflammable, and how a fabric is to be ironed without its melting or disintegrating.

• *Cotton.* Cotton is highly resistant to degradation by heat. It scorches at about 300 degrees Fahrenheit but does not burn until the temperature is 475 degrees Fahrenheit.

• *Linen.* The reaction of linen to heat is similar to that of cotton. However, because of the greater natural stiffness of linen, it should be very damp when ironed, and the iron should be hotter than ordinarily used for cotton.

• *Wool.* Although wool will start to decompose at 266 degrees Fahrenheit, it does not flame. It will support combustion at 572 degrees Fahrenheit.

Wool should be pressed with a steam iron, or a very damp pressing cloth should be used with an ordinary iron.

• *Silk*. Silk is less resistant to heat than wool. It will decompose at about 330 degrees Fahrenheit.

• *Rayon*. Both viscose and cuprammonium rayons burn rapidly, once the kindling point of about 350 degrees Fahrenheit is reached. A slightly cooler iron is recommended for these fibers than for cotton.

• *Acetate*. Acetate will stick to the iron at about 350 degrees Fahrenheit. At higher temperatures it will char, sputter, and flame. A cooler iron should be used for acetate than for rayon. Cigarette sparks and glowing embers falling on acetate fabrics will melt holes in the fabric on contact.

• *Nylon*. Nylon will melt at 482 degrees Fahrenheit. However, it may discolor or yellow at lower temperatures. It is advisable to iron nylon in the same manner as acetate. Nylon garments may be commercially heat-set to retain their shape after washing or dry cleaning without further pressing or ironing. As with acetate fabrics, cigarette sparks and glowing embers will melt holes in nylon fabrics.

• *Orlon*. Orlon fabrics also can be permanently heat-set. If Orlon is to be ironed, it should be treated similarly to nylon.

• *Acrilan*. Acrilan starts to shrink at 356 degrees Fahrenheit and begins to soften at 464 degrees Fahrenheit. Its color turns yellow to orange to brown on prolonged heating at elevated temperatures.

• *Dynel*. Dynel will not support combustion but will soften at about 300 degrees Fahrenheit and will melt at higher temperatures. Dynel can be heat-set to hold a permanent shape and creases.

• *X–51*. The incipient melting point or sticking temperature of X–51 is about 560 degrees Fahrenheit as determined on a hot surface. However, the fiber shrinks and shrivels below this temperature, in common with other thermoplastic fibers, and may ignite when an open flame is applied. Cigarette sparks and glowing embers will not ignite fabrics produced from staple, or cause pinholes.

• *Dacron*. Dacron melts at 480 degrees Fahrenheit. It should be ironed in the same manner as nylon and Orlon. However, it, too, can be heat-set to hold a permanent shape or crease.

• *Vicara*. Vicara loses strength above 350 degrees Fahrenheit and melts at about 470 degrees Fahrenheit. Therefore, it should be ironed in the same manner as rayon or acetate.

• *Vinyon N*. Vinyon N will not support combustion but can soften at a temperature as low as 170 degrees Fahrenheit. Therefore, it is difficult to iron. However, it can be permanently heat-set and thus avoid ironing.

• *Saran.* Saran is self-extinguishing. It softens at a low temperature of about 167 degrees Fahrenheit. Ironing is therefore difficult.

• *Fiberglas.* Temperatures must be extremely high to damage Fiberglas. It begins to lose some strength at 600 degrees Fahrenheit and softens at 1,500 degrees Fahrenheit. Obviously, ironing not only will not affect Fiberglas but is actually a waste of time and effort.

Effect of Mildew on Fibers.   Mildew often attacks textiles, particularly where there is dampness. Mildew stains and deteriorates fabrics and leaves a musty odor. It is well to know which fibers are resistant to mildew.

The following fabrics are wholly resistant to mildew: *nylon, Orlon, Acrilan, Dynel, X–51, Dacron, Vinyon N, saran, Fiberglas.* If any of these fibers ever appear to get moldy, it is actually the finish on the fiber, and not the fiber itself, that is mildewing.

• *Acetate* is highly resistant to mildew but may discolor.

• *Wool* and *Vicara* have good resistance to mildew but in time will succumb.

• *Silk* has good resistance to mildew but eventually will be damaged under extreme conditions of dampness and darkness.

• *Cotton, linen,* and *rayon* will definitely be attacked by mildew.

Effect of Sunlight on Fibers.   Textiles are constantly exposed to the outdoors and light. Some need to be very resistant to degradation by sunlight.

The reaction of the textile fibers to sunlight is as follows:

• *Cotton.* Cotton loses strength and has a tendency to yellow.

• *Linen.* Linen is much more resistant to light than cotton.

• *Wool.* Wool loses strength. However, its dyeing properties are improved on exposure of the fiber to sunlight.

• *Silk.* Silk will be deteriorated by sunlight more quickly than will cotton or wool.

• *Rayon.* Viscose and cuprammonium lose strength after prolonged exposure.

• *Acetate.* Acetate will lose some strength but not as much as rayon.

• *Nylon.* Nylon will lose some strength after exposure over a relatively long period of time. Bright nylon is more resistant to sunlight than is the semidull or dull nylon.

• *Orlon* and *Acrilan.* Both of these fibers are extremely resistant to degradation by sunlight.

• *Dynel.* Dynel darkens somewhat after prolonged exposure and loses some strength.

• *Dacron.* Dacron also loses some strength after prolonged exposure. However, there is no discoloration. It is much more resistant behind glass than in direct sunlight.

• *Vicara.* There is a very slow deterioration and loss of strength under sunlight.

• *X–51.* Limited information in 1954 indicates that the filament is relatively resistant to degradation by sunlight. Tests are being continued for staple X–51.

• *Vinyon N.* There is a slight loss of strength.

• *Saran.* Saran darkens slightly. It is not deteriorated by sunlight, and as a result is used a great deal for window screens.

• *Fiberglas.* Sunlight and outdoor exposure have no effect on Fiberglas.

Reaction of Fibers to Alkalies and Acids. In studying textiles, a knowledge of the reaction of the textile fibers to alkalies and acids is important. Alkalies destroy animal fibers; acids, even in a weak solution, destroy vegetable fibers. For example, chemical tests for determining the fiber content of fabrics are made by noting the disintegration of wool and silk when exposed to a strong alkali, and a similar reaction when cotton and linen are exposed to acids.

Good results in the bleaching, finishing, and dyeing processes are dependent on the reaction of the fibers to alkali or acid chemical agents.

Not only is this reaction important in testing and manufacturing; it also closely touches the consumer when the care of fabrics is considered.

This reaction to alkalies and acids is most important to the consumer when fabrics are washed. As the brown soap sometimes used for household laundry is a strong alkali, it must not be used for silk or wool fabrics. Synthetic detergents, which are neutral, should be used for these protein fibers. For cotton and linen, synthetic detergents as cleansing agents are not as effective as soap.

• *Cotton.* Cotton is destroyed by concentrated inorganic acids—such as hydrochloric, hydrofluoric, sulphuric, and nitric—and is damaged when such acids are in dilute solutions. It is not injured by alkalies even in hot, strong solutions; strong soap may be used for washing cotton.

• *Linen.* The reaction of linen to acids is similar to that of cotton. Although linen is not readily damaged by alkalies, strong soap should not be rubbed on linen fabrics because a strong caustic soap bath turns linen yellowish.

• *Wool*. Dilute acids do not injure wool, but concentrated acids destroy it. Wool is quickly destroyed by strong alkalies; it dissolves if completely immersed in a boiling alkali. A neutral or mild soap must be used for washing wool.

• *Silk*. The organic acids—acetic, tartaric, stearic, and formic—have little effect on silk. Weak inorganic acids also have little effect, but strong solutions injure silk. A dilute solution of nitric acid produces a bright yellow color in silk, and this reaction identifies silk from wool when testing.

Silk is destroyed by strong alkalies; strong soap should be avoided when washing silk. Compared with wool, silk is more resistant to alkalies but less resistant to strong acids.

• *Rayon*. Hot dilute solutions or cold concentrated solutions of strong inorganic acids, such as sulphuric, hydrochloric, hydrofluoric, and nitric, destroy rayon. The organic acids, formic and acetic, do not affect viscose or cuprammonium rayon. Rayons are not readily damaged by alkalies, but are less resistant than cotton or linen. Both viscose and cuprammonium lose tensile strength when exposed to a weak solution of a strong alkali, such as caustic soda.

• *Acetate*. Strong acids will destroy acetate. However, acetate will withstand solutions of organic acids as strong as 28 per cent. Acetate is easily affected by alkalies, especially if the water is very hot. Therefore, mild soaps and lukewarm water should be used when laundering acetate.

• *Nylon*. Nylon is affected by concentrated solutions of the strong mineral and organic acids. Alkalies, however, have virtually no effect on nylon.

• *Orlon*. Orlon has good-to-excellent resistance to mineral acids and fair-to-good resistance to weak alkalies. Nor is it harmed by the organic acids.

• *Acrilan*. Acrilan has good resistance to the mineral and organic acids and fair-to-good resistance to weak alkalies.

• *Dynel*. There is little or no effect of either the acids or alkalies on Dynel.

• *X-51*. In general, X-51 has very good resistance to acids, although there is a tendency to bleach. Its resistance to alkalies is fair, with a tendency to yellow under severe conditions. Higher concentrations and higher temperatures cause more severe attack.

• *Dacron*. Dacron has good resistance to most mineral acids, although a concentrated solution of sulphuric acid will decompose it. Dacron also has good resistance to weak and strong alkalies. However, it will be disintegrated by strong alkalies at boiling temperatures.

• *Vicara.* Although Vicara is protein in nature, it has great resistance to concentrated solutions of mineral acids. Furthermore, Vicara is very resistant to the action of alkalies.

• *Vinyon N.* Acids and alkalies have little or no effect on Vinyon N.

• *Saran.* Saran has fair resistance to concentrated sulphuric acid and good resistance to others. It is unaffected by most alkalies but is affected to a limited extent by ammonium hydroxide.

• *Fiberglas.* Fiberglas is affected by hydrofluoric and hot phosphoric acids only. It is attacked by hot solutions of weak alkalies and cold solutions of strong alkalies.

Affinity of Fibers for Dyes. The readiness with which a fiber absorbs and retains dye affects the appearance and serviceability of a fabric. Affinity for dyes is usually determined by the porosity of a fiber.

• *Cotton.* While cotton does not have a natural affinity for dyes, it is usually treated in a manner that will assure fastness of color. Mercerized cotton, for example, absorbs and retains dyes better than do cottons that have not been so treated.

• *Linen.* Linen fibers have a poor affinity for dyes. The hard nonporous surface of the fiber and its natural gum content (pectin) do not allow even penetration of the dyestuff. A more favorable reaction can be induced by removing the pectin by a strong bleaching process, but this may entail some sacrifice in the durability of the fabric. For this reason, unbleached linens are preferable when extreme whiteness is not a primary consideration.

• *Wool.* Wool has a very high affinity for dyes. Wool fabrics dye well and evenly.

• *Silk.* Silk has a good affinity for most dyestuffs.

• *Rayon.* Rayon also reacts favorably to dyes. The dyestuff is absorbed evenly, and the material is consequently dyed successfully.

• *Acetate.* Acetate requires special dyes. Some colors, such as grays and blues, tend to gas-fade and turn red or purplish. Like cotton, the affinity of acetate for dyes can be increased by an alkali treatment. Special processes have been developed whereby the coloring pigment can be added to the acetate solution before the fiber is actually formed. This technique makes the color a permanent part of the fiber.

• *Nylon.* Nylon dyes fairly well. The colors are generally fast.

• *Orlon* and *Acrilan.* These fibers may be dyed with some difficulty. The pastel and medium shades are more easily obtained. The colors have excellent washfastness. Lightfastness is very poor.

	Structure	Length	Luster	Strength *	Elasticity †	Heat Conductivity ¶	Absorbency §
Cotton	Flat, twisted, ribbonlike, with a wide inner canal	½ to 2½ inches	Little to none	7	13 Wrinkles very easily but can be treated	2	6
Linen	Bamboolike	12 to 20 inches	High	4	14 Wrinkles very easily but can be treated	1	5 Dries more quickly than cotton
Wool	Roughly cylindrical, covered with overlapping scales	1 to 8 inches	None	13	3 Very resilient	12	1
Silk	Smooth, lustrous; slightly uneven when gum is on	1,200 to 4,000 feet	High	3	6 Very resilient	10	2
Viscose rayon	Threadlike longitudinal lines; serrated surface	Any length	Bright, semidull, dull	12	10 Wrinkles easily but can be treated	4	3
Cuprammonium rayon	Fine, smooth, round	Any length	Bright, semidull, dull	12	10 Wrinkles easily	3	3
Acetate	Striated due to crenulated surface	Any length	Bright, semidull, dull	15	9 More resilient than rayons	5	8 Dries faster than rayon, slower than nylon. Clammy when wet
Nylon	Fine, smooth, round	Any length	Bright, semidull, dull	2	2 Very resilient	6	9 Dries quickly. Feels clammy when wet.
Orlon	Dog-bone shape	Any length	High	5	11 Excellent resilience	9	10 Not very absorbent. Resists stains
Acrilan	Dog-bone shape	1 to 6 inches	Semidull	10	11 Excellent resilience	9	7 Not very absorbent. Resists stains
Dynel	Irregular ribbon	1 to 6 inches	Semidull	10	7 Excellent resilience	9	12 Not very absorbent. Resists stains
X-51	Substantially round with a skin effect	Any length	Semidull	8	12 Excellent resilience	8	11 Not very absorbent. Resists stains
Dacron	Substantially round with dots in the cross section	Any length	High	6	8 Excellent resilience	7	13 Not very absorbent. Resists stains
Vicara	Cylindrical, translucent rod	1 to 6 inches	Semidull	14	1 Excellent resilience	11	4
Vinyon N	Dog-bone with false lumen	Any length	Soft luster	9	4 Good resilience	(See text)	14
Saran	Featureless, round	Any length	Soft luster	11	5 Good resilience	(See text)	15 Absorption practically nil
Fiberglas	Featureless, fine, round	Any length	High	1	15 Flexible	(See text)	15 Absorption practically nil

*. Indicates strongest   † Indicates most elastic   ¶ Indicates coolest   § Indicates most absorbent

QUALITIES OF TEXTILE FIBERS

Cleanliness and Washability	Reaction to Bleaches	Effect of Heat	Effect of Mildew	Effect of Light	Reaction to Alkalies	Reaction to Acids	Affinity to Dyes
13 Gets dirty easily; will shrink	Weakens; may be used with care	Will scorch and burn	Damaged	Loses strength; yellows	Not affected	Easily affected	Excellent
12 Will shrink	Weakens; use with care	Will scorch and burn	Damaged	More resistant than cotton	Not affected	Easily affected	Very good
14 Weakens when wet; will shrink, pill, felt	Deteriorates	Does not flame, will char	Good resistance	Weakens	Easily harmed	Not affected	Excellent
9 Must be washed with care	Deteriorates	Less resistant than wool	Good resistance	Less resistant than cotton or wool	Destroyed	Somewhat affected	Excellent
11 May shrink; weakens when wet	Deteriorates	Reacts like cotton, but at lower temperature	Damaged	Loses strength over prolonged period	Less resistant than cotton	Like cotton	Very good
11 May shrink; weakens when wet	Deteriorates	Reacts like cotton, but at lower temperature	Damaged	Loses strength over prolonged period	Less resistant than cotton	Like cotton	Very good
10 Use mild soap, warm water; shrinks	Deteriorates	Melts and burns. Use cooler iron than for rayons	Highly resistant; may discolor	More resistant than rayons	Less resistant than cotton	Slightly more resistant than rayons	Fair; gas-fades
4 Retains shape; filament dries quickly	Deteriorates	Quickly damaged by cigarette sparks. Use warm iron	Wholly resistant	Bright, more resistant than most fibers; semidull, dull, good resistance	No effect	Weakened	Good
6 Retains shape; does not shrink	Resistant	Reacts like nylon	Wholly resistant	Extremely resistant	Resistant to weak alkalies	Good resistance	Not too good; poor lightfastness
6 Retains shape; does not shrink	Resistant	Reacts like nylon	Wholly resistant	Highly resistant	Resistant to weak alkalies	Good resistance	Not too good; poor lightfastness
5 Retains shape; will not felt, pill, or shrink	Resistant	Will not support combustion, but will melt	Wholly resistant	Darkens somewhat; loses some strength	No effect	No effect	Good
6 Retains shape; does not shrink	Resistant	More resistant than nylon. Will melt	Wholly resistant	Fairly resistant	Fair resistance. Affected by high heat	Good resistance. Tendency to bleach	Good
3 Most stains wash out readily. Dries quickly, does not shrink. Retains shape	Resistant	Similar to nylon	Wholly resistant	Loses some strength over prolonged period	Good resistance	Good resistance except to sulphuric acid	Very good; fair lightfastness
8 Will not pill, felt, or shrink	Resistant	Melts. Should be ironed like acetate	Good resistance	Slow deterioration	Very resistant	Good resistance	Excellent
7 Retains shape; will not shrink	Resistant	Will not support combustion. Melts at 170° F.	Wholly resistant	Slight loss of strength	No effect	No effect	Very poor
2 Water must not be too hot	Resistant	Self-extinguishing. Melts at 167° F.	Wholly resistant	Darkens slightly. No loss of strength	Slightly affected by ammonium hydroxide	Good resistance	Color must be added before extrusion
1 Dirt wipes off	Resistant	Incombustible. Melts above 1500° F.	Wholly resistant	No effect	Affected by hot weak, or cold strong, solutions	Damaged by hydrofluoric & hot phosphoric acids	Takes dye by special process

• *Dynel.* Dynel can be dyed many colors without too much difficulty.

• *X-51.* Different techniques must be used, and different results are obtained depending on whether filament or staple fiber is being dyed. In general, it may be stated that X–51 can be dyed with a variety of dyes: acetate, acid and direct, basic, vat, and soluble vat. The results produced may be a wide range of colors and shades including pastels and bright colors. Depending on the dye used, the colors can be lightfast and washfast as well as resistant to perspiration, gas fading, and crocking.

• *Dacron.* Dacron can be dyed to a complete range of shades with good-to-excellent washfastness and fair-to-good lightfastness.

• *Vicara.* Vicara can be dyed with a wide variety of dyestuffs and gives excellent results.

• *Vinyon N.* Due to the high resistance of Vinyon N to water, it is difficult to dye. Special dyes producing limited colors must be used.

• *Saran.* Saran can be dyed only by including the color before the fiber is extruded.

• *Fiberglas.* A special technique that causes the dye to stick to the surface of the Fiberglas is used.

▶ **TEST YOURSELF ON THIS CHAPTER**

1. How may a knowledge of textiles help the consumer?
2. What is the sequence of development of fiber into fabric?
3. What practical significance has the quality of absorbency in apparel?
4. Explain how length of staple affects the quality of a fabric.
5. What quality of acetate makes it desirable for winter underwear?
6. What type of rayon would make the best-wearing coat lining? Why?
7. Why is elasticity important in textiles? How may elasticity in textile fabrics be improved?
8. What qualities of linen make it suitable for (*a*) towels and handkerchiefs, (*b*) summer suits, (*c*) draperies, (*d*) summer shoes?
9. What qualities of silk make it suitable for (*a*) women's dresses, (*b*) fishlines, (*c*) neckties, (*d*) ribbons?
10. Why is cotton used so extensively for infants' wear?
11. What qualities of rayon make it a poor fiber to use for (*a*) sewing thread, (*b*) stockings, (*c*) winter underwear?
12. What specific qualities have spun rayon fabrics that are not found in long-staple rayons?
13. What properties may wool fabric be expected to have? How do they affect the serviceability of wool?

14. How does a napped surface affect the hygienic quality of a fabric?

15. Why does a cotton bathing suit feel cooler than a woolen one?

16. Why does a fabric of nylon filament yarn dry faster than one of nylon spun yarn?

17. What one characteristic do all the acrylic fibers have that is of great advantage to the consumer and homemaker?

18. Why is the use of saran limited?

19. Which textiles will be damaged quickly by cigarette sparks?

20. Which textile would be considered best for curtains? Why?

21. Obtain as many samples of fabrics as you can, and cut them into small square pieces, three by three inches. Mount them on small cards. Determine the fiber content of each sample, and record your data on the card. Give all the possible uses for each fabric. Give the reasons for your answers in terms of the basic qualities of the fibers.

22. Observe carefully the various contents of your home furnishings, and make a record of every item that uses any textile fibers. Add the name of the fiber used, indicating if this is a guess or the result of observation and analysis. Give reasons for each answer.

3 | TESTING FIBERS

For Identification

Textile fibers are ordinarily classified according to their substance. In other words, cotton and linen are called vegetable fibers because they are derived from plants; wool and silk are called animal fibers because they are derived from sheep and silkworms respectively. Rayon may come under the vegetable classification because, although rayon is a man-made fiber, it is made from cellulose, an important ingredient of all plant life. Acetate also has its origin in cellulose.

With the exception of Vicara, which is derived from corn protein, called zein, all the newer fibers are synthetics. These fibers have no counterpart in nature but rather are creations of chemists. Chemically, nylon is an amide; Orlon, Acrilan, Dynel, and X–51 are acrylics; Dacron is a polyester fiber; Vinyon N is composed of a vinyl resin; saran is vinylidene chloride; and Fiberglas is, of course, a form of glass.

The value of classifying fibers according to substance is evident in many textile operations. Its immediate application is indicated in various physical and chemical tests for identification purposes: (1) testing by microscope, (2) the feeling test, (3) the burning test, (4) the breaking test, (5) chemical tests, (6) nontechnical tests for distinguishing linen from cotton.

Limitation of Tests. No single test, other than by microscope, can be depended on to give at all times immediate recognition of every fiber; limitations will be encountered in all the tests. In practice, therefore, identification tests are used in combination. Certain tests cannot be made freely or easily in the retail store by the consumer at the time of purchase. At that time, the consumer is forced to make use of what might be called nontechnical tests. These are inadequate, yet they convey a certain amount of information if they have been used frequently enough to insure correct observations.

Testing by Microscope. Identification by microscope is the most reliable test that can be used to distinguish the fibers. Such identification has already been used in Chapters 1 and 2 to introduce the fibers and to describe their essential qualities. Knowing what the fibers look like under the microscope helps the consumer to understand other identification tests.

It has already been pointed out that certain manufacturing and finishing processes, such as mercerizing and delustering, affect the appearance of a fiber under the microscope. In addition, a dark-colored fabric cannot be identified under the microscope until the dyestuff is removed; the light that is necessary for identification cannot pass through a dark fabric. The dyestuff must be removed, or "stripped," by the use of a bleaching chemical. The choice of the stripping chemical is determined by the composition of the fabric. If the fabric is of vegetable substance, its color can be removed by chlorine water or by sodium hydrosulphite (3 per cent solution, boiling); if of animal substance, a ½ per cent solution of caustic soda will remove the dye.

Feeling Test. The feeling test requires skilled perception if the test is to be of any value to the consumer when on a shopping tour. Skilled perception is acquired only after handling many different fabrics over a period of time.

To understand what is meant by "to feel" a fabric, place your finger on a sample of wool. The heat generated by the finger remains in the area because wool is a nonconductor of heat. Consequently, wool fabric "feels warm to the touch." If your finger is placed on a sample composed of the vegetable fibers—that is, cotton, linen, or even rayon—the heat of the finger passes off because such fibers are conductors of heat. Therefore, the fabrics "feel cool to the touch."

Identification of the natural fibers by the feeling test may be summarized as follows:

Cotton. Cotton is cool to the touch and feels soft and inelastic.

Linen. Linen is cold and smooth and has a leathery feel.

Wool. Wool is warm to the touch and feels elastic and springy.

Silk. Silk feels warm, smooth, and elastic.

LIMITATION OF THE FEELING TEST. The man-made and synthetic fibers cannot be detected by feeling alone. For example, spun rayon can be made to look and feel like cotton, wool, or linen; spun nylon can be made to look and feel like cotton or linen; Vicara can be made to look and feel like wool or cashmere. Some of these newer fibers may even look and feel like each other in fabric form.

Courtesy U.S. Department of Agriculture

Pure-dye silk burns (at left) with a small flame that soon dies, leaving an ash in the form of small, brittle, shiny black balls along the edge of the fabric.
Weighted silk burns (at right) without showing a visible flame. It chars and leaves a coherent ash, a skeleton of the original fabric.

Burning Test. To recognize the composition of fabrics by the burning test, the tester must note three things: (1) how the yarn ignites when flame is applied; (2) the condition of the burned portion; (3) the odor produced by the burning.

If both the lengthwise and the crosswise yarns in a fabric are known to be of the same substance, the sample may be tested as a whole. Different kinds of yarn, however, are sometimes used in a fabric. When the presence of yarns of different substances is suspected, the lengthwise yarns should be separated from the crosswise yarns, and each set should be tested separately.

To avoid burning the fingers, a candle flame rather than a lighted match should be used when the burn test is made. Also, the sulphur odor from the match causes confusion when testing for odor. Additional precaution should be taken to protect the fingers from the flame by holding the sample with tweezers or any metal holder.

• *Cotton.* Cotton yarn blazes quickly when it comes in contact with the flame because the cellulose ingredient is highly inflammable. The ash is light and feathery and has a vegetable odor similar to that of burned paper; mercerized cotton produces a black ash. Because cotton is highly inflammable, the prudent homemaker will not use cotton where its proximity to flame becomes a fire hazard; for example, pot holders should be made of wool, never of cotton.

Courtesy U.S. Department of Agriculture

Acetate blazes (at left) as it burns The fabric puckers, curls, and fuses into an irregular black residue that hardens when cooled.
Wool burns slowly (at right) with a small flickering flame. The fabric sizzles and curls. The ash is black, irregular, and crisp.

• *Linen.* Linen, when burned, produces an ash similar to cotton ash because both fabrics are of vegetable substance. Linen ash is also light and feathery and has the odor of burned paper. Linen as a fabric, however, burns somewhat more slowly than cotton because linen yarns are heavier than cotton yarns. The pace of burning, however, is not sufficiently different to aid in distinguishing linen from cotton.

• *Wool.* Wool is slow to ignite and has a characteristic small, slow, flickering flame that sizzles and curls. It can be extinguished easily, as the fabric ceases flaming when the fire is withdrawn. Wool ash is dark and crisp. It falls into an irregular shape and can be crushed easily. The ash has a strong animal odor resembling burning feathers or hair. This odor indicates the presence of an animal substance or of a fiber obtained from an animal. The offensive odor characteristic of burned wool is due to the sulphur ingredient.

• *Silk.* Pure silk also burns slowly and ceases flaming when the fire is withdrawn. The ash of silk appears in the form of round, crisp, shiny black beads that, like the ash of wool, can be crushed easily with the fingers. The ash gives forth an animal odor, but one that is less pronounced than that of wool, as silk does not contain sulphur.

In textile manufacturing, additional body is given to silk fabrics by weighting them with metallic fillers. Weighted silk burns without showing a visible flame. The burned part becomes incandescent; it chars and gradually smolders away, leaving a coherent ash that is a screenlike skeleton of the original fabric. The odor of the ash of weighted silk, however, is similar to that of pure silk.

• *Rayon.* Like cotton, rayon ignites quickly. It burns with a bright yellow flame, sometimes more rapidly than cotton because rayon is essentially

SUMMARY OF THE BURNING TEST FOR FIBERS

Yarn	Flame	Odor	Ash
Cotton	Large yellow flame; burns quickly	Like burned paper	Light, feathery grayish ash; black ash denotes mercerized cotton
Linen	Like cotton; sometimes slower if yarns are heavier	Like burned paper	Like cotton; sometimes heavier if yarn is thicker
Wool	Small, slow flickering flame; sizzles and curls; ceases flaming when withdrawn from flame	Strong animal stench like burning feathers or hair	Crisp dark ash; irregular shape that can be crushed easily
Silk (pure dye)	Burns slowly; ceases flaming when withdrawn from flame	Gives off an animal odor, but less pronounced than wool	Round, crisp, shiny black beads that can be easily crushed with the fingers
Silk (weighted)	No flame; burned part becomes incandescent and chars	Same as pure silk	Screenlike skeleton of original sample
Rayons	Ignites quickly like cotton, sometimes faster	Like burned paper	Like cotton
Acetate	Flames quickly; material puckers, sputters, melts; drips like tar	Acid, like vinegar	Brittle black ash, difficult to crush between the fingers; unlike ash of any other fibers

a purified cellulose. The ash of rayon has the same odor as that of cotton and linen ash and is similarly light and feathery.

• *Acetate.* Acetate blazes as it burns. The edge of the fabric puckers and curls as the material fuses and melts into a hard mass. Acetate sputters and drips like tar. The ash of acetate is hard and brittle, and is difficult to crush

SUMMARY OF THE BURNING TEST FOR FIBERS

Yarn	Flame	Odor	Ash
Nylon	Melts and shrinks from flame before burning	Pungent	Hard round bead that cannot be crushed
Orlon	Melts; burns rapidly like acetate	Acrid	Hard black bead
Acrilan	Melts; burns rapidly	Acrid	Hard black bead
Dynel	Shrinks; will not support combustion	Disagreeable	Hardens; becomes brittle
X-51	Melts		Hardens
Dacron	Melts before burning; burns slowly	Slightly sweetish	Brittle, beady ash
Vicara	Somewhat like wool	Burning chicken feathers	Small bead, easily crushed
Saran	Melts, shrinks from flame; does not support combustion		Hard bead
Vinyon N	Similar to saran, but melts more quickly		Irregular, brittle bead
Fiberglas	Will not burn; melts at temperature over 1,500° F.		Melts

between the fingers; it is unlike the ash of any other fiber. Because of the acetic acid that is used in the manufacture of acetate, the ash has an acid odor similar to that of vinegar.

• *Nylon.* Nylon melts before burning. As it burns, it shrinks from the flame and forms a hard round bead that cannot be crushed between the fingers. While burning, it has a pungent odor.

• *Orlon.* Orlon melts and burns, leaving a hard black bead. It burns at a rapidity between that of cotton and acetate.

• *Acrilan.* Acrilan also melts and burns very much like Orlon.

• *Dynel.* Dynel will not support combustion. It will shrink, harden, and become brittle, leaving a disagreeable odor.

• *X–51.* In common with other thermoplastic fibers, X–51 will shrink, melt, and become brittle.

• *Dacron.* Dacron melts before burning. When it burns, it does so slowly, leaving a brittle beady ash. While it burns, Dacron has a slightly sweetish odor.

• *Vicara.* Vicara burns with a small bead that can be easily crushed. The odor is like that of burning chicken feathers. In fact, being a protein fiber, Vicara reacts to flame in a manner similar to that of silk and wool.

• *Saran.* Saran does not support combustion. It will melt, shrink from the flame, and form a bead.

• *Vinyon N.* Vinyon N reacts similarly to saran, except that it melts much more quickly and leaves an irregular brittle bead.

• *Fiberglas.* Fiberglas will not burn. Of course, if the temperature is over 1,500 degrees Fahrenheit, it will melt.

LIMITATION OF THE BURNING TEST. As cotton, linen, and rayon show a large yellow flame, rapid burning, and a light feathery ash that gives off an odor similar to that of burned paper, the burning test is of no value in distinguishing these three fibers from one another. But this test is important in distinguishing cotton, linen, and rayon from the other fibers.

Furthermore, it will be noted that many of the man-made and synthetic fibers react similarly. Nylon, Orlon, and Acrilan melt before burning and leave a hard round bead. Dynel, Vinyon N, and saran do not support combustion, but they melt and leave a brittle bead.

In fact, these limitations or similarities provide a basic means of preliminary examination and elimination. This can be summarized as follows:

1. Burns, forming a light feathery ash and leaving an odor of burning paper. This category would indicate cotton, linen, or rayon.

2. Burns, forming a bead with the odor of burning feathers. This category would indicate a wool, pure silk, or Vicara.
3. Burns, leaving a skeleton of ash with the odor of burning feathers. Indicates weighed silk.
4. Shrinks from flame, melts, burns, and forms a bead. This category would include nylon, Orlon, Acrilan, X–51, and acetate (which has the odor of acetic acid).
5. Does not support combustion but will shrink, harden, and become brittle. This category includes Dynel, Vinyon N, and saran.
6. Incombustible but with sufficient heat will melt and shrink from flame. This is true only of Fiberglas.

Breaking Test.   The breaking test is nontechnical, yet it affords a convenient means of identifying fabrics. Recognition of a yarn by the breaking test requires observation of the fiber ends when the yarn is broken apart. A piece of yarn about 12 inches long is required for this test. The yarn must be untwisted very gently to restore the natural formation of the fiber before twist was inserted by the spinning operation. Sometimes, two or more strands

To examine the breaking pattern of cotton or rayon yarn, untwist the yarn and tear it apart, using both thumbs. Rayon yarn will show lustrous, inelastic filaments. Cotton yarn will show brushlike ends that are short, even, and fuzzy. To examine the breaking pattern of linen yarn, untwist the yarn, and tear it apart, using the index fingers as well as the thumbs. Linen yarn will break unevenly, showing long, pointed ends that are inelastic and lustrous.

are combined to make up a single yarn. In such cases, the yarn must be untwisted gently until a single strand is obtained. Care must also be used when pulling a yarn apart; otherwise, the broken fiber ends will not take their characteristic pattern.

• *Cotton.* Because cotton yarns are made from short-staple fiber, the breaking of a cotton yarn will show fiber ends that are short, even, fuzzy, and brushlike. There is a characteristic curl to the ends, caused by the natural twist of the fiber. The inelasticity of cotton yarn causes the yarn to snap when pulled apart.

• *Linen.* When it is suspected that a yarn is composed of linen fiber, a long piece of yarn is necessary for testing because long staple may be anticipated. If a break does not occur readily when the yarn is untwisted and gently pulled apart, the span must be increased to exert tension on a longer staple. Untwisting should be continued along the span, and the yarn again pulled gently. If necessary, the span should be increased again. The breaking pattern of a linen yarn shows long, straight, lustrous fiber ends that are pointed and uneven at the tips. The fiber ends never curl; instead, they point outward with marked stiffness that indicates the lack of flexibility of the linen fiber.

• *Wool.* A wool yarn has a characteristic fuzzy surface. When the yarn is pulled gently for the breaking test, it stretches easily because of its remarkable elasticity. The breaking pattern shows fiber ends that are wavy and spiral in shape.

• *Silk.* A silk yarn stretches easily when pulled because silk ranks close to wool in elasticity. Because of its strength, the silk yarn stretches a considerable degree, breaking apart finally with a snap, but only after it has exceeded its limit of stretching. The fiber ends, when broken, appear fine and lustrous.

• *Rayon.* If tension is exerted on a dry rayon yarn, the yarn appears to be comparatively strong, though inelastic, and does not break easily. When a rayon yarn is moistened with the tongue, a slight pull breaks the yarn easily. When broken, the fiber ends create a pattern similar to that of a tree

Rayon's loss of strength when wet can be readily detected by the moisture test. Moisten rayon yarn slightly, and then pull both ends.

with numerous stiff branches. This effect is produced by the explosivelike bursting of the separate filaments.

LIMITATION OF THE BREAKING TEST. One limitation of the breaking test is indicated in testing spun rayon. As spun rayon can easily simulate wool, linen, or even cotton, the breaking pattern of this rayon is similar to the characteristic pattern of wool or of linen. When the burning test is used as an additional means of identification, the rayon yarn that resembles wool reveals the lack of animal odor that is characteristic of wool. Rayon yarn that resembles linen can be detected by exerting tension on the yarn after moistening it with the tongue. The characteristic loss of strength that rayon shows when wet is evident.

Of course, spun rayon is only one example of the limitation of this test. It would be difficult to determine accurately whether a yarn is composed of nylon, Orlon, Dacron, or any of the other stronger synthetic fibers. These fibers are relatively strong, and the degree of tension used in trying to break these yarns by hand cannot be measured accurately. Furthermore, when broken, the ends of these yarns may look like each other, or like wool, cotton, or some other fiber, depending on whether filament, artificially crimped staple, or staple fibers were used in the manufacture of the yarn.

Chemical Tests.

In addition to the microscope, chemical tests provide positive means of identifying fibers. But chemical tests are not intended for the general consumer. Their value is demonstrated, however, by the fact that some retail stores have their own laboratories for testing fabrics.

• *To Distinguish Animal from Vegetable Fibers with an Alkali.* As strong alkalies destroy animal substances, a 5 per cent solution of lye in water (½ teaspoon of lye in a glass of water) can be used to eliminate wool and silk fibers from a sample that contains a mixture of fibers. The action of this chemical (also known as caustic soda or sodium hydroxide) is hastened by boiling the solution before the sample is immersed. The wool and silk fibers will be completely dissolved. The vegetable fibers will not be affected. Another test is necessary to identify those fibers.

• *To Distinguish Vegetable from Animal Fibers with an Acid.* As dilute acids destroy vegetable fibers, a 2 per cent solution of sulphuric acid may be used to distinguish vegetable from animal fibers. A drop of the solution is placed on a sample of the fabric, which is then placed between two blotters and pressed with a hot iron. The spotted area will become charred if the fabric is cotton, linen, or rayon.

• *To Distinguish Silk from Wool.* If the fibers in a sample are known to consist of silk and wool, and identification of each is desired, the use of concentrated hydrochloric acid (cold) will dissolve the silk and cause the wool fiber to swell.

• *To Distinguish Linen from Cotton.* Before any chemical test is made to distinguish linen from cotton, all surface dressings should be removed from the samples by boiling them for a few minutes in a solution of dilute sodium hydroxide, about ½ per cent. Then any of the following tests can be made.

Immersing cotton and linen samples in a 1 per cent solution of fuchsin in alcohol produces a rose-red color in both samples. After the samples have been washed and then immersed in ammonia, linen retains the red coloration, but cotton does not. This test is sometimes made with a 1 per cent solution of magenta, a red dyestuff.

If samples of cotton and linen are immersed in an alcoholic solution of rosalic acid for a few minutes, then washed and immersed quickly in strong caustic soda and washed again, linen turns rose red, and cotton appears only slightly colored.

Cotton fibers are weakened more than linen fibers if samples are immersed in concentrated sulphuric acid for two minutes. After the samples are rinsed and immersed in weak ammonia, the cotton fibers dissolve, leaving the linen fibers unaffected.

When cotton and linen samples are immersed in a solution of iodine and zinc chloride (Herzberg's stain), cotton is stained reddish purple, and linen is stained blue to purple.

When samples are immersed in a caustic soda solution, cotton remains white and linen turns yellowish.

• *To Distinguish Viscose, Cuprammonium, and Acetate.* A solution containing equal parts of concentrated sulphuric acid and iodine (crystals) may be used to distinguish each of the different fibers. When samples are immersed in this solution, a dark-blue coloration indicates viscose; a light-blue coloration indicates cuprammonium; a yellow coloration indicates acetate.

Another test to distinguish acetate from rayon, when both types are known to be used in a fabric, is to immerse the sample in a 50 per cent solution of acetic acid. The acetate dissolves; rayon is not affected.

• *To Distinguish Acetate from Other Fibers.* If a sample of acetate is immersed in acetone (a chemical used in nail-polish removers), the acetate fibers are completely dissolved; other fibers, with the exception of Dynel and Vinyon N, are not affected. Vinyon N will dissolve in acetone only if it is a 100 per cent concentration.

• *To Distinguish Nylon from Other Fibers.* Nylon can be distinguished from acetate by attempting to dissolve it in acetone. Nylon, of course, will not dissolve in acetone.

If the yarn or fabric is thought to contain wool and/or nylon, the fabric may be immersed in a boiling solution of sodium hydroxide. The nylon is insoluble in such a solution, but wool will dissolve. In fact, nylon's insolubility in boiling sodium hydroxide makes it easily distinguishable from most other fibers.

The only common solvents in which nylon is soluble are concentrated formic acid, phenol, and cresol.

• *To Distinguish Orlon from Other Fibers.* Orlon is often blended with wool, cotton, silk, rayon, acetate, and nylon. Even when it is not, Orlon may be mistaken for one of the other fibers. If the fiber is Orlon, it will not be affected by these common solvents: glacial acetic acid, chloroform, acetone, and 88 per cent formic acid.

• *To Distinguish Dynel from Other Fibers.* Although Dynel is often used alone, it may be blended with other fibers. However, it is easily distinguishable from other fibers by chemical tests. It is highly resistant to a wide variety of inorganic acids, bases, salts, hydrocarbons, and most organic solvents. Acetone, cyclohexanone, and dimethylformamide are solvents in varying degrees. Other cyclic ketones and certain amines cause some solvent or swelling action at high temperatures.

• *To Distinguish Dacron from Other Fibers.* Like acetate and nylon, Dacron is soluble in hot metacresol. However, unlike acetate, it is not soluble in acetone; and unlike nylon, it is not soluble in concentrated formic acid.

• *To Distinguish Vicara from Other Fibers.* Vicara is used primarily as a blending fiber, particularly with wool, cotton, rayon, and nylon. It can be distinguished from wool by the use of caustic soda of up to 10 per cent concentration. Under these conditions, the wool will dissolve, but the Vicara will not.

Hydrochloric acid will distinguish Vicara from cotton, rayon, acetate, and nylon. This acid will dissolve the latter four fibers, but it will not affect Vicara.

• *To Distinguish Vinyon N from Other Fibers.* Methylene dichloride is a specific solvent for Vinyon N. The use of such a solution will immediately indicate the presence of Vinyon N.

• *To Distinguish Saran from Other Fibers.* For quick differentiation from Vinyon N, acetone may be used. A 100 per cent solution of acetone will dissolve Vinyon N but will not affect saran. At elevated temperatures, saran will dissolve in dioxan and cyclohexanone. Saran is also soluble in ammonium hydroxide.

• *To Distinguish Fiberglas from Other Fibers.* Two specific solvents for quick identification of Fiberglas are hydrofluoric acid (which, incidentally, is used for etching glass) and hot phosphoric acid. In fact, these are the only two acids that will affect Fiberglas.

Nontechnical Tests for Distinguishing Linen from Cotton.

The identification of linen and cotton fabrics has always been of special interest to the analytical consumer. Because cotton can be made to simulate linen, additional nontechnical tests for distinguishing linen from cotton are evaluated here. Some of these tests are adequate; others are not recommended because finishing substances that are commonly used in the manufacturing process interfere with the expected reaction.

• *Squeezing Test.* A simple method of distinguishing linen from cotton is the pulling of a yarn through two tightly compressed finger tips. If the yarn emerges stiff and straight, it is linen; if the yarn is limp and drooping, it is cotton.

• *Curl Test.* If the end of a single filament turns in a clockwise direction when squeezed between the moistened thumb and finger, the fabric is linen. If the tip turns counterclockwise, the fabric is cotton.

• *Tearing Test.* Linen fabrics do not tear readily, but they do tend to slip apart when subjected to strain. A sample may be identified as cotton if it tears readily with a characteristic shrill sound.

• *Reaction to Oil.* If lightweight oil or glycerine is dropped on a sample of linen, a translucent area appears on the fabric; if dropped on cotton, the area is opaque.

• *Ink Test.* If a drop of ink is placed on a linen fabric, the ink spreads evenly in a circular form. In contrast, a drop of ink on a cotton fabric tends to spread outward with a fading density toward the outer edge, making a slightly irregular outer rim, more oval than circular. The ink test, however, is not considered reliable because finishing substances may interfere with the reaction just described.

• *Moisture Test.* A common practice is to attempt to identify linen by noting the pace of absorption when a drop of saliva is placed on the undersurface of the fabric. As linen absorbs water quickly, it is believed that this test will identify the linen fiber. But finishing substances prevalent in the dressing of linens interfere with this test; therefore, it is not recommended.

Also, sheer cotton fabrics absorb a drop of saliva even more quickly than any fine linen.

▶ TEST YOURSELF ON THIS CHAPTER

1. Why is the classification of fibers according to their substance important for identification purposes?
2. List the advantages and the limitations of the burning test when it is used to differentiate cotton, linen, silk, wool, acetate, and rayon.
3. Describe three tests used to differentiate cotton and linen.
4. Describe the chemical test used to differentiate acetate, viscose, and cuprammonium.
5. Describe the breaking test as applied to cotton, linen, wool, silk.
6. Describe the differences between cotton and wool in the burning test.
7. Assume that you have samples of linen, cotton, silk, and wool materials, all unmarked. What chemical processes would you use to distinguish the animal fibers from the vegetable fibers? To distinguish cotton from linen?
8. Why is spun rayon difficult to identify by the feeling test or the breaking test?
9. What two positive tests permit identification of viscose, cuprammonium, and acetate?
10. What are the three tests by which silk may be differentiated from rayon?
11. Compare the effect of burning on acetate and on rayon in regard to flame, odor, and ash.
12. Compare the results of the breaking test on viscose and on linen yarn.
13. In selecting yard goods for a skirt, what tests can be used to determine whether the material is wool or cotton or a mixture?
14. Why would you choose a woolen blanket instead of a cotton blanket to put out a flame?
15. A consumer used the moisture test to determine whether sheets were linen or cotton. Why could the moisture test fail? What other tests would you suggest? Explain fully.
16. What three fibers will be dissolved by acetone?
17. What is a sure solvent specific for Vinyon N?
18. By what chemical tests can Vicara be distinguished from wool? Describe the results.
19. By what chemical tests can Dynel be distinguished from Vicara? Describe the results.
20. By what chemical tests can nylon be differentiated from other fibers? Describe the results.

4 | SPINNING

Fiber to Yarn

The formation of yarn becomes possible when fibers have surfaces that are capable of cohesiveness. This quality is exemplified by the serrations of the wool fiber, the convolutions of the cotton fiber, and the roughness of the flax fiber. Elasticity or flexibility permits the fibers to be twisted around one another.

Primitive man discovered that a succession of fibers could be twisted into a continuous yarn. This was probably accomplished slowly and laboriously at first, but the greater strength thus produced and the many uses soon found for articles made from continuous yarns led to the invention of hand implements to aid and improve the process of twisting and spinning. Many such implements and methods are still used by the more primitive peoples in various parts of the world as well as by persons who are interested in reviving artistic handicraft.

At the same time that a method of twisting fibers into yarn was discovered, it was necessary to invent simple methods of disentangling, separating, and arranging the fibers according to their length, other than by just

Spinning cotton on a Saxony wheel.

Courtesy Spool Cotton Co.

A tangled bunch of cotton fiber is carded into orderly arrangement, drawn out, condensed to a ropelike sliver, then further condensed and twisted into yarn.

using the fingers. Thus, crude methods of carding were invented to separate the fibers according to their length of staple. Uniformity of staple gives yarns a required evenness and improves the quality of the yarn.

Development of Fiber into Yarn. The value and character of a yarn are determined by (1) the kind and quality of the fiber; (2) the amount of processing necessary to produce fineness; and (3) the amount of twist, which increases tensile strength in the finished yarn. The purpose of the yarn must be anticipated, as this determines the number and kind of manufacturing operations.

The development of fiber into yarn, when stated in terms of basic manufacturing processes, is as follows: carding, combing, drawing out, twisting, and winding. As the raw fiber passes through these processes, it is successively called *lap, sliver, roving,* and finally *yarn.* The manufacturing operations in which these stages occur may be summarized as follows:

1. Lap to card sliver by the carding process.
2. Card sliver to comb sliver by the combing process (if the fiber is to be combed).
3. Sliver to roving by the drawing-out process.
4. Roving to yarn by the twisting process.
5. Reeled on bobbins, spools, or cones by the winding process.

Because the production of cotton yarn lends itself to a simple description of the manufacturing operations that make fiber into yarn, cotton fiber has been used in this chapter to illustrate the spinning process. It must be remembered, however, that all other raw fibers pass through similar spinning operations, although, of course, there are differences that will be explained in the chapters dealing with the various fibers. One such difference occurs when filaments are used rather than staple. In such instances, the required number of filaments are simply twisted together in a ropelike fashion.

Opening and Blending. When bales are opened at the mill, the compressed masses of raw fiber are loosened and exposed to the atmosphere. Variation in the raw material is eliminated by mixing together parts of several bales and feeding the material into the opening machines. This blending of the raw material results in greater uniformity. Hard lumps in the fibers are loosened, and the heavier impurities—such as dirt, leaves, burs, and any remaining seeds—are removed by three machines known as pickers: breaker, intermediate, and finisher. These machines clean and form the cotton into *laps,* or rolls, that resemble cotton batting; the laps are 40 inches wide and 1 inch thick, and weigh about 40 pounds each.

Carding. In the lap stage, the fibers are still in a tangled condition, containing waste material. Before this raw stock can be made into yarn, these impurities must be removed, and the fibers must be straightened. Such straightening or smoothing is necessary for all natural fibers; otherwise, it would be impossible to produce fine yarns from what is originally a tangled mass. This initial process of arranging the fibers in a parallel fashion is known as *carding.* The work is done on a carding machine, where the lap is unrolled and drawn on a revolving cylinder that is covered with very fine hooks or wire brushes. On top of this cylinder there is a moving belt, also covered with wire brushes.

The cylinder pulls the fibers in one direction, disentangles them, and arranges them parallel in the form of a thin film. This film is drawn through a funnel-shaped device that molds the film into a round ropelike mass called *card sliver,* about the thickness of a broomstick.

Card sliver produces yarns whose serviceability is good enough for ordinary purposes. These yarns are identified as *carded yarns* or *carded cottons* and are used for inexpensive cotton fabrics.

Combing. When the fiber is intended for fine yarns, the sliver is put through an additional straightening called *combing.* In this operation, fine-toothed combs continue the process of straightening the fibers until they are arranged with such a high degree of parallelism that the short fibers, called *noils,* are combed out and completely separated from the longer fibers.

The combing process forms a *comb sliver* made of the longest fibers, which, in turn, produce a smoother and more even yarn. This operation eliminates as much as 25 per cent of the original card sliver; thus almost one-fourth of the raw cotton becomes waste. Therefore, the combing process is identified with consumers' goods of better quality.

Since long-staple yarns produce stronger, smoother, and more serviceable fabrics, quality cotton goods carry labels indicating that they are made from *combed yarns* or *combed cottons*.

Doubling. After carding (or combing in the case of better-grade yarns), several slivers are combined and put through drawing frames for continued condensation of the cotton stock to a denser sliver of smaller diameter.

Courtesy Spool Cotton Co.

The ring spinning frame completes the manufacture of yarn by drawing out the roving, inserting twist, and winding the yarn on bobbins—all in one operation.

Drawing Out. The combining of several slivers for the drawing-out process eliminates irregularities that would cause too much variation if the slivers were put through singly.

The drawing frame has several pairs of rollers, each set of which revolves at a progressively faster speed. After several stages of drawing out, the condensed sliver is taken to the slubber, where rollers similar to those in the drawing frame draw out the cotton further. Here the slubbing is passed to the spindles, where it is given its first twist and is then wound on bobbins.

Roving. These bobbins are placed on the roving frame, where further drawing out and twisting take place until the cotton stock is about the diameter of a pencil lead.

There are two stages of roving: intermediate and fine. The operations are identical, but each machine yields a finer product than the stock it received.

Roving is the final product of the several drawing-out operations. It is a preparatory stage for the final insertion of twist. To this point, only enough

Courtesy Bibb Manufacturing Co.

The principle of the ring spinning process is shown here. The roving (1), on bobbins, is fed between sets of drafting rolls (2) to draw the strand down to the final desired size. The spindle (3) turns the bobbin (4) at a constant speed. The front set of rolls is adjusted to deliver the yarn at a rate of speed so that the desired amount of twist is inserted as the strand moves along. The traveler (5) glides freely around the ring (6). The tension caused by the drag of the traveler causes the yarn to wind on the bobbin at the same rate as it is delivered by the rolls.

twist has been given the stock to hold the fibers together. Roving has no tensile strength; it will break apart easily with any slight pull.

Spinning. The roving, on bobbins, is placed in the spinning frame, where it passes through several sets of rollers running at successively higher rates of speed and is finally drawn out to *yarn* of the size desired.

Spinning machines are of two kinds: ring frame and mule frame. The ring frame is a faster process, but produces a relatively coarse yarn. For very fine yarns, the mule frame is required because of its slow intermittent operation. The ring frame is more suitable for the manufacture of cotton yarns for mass production because of its hundreds of spindles whirling thousands of revolutions a minute and its constant spinning action, which provides a fast operation.

In ring spinning, the roving is passed through an eyelet guide to a small metal loop called a traveler, which runs around a metal ring at a very high speed. Inside the ring, a spindle revolves, pulling the traveler after it, and inserts a stipulated number of twists to the finished yarn.

Courtesy Spool Cotton Co.

After spinning, yarn is sometimes reeled from bobbins into large skeins ready for bleaching, mercerizing, and dyeing.

The ring spinning frame completes the manufacture of yarn (1) by drawing out the roving, (2) by inserting twist, and (3) by winding the yarn on bobbins—all in one operation.

Preparation for Weaving. In the weaving operation, the lengthwise yarns that form the basic structure of the fabric are called the *warp.* The crosswise yarns are the *filling,* also referred to as the *weft* or the *woof.* The filling yarns undergo little strain in the weaving process. Therefore, in preparing them for weaving, it is only necessary that they be spun to the desired size and that they be given the amount of twist required for the type of fabric for which they will be used.

Yarns intended for the warp must pass through such operations as spooling, warping, and slashing to prepare them to withstand the strain of the weaving process. These operations are not intended to improve the quality of the yarn.

Courtesy Bibb Manufacturing Co.

*From spools or cones, mounted on a creel, separate yarns
are wound on a warp beam.*

Courtesy Wool Bureau, Inc.

This operation in a woolen mill tests twist per inch of yarn run.

In *spooling,* the yarn is wound on larger spools or cones, which are placed on a rack called a *creel.* From this rack, the yarns are wound on a *warp beam,* which is similar to a huge spool. An uninterrupted length of hundreds of warp yarns results, all lying parallel to each other.

These yarns are unwound to be put through a starch bath called *slashing* or *sizing.* The slasher machine covers every yarn with a starch coating, which serves to prevent chafing or breaking during the weaving process. The yarns are passed over a large copper drum and are heated by steam, to set the sizing. They are then wound on a final warp beam and are ready for the loom.

Amount of Twist. The amount of twist to the inch is an important factor in finished consumers' goods. It determines the appearance as well as the durability and serviceability of a fabric. Fine yarns require more twist than coarse yarns. Warp yarns are given more twist than are filling yarns. The amount of twist also depends on the type of fabric for which the yarns will be used. For example:

1. Yarns intended for soft-surfaced fabrics are given only a slack twist. They are called *soft-twisted yarns.*

2. Yarns intended for smooth-surfaced fabrics are given many twists to the inch. Such *hard-twisted yarns* contribute strength, smoothness, elasticity, and some crease resistance to fabrics.

*The S twist and Z twist are diagrammed here. The impor-
tance of the direction of the twist is illustrated in the diagrams of thrown silk threads shown in Chapter 12.*

3. Yarns intended for crepe-surfaced fabrics are given a maximum amount
of twist. In this case, the direction of twist is also important and contributes
crease resistance. Direction of twist may be observed by holding a yarn in a
vertical position. If the spirals conform to the direction of the slope of the
central part of the letter S, the yarn has an S twist; if they conform to the
slope of the letter Z, the yarn has a Z twist.

Permanent crepe effects, such as chiffon, georgette, crepe de chine, canton,
flat, and French crepes, are produced by the use of hard-twisted yarns, some
of which have left twist, others right twist. These yarns are placed alternately
in the warp or in the filling, or in both. When the finished fabric is later
washed or dyed, such yarns kink in different directions, producing the crepe
surface.

Another satisfactory method of obtaining crepe effects during the construction of the fabric is by the use of slack warp yarns, which may or may not be
wound on a separate warp beam. These yarns are held less taut than the
other warp yarns and produce a permanent crinkled pattern. Seersucker and
matelassé are produced in this way and prove very serviceable.

Yarn Count. In the spinning process, there is always a fixed relation between the weight of the original quantity of fiber and the length of the yarn
produced from that amount of raw material. This relation indicates the thickness of the yarn. It is determined by the extent of the drawing-out process and
is designated by numbers, which are called the *yarn count.*

The standard for the yarn count in cotton is 1 pound of fiber drawn out
to make 840 yards of yarn; the resultant thickness or size is known as count
No. 1. If the yarn is drawn out farther, so that 1 pound makes twice 840

Courtesy Wool Bureau, Inc.

Testing uniformity of yarn sample in a woolen mill. The yarn is wound on a black card. The distance between each strand is carefully controlled so that when the sample card is completed the inspector can readily judge whether the yarn is being spun to proper evenness.

yards, it is identified as No. 2. Thus, a No. 2 yarn will be finer than a No. 1. No. 10 denoted a still finer yarn, as it indicates that 1 pound of cotton is drawn out to ten times 840 yards. The higher the number of the yarn count, the finer the yarn in size.

Yarn counts up to 20 are called coarse yarns; 20 to 60 are medium yarns; above 60 are fine yarns. Up to 20, the count rises by single numbers. Only even numbers are used between 20 and 60. Above 60, the count rises by intervals of 5 until 100, after which an interval of 10 is used.

The size of mercerized cotton sewing thread used for general purposes is No. 50 or No. 60. The finest yarn ever made in the United States was No. 160, the product of 1 pound of cotton drawn out to a strand 134,000 yards long (over 76 miles). The very finest cotton yarns spun in England have been as high as No. 400; but extremely fine yarns are difficult and costly to manufacture because of the greater care required in spinning and the greater amount of twist to the inch.

The size of yarn to be used in a certain fabric is determined by the pur-

Courtesy Wellington Sears Co.

This sample of duck fabric shows how the use of ply yarns produces compactly woven cloth of great strength.

pose of the fabric. Yarns of varying sizes may be used to obtain the nubbed or novelty effects and rough textures characterized by ratiné, bouclé, or éponge.

Ply Yarns. When two or more strands or yarns are twisted together, they are designated as *ply yarns*. They are termed two-ply, three-ply, and so on, according to the number used in their construction.

A single yarn may be of relatively good quality; but where durability is all-important, ply yarns are preferable, assuming that the yarns have the same length of staple. Good-quality broadcloth for men's shirtings, for example, is made with ply yarns.

Yarn construction and yarn count are expressed in the following manner. The term 1/30s denotes the use of a single yarn having a yarn count of 30. In the same way, 3/30s denotes the use of a three-ply yarn—that is, three strands twisted together, each having a separate yarn count of 30. A three-ply yarn, indicated by 3/30s, would be equivalent to a single yarn having a yarn count of 10. In the same way, 2/10s (containing two single strands of 10s) is equivalent in size to 1/5s.

When the number of yards in a pound of cotton is to be calculated for any given size of yarn, the yarn count is multiplied by 840 yards. For example, if the required size of a yarn is 2/10s, the fraction should be reduced to 1/5s; then the 5 is multiplied by 840; and the result is 4,200 yards.

Doubled Yarns. Another type of yarn construction is the *doubled yarn*. This consists of two or more single strands treated as one in the weaving process; but the strands are not twisted together. The doubled yarn must not be confused with ply yarns, which are stronger because they are twisted. Doubled yarns are used for ornamental effect; they do, of course, contribute a certain amount of additional strength. Because doubled yarns have little twist, they produce luster and softness.

Slub Yarns. The consumer's desire for ornamental effects has popularized the production of yarns that are given only a small amount of drawing out. Such yarns, which are called *slub yarns,* have soft untwisted areas at frequent intervals throughout their length. They are coarse, with slight twist, having varying diameters that show irregularities typical of an incomplete spinning operation.

If simulation of linen is desired, the use of slub yarns is easily understood. Where durability is a main consideration, however, their practicability is justly questioned, because a heavy yarn protruding above the level of surrounding yarns is subjected to friction, and the fabric soon shows signs of wear at those points after continued use.

In the past, slub yarns were generally used in fabrics that possessed an especially compact construction and consequently were characterized by marked durability. Today, slub yarns do not always imply compact construction in the fabric of which they are a part. They do furnish ornamental

The soft untwisted parts of slub yarns, which are the result of an incomplete spinning process, produce interesting irregularities in finished cloth.

Courtesy American Viscose Corp.

effects, and are frequently used for that purpose in cotton broadcloths and tweeds.

Complex Yarns. The spinning process can produce decorative effects also by varying the amount of twist or by twisting together yarns of different diameters. Bouclé and ratiné fabrics are the most common examples of complex yarns. They are made by twisting together two or more yarns under different spinning tensions, thus producing irregularities at intervals along the surface of the yarn.

Other novelty effects can be obtained by using one yarn as a core or base and winding a second yarn around this core. Although the core gives strength with lessened cost, when the inner yarn is of an inferior grade, the product may be regarded as an adulteration.

A safe rule for the consumer is to remember that longer service may be expected from fabrics made from evenly spun yarns rather than from novelty yarns of complex character.

Thread Count. The durability of a fabric depends on: (1) the kind and quality of the fiber, (2) the tensile strength of the yarn, (3) the amount of twist in the yarn, (4) the use of ply yarns as compared with singles, and (5) compactness of construction.

Compactness is one of the most significant factors when considering the durability of a fabric. It is determined by the closeness of the yarns after the fabric is woven. A closely woven fabric has a larger quantity of yarns than a loosely woven one, and is therefore more serviceable. A garment made from such a fabric shrinks less in washing, slips less at the seams, and is more apt to keep its shape.

Novelty yarns produce the attractive nubby effects seen in tweeds.

A fabric of compact construction has a high thread count. *Thread count,* also known as *cloth count,* is determined by counting the number of warp yarns and filling yarns in 1 square inch. These yarns are commonly referred to as *ends* and *picks,* terms that are synonymous with *warp* and *filling,* respectively.

To ascertain the thread count, it is necessary to have a pick glass, sometimes called a thread counter, which is a magnifying glass mounted on a small stand with a square opening in its base. Through this opening, warp and filling yarns are magnified and counted. If the square opening is a ¼-inch size, the number of yarns counted in the quarter inch, when multiplied by 4, gives the number of yarns in 1 inch of the fabric. Some pick glasses have a ½-inch square opening; others have a full square inch. The largest size is preferable as the possibility of error in computation is minimized.

Thread count should not be confused with yarn count. Yarn count measures the degree of fineness in yarns; thread count measures the number of warp and filling yarns in a square inch of fabric. While these counts are separate devices of measurement, there is a direct relationship between them. If coarse sheeting with a low thread count is to be constructed, for example, thick or coarse yarns will be used. These give the fabric greater resistance to hard wear.

• *Typical Thread Counts.* Thread counts range from as low as 20 threads to the inch, used in tobacco cloth, to as high as 350 threads to the inch, found in typewriter-ribbon fabrics.

An example of thread count used as a standard may be illustrated by the Summary of Types of Muslin and Percale Sheets in Chapter 9. A total thread count of 140 threads to the square inch, for example, means that each sheet must have 74 warp yarns and 66 filling yarns to the square inch. The first number indicates the warp; the second is the filling.

With some finished goods, such as sheeting, thread count is sometimes given as a single number, which is the addition of warp and filling. Thus a 74 × 66 is described as a 140.

• *Balanced Construction.* A fabric is said to be well balanced if the number of warp yarns and filling yarns are almost equal. For example, a piece of muslin with a thread count of 64 × 60 is considered well balanced. A piece of gauze with a thread count of 28 × 24 is also well balanced.

In contrast, a broadcloth with a count of 100 × 60 has poor balance. Although good balance of warp and filling produces a fabric with good wearing qualities, a balanced construction is not always obtainable with

Perfectly balanced cloth construction is shown in this sample of sheeting; the number of warp and filling yarns is the same.

Courtesy Wellington Sears Co.

certain staple fabrics. Broadcloth shirting, for example, uses approximately twice as many warp yarns as filling yarns. Therefore, the nature of its construction makes it impossible for it to be well balanced according to thread count; yet it is a durable fabric if its thread count is high.

Sometimes, a fabric may have good balance in its thread count, but it may be altogether unsatisfactory because of weakness in either warp or filling yarns. Therefore, the factor of tensile strength of both sets of yarns must always be taken into consideration when a fabric is being judged. Both yarn count and thread count determine the suitability and value of finished goods. A safe rule for the consumer to remember is that a high-count fabric even with poor balance will give better wear than a low-count fabric with good balance.

▶ TEST YOURSELF ON THIS CHAPTER

1. How are fibers made into yarns?
2. Describe the carding process and what it does to the cotton fibers.
3. Explain why a fabric woven from slub yarns may not wear well.
4. Why would it be difficult to make fabric directly from roving?
5. What is meant by yarn count? Why is it important?
6. Why is thread count especially important?
7. In what way do differences in the raw material affect the formation of yarn?
8. Compare the carding and the combing processes.
9. Explain the processes involved in the manufacture of yarn. Use a rough diagram to illustrate your explanation.

10. What are the qualities that determine the value of the yarn?
11. Explain the meaning of 1/60s, 4/20s, 3/30s.
12. Explain the difference between ply yarns and doubled yarns.
13. How is variation in yarns obtained in the spinning process?
14. How does twist in a yarn affect the finished fabric?
15. For what kind of fabrics are yarns given a very slack twist in spinning?

5 | WEAVING

Yarn to Fabric

The second stage of development of fiber into fabric is the weaving process. Although there are other methods of cloth construction, that of weaving, or interlacing, yarns has foremost place.

It is believed that the interlacing or weaving process became known to primitive man before spinning. At first, materials available for weaving were used in their natural state, just as they grew. As time passed, spinning slowly developed because man discovered that the raw materials could be changed somewhat and improved before they were woven.

It is not known how knowledge of interlacing was first acquired, but primitive man may have observed the interlaced grasses and twigs in the nests of birds, and thus discovered how he could make protective clothing for himself, baskets and nets, and thatchlike huts and fences. Or he may have seen rushes naturally interlacing as they grew.

In the course of time, rude looms were made, which were crudely simple and hand operated. Yet the modern power loom used in the textile industry today contains essentially the same parts and performs the same operations as the simplest hand-operated loom.

Essential Weaving Operations. On the modern loom, the warp yarns are wound on a cylinder called the *warp beam,* which is at the back of the loom. The warp extends to another cylinder called the *cloth beam* at the front of the loom, on which the fabric is rolled as it is constructed. Supported on the loom frame between these two cylinders, the warp yarns are ready to be interlaced by the filling yarns, which thus produce the woven fabric.

In any type of weaving, four operations are fundamental. They are performed in sequence and are constantly repeated. If these operations are carefully noted, the more varied and advanced constructions of fabric will be readily understood.

The essential parts of the loom are: warp beam, cloth beam, harness or

64

Courtesy American Woolen Co.

This loom in operation shows how the harness and heddles (in the upper left) are lifting and lowering units of warp yarns to form the shed through which the shuttle is passing. The reed automatically moves forward to batten each newly woven yarn.

heddle frame, shuttle, and reed. These parts are used to perform the following operations.

1. Shedding—raising warp yarns by means of the harness or heddle frame.
2. Picking—inserting filling yarns by means of the shuttle.
3. Battening—pushing filling yarns firmly in place by means of the reed.
4. Taking up and letting off—winding the finished fabric on the cloth beam, and at the same time releasing more of the warp from the warp beam.

• *Shedding.* On a primitive loom, the weaver had to raise each alternate warp yarn with his finger or with a stick to insert the filling yarns into the

The bobbin of filling yarn lies inside the shuttle, and the yarn is pulled through a small opening in the side as the shuttle moves swiftly across the loom.

This drawing shows how a harness frame holds several heddles in one unit. Warp yarns pass through the eyes of the heddles (shown in center), and are raised or lowered as one unit in the weaving operation.

warp. Weaving was therefore a very slow process. The raising of the warp yarns formed an opening, or shed, through which the filling yarn was inserted. This first weaving operation therefore became known as *shedding.*

On the modern loom, simple and intricate shedding operations are performed automatically by the heddle frame. This is a rectangular frame to which a series of wires, called heddles, are attached. As the warp yarns come from the warp beam, they must pass through openings in the heddles. Each opening may be compared to the eye of a needle. The operation of drawing each warp yarn through its appropriate heddle is known as *drawing in.*

In the simplest weave construction, the heddle frame raises or lowers certain groups of alternate warp yarns so that the filling yarns alternate in passing under one group of warp yarns and over another. The heddle frame is better known as the *harness,* and that term is used hereafter because it will be necessary to refer to the number of harnesses used for the different types of weaves.

• *Picking.* As the harnesses raise the heddles, which raise the warp yarns, the filling yarn is inserted through the shed by a small carrier device called a shuttle. The shuttle contains a bobbin of filling yarn, which emerges through a hole in the side as the shuttle moves across the loom. One passage of the shuttle from one side of the loom to the other is known as a *pick.*

• *Battening.* All warp yarns pass through the heddle eyelets and through openings in another frame that resembles a comb and is called a *reed.* With each picking operation, the reed pushes automatically, or battens, each filling yarn against the portion of the fabric that has already been formed. This third essential weaving operation is therefore called *battening.* It gives the fabric a firm compact construction.

• *Taking Up and Letting Off.* With each shedding, picking, and battening operation, the newly constructed fabric must be wound on the cloth

The reed resembles a large comb. The warp yarns are evenly separated and held parallel as they pass between the teeth.

Courtesy National Association of Wool Manufacturers

*In the drawing-in process, each warp yarn must be
drawn through its assigned heddle. This is determined
by the construction design on the white card, which
can be seen in this picture on the top of the machine.
The warp units are then drawn through the reed.*

beam. This process is known as *taking up*. At the same time, the warp yarns
must be released from the warp beam; this is referred to as *letting off*.

Classification of Weaves.

The manner in which groups of warp yarns
are raised by the harnesses to permit the insertion of the filling yarn determines the pattern of the weave, and in large measure the kind of fabric produced. Weave patterns can create varying degrees of durability in fabrics,
adding to their usefulness and also to their appearance.

In a simple weave construction, consisting of under one warp and over
the next, two harnesses are needed: one to lift the odd-numbered warp yarns,
and a second to lift the even-numbered warp yarns. For advanced weaves,
more than two harnesses are required, and as many as forty may be necessary
for the figured weaves.

The three basic weaves in common use for the majority of fabrics are plain, twill, and satin, with respective variations. Important constructions are also obtained from the following weaves: pile, double cloth, gauze, swivel, lappet, dobby, and Jacquard.

Construction of Cloth Designs. In the textile industry, a pattern of the weave to be used in the construction of a fabric is designed on cross-sectioned paper. A draft of the design of the weave is indispensable when setting up a loom for a particular weave or color effect, as it indicates the particular harness and heddle through which each warp yarn is to be drawn. Textile designers use such graph paper to plot out fabric weave designs. The horizontal squares represent the filling yarns; the vertical squares represent the warp.

The student may obtain a working knowledge of weaves by reproducing such designs on graph paper and then carrying out the actual weaving operations on a miniature loom made of stiff cardboard or a cigar box.

Plain Weave. The plain weave is sometimes referred to as the tabby, homespun, or taffeta weave. It is the simplest type of construction, and is consequently inexpensive to produce. On the loom, the plain weave requires only two harnesses.

Each filling yarn goes under and over the warp yarns across the width of the fabric; on its return, the yarn alternates the pattern of interlacing. If the yarns are close together, the plain weave has a high thread count, and the fabric is therefore firm and will wear well.

As the manufacture of the plain weave is relatively inexpensive, it is used extensively for cotton fabrics and for fabrics that are to be decorated with printed designs, because the surface that it produces is especially receptive to a direct print.

The appearance of the plain weave may be varied by differences in the closeness of the weave, by different thicknesses of yarn, or by the use of contrasting colors in the warp and filling. The last method gives the effect of a design. In addition, two variations of the plain weave afford simple decorative effects; namely, the basket weave and the ribbed, or corded, weave.

Fabrics in Plain Weave. In cotton: batiste, broadcloth, bunting, calico, cambric, challis, chambray, cheesecloth, chintz, crash, crepe, crinoline, cretonne, duck or canvas, flannelette, gingham, Indianhead, lawn, longcloth, muslin, madras, nainsook, oilcloth, organdy, osnaburg, outing flannel, percale, percaline, ratiné, seersucker, scrim, sheeting, tarlatan, voile.

The construction design for the plain weave resembles the familiar checkerboard. The way in which filling yarns pass under and over alternate warp yarns is shown at the right. When fabric is closely constructed in the plain weave, there is no distinct pattern.

In linen: airplane cloth, art linen, cambric, crash, dress linen, handkerchief linen, sheeting, theatrical gauze.

In wool: albatross, blanket cloth, challis, flannel, homespun, nun's veiling, tweed.

In silk, rayon, or other filament yarns: canton crepe, chiffon, China silk, flat crepe, georgette, habutai, mousseline de soie, radium, shirting silks, taffeta, voile, crepe de chine.

• *Basket Weave.* The variation of the plain weave known as the basket weave uses doubled yarns to produce the design that resembles the familiar pattern of a basket. Two or more filling yarns with little or no twist are interlaced with a corresponding number of warp yarns. They are woven in a pattern of 2 × 2, 3 × 3, or 4 × 4, instead of 1 × 1, which is the plain weave.

The weave used in the popular oxford shirting varies slightly from the regular basket weave in that it has a 2 × 1 construction; but the size of the single yarn—a coarser yarn used as the filling—is approximately equivalent in size to the two separate warp yarns. As the coarser yarn has no twist, the fabric is of soft texture and has a degree of luster.

Many variations of the yarn construction of the basket weave are possible.

The basket weave is a variation of the plain weave. Two (instead of one) filling yarns pass under and over two (instead of one) warp yarns. This weaving method results in a simple, attractive pattern, so named because baskets have long been woven in this manner.

This picture of monk's cloth shows how the interweaving of two filling yarns with two warp yarns constructs a loosely woven fabric with an attractive basket-weave pattern.

Courtesy American Viscose Corp.

For example, there may be a 3 × 2 or a 5 × 3, and so on. However, the size or thickness of the combined warp yarns will always equal the size or thickness of the corresponding filling yarns. This provides a certain degree of balance and pattern to the fabric.

The basket weave produces an attractive loosely woven fabric that stretches easily and hangs well. It is therefore suitable for drapery and covering fabrics, such as monk's cloth. Due to the characteristic looseness of construction and the low tensile strength of yarns that have little or no twist, this weave is not considered desirable for clothing purposes where the factor of durability is a primary consideration.

Fabrics in Basket Weave. In cotton: monk's cloth, hardanger cloth, oxford shirting or suiting, panama cloth.

In wool, silk, rayon, or other filament yarns: shepherd's check or plaid.

• *Ribbed Effects.* Ribbed, or corded, effects are further variations of the plain weave. The rib may be produced in the warp or in the filling by alternating fine yarns with coarse yarns, or single yarns with doubled yarns.

Ribbed effects are popular; but the consumer should remember that

The design for oxford cloth shows how a large filling yarn having no twist is woven under and over two single, twisted warp yarns.

The left drawing shows a ribbed or corded effect running in the direction of the warp. The right shows the ribbed effect running in the direction of the filling.

sometimes inferior yarns are used in their manufacture, especially when the yarns that make the rib are hidden in the thickness of the cloth. As these yarns do not show on either side of the fabric, sometimes extremely short-staple yarns or yarns with insufficient twist are used.

A ribbed fabric will not be durable if the ribs are too pronounced, be-cause the coarse yarns that produce the rib tend to pull away from adjacent fine yarns. Also, in ribbed effects, an entire yarn is exposed to friction, thus lessening the durability of the fabric.

Fabrics in Ribbed Effects. Filling-ribbed fabrics include: poplin and broadcloth in cotton; bengaline, faille, taffeta, and ottoman in silk, rayon, and other filament fibers. Warp-ribbed fabrics, usually referred to as *waled* or *corded,* include Bedford cord, piqué, and dimity.

Twill Weave. A distinct design in the form of diagonals is characteristic of the second basic weave, called the twill. Changes in the direction of the diagonal lines produce variations, such as the herringbone, corkscrew, entwin-

When too coarse a yarn is combined with fine yarns for a ribbed effect, the fine yarns adjacent to the rib soon break when subjected to strain or to heavy wear.

Courtesy U.S. Department of Agriculture

The twill weave gives a distinct design in the form of a diagonal. This drawing shows a three-shaft twill; that is, two warp yarns are interlaced with one filling yarn to form the diagonal.

The basic diagonal of the twill weave is shown in all these drawings. The direction of the diagonal and the number of harnesses used produce different surface designs. The drawings at the left show left-hand twills; those at the right are right-hand twills.

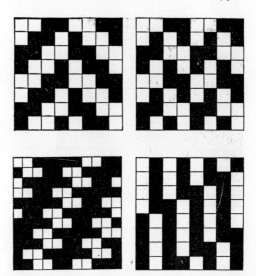

These variations of the twill weave show broken twills (herringbone) in the two upper drawings, a gabardine in the lower left, and a corkscrew twill in the lower right.

ing, and fancy twills. Increased ornamentation may be obtained by varying the diagonal, but the chief values of the twill weave are its strength, firmness, and drapability. The yarns are usually closely battened, making an especially durable fabric. Twill weaves are therefore commonly used in men's suit and coat fabrics and for work clothes, where strong texture is essential.

In the twill weave, the filling yarn interlaces more than one warp yarn, but never more than four, as strength would be sacrificed by so doing. On each successive line, or pick, the filling yarn moves the design one step to the right or to the left, thus forming the diagonal. Whichever the direction of the diagonal on the face of the fabric, the design runs in the opposite direction on the reverse side.

The characteristic diagonal of the twill weave can be seen in this sample of a twill fabric.

The common herringbone twill.

*Courtesy National Association
of Wool Manufacturers*

Twill weaves are named according to the number of harnesses required to make the design. A three- or four-harness twill is a frequently used term. The words "shaft" or "leaf" are sometimes substituted for "harness"; hence the term *three-shaft* or *four-shaft twill.*

Twill weaves are also classified as *even* or *uneven* according to the number of warp and filling yarns that are visible on the face of the fabric. The even twill, for example, shows an equal number of warp and filling yarns in the recurring design, such as two over and two under. This pattern makes what is called a four-shaft twill, and it requires four harnesses.

Most twill weaves are uneven. An uneven twill may show more warp than filling yarns in the recurring design; this is called a *warp-face twill.* If more filling yarns than warp yarns show on the face, the weave is called a *filling-face twill.* An example of an uneven twill is three and one, or three up and one down, indicating the manner in which the harnesses are lifted and lowered. The result is a warp-face twill.

Fabrics in Twill Weave. Wool fabrics are usually right-hand twills, as the diagonal lines run from the upper right-hand corner toward the lower left. Wool twill-weave fabrics are: broadcloth, cashmere, cheviot, covert, flannel, gabardine, mackinaw, melton, pilot cloth, serge, tweed, whipcord, worsted cheviot.

Silk fabrics are also right-hand twills. They include foulard, merveilleux, peau de soie, silk serge, and surah.

Cotton fabrics are usually left-hand twills, as the diagonal lines run from the upper left to the lower right corner. They include canton flannel, covert cloth, coutil, denim, drill, gabardine, hickory shirting or hickory stripe, jean, khaki, middle twill, outing flannel, silesia, ticking, venetian cloth, whipcord.

The twill weave is not used much in the production of linen, as linen yarns make a naturally strong fabric. It may be found in linen ticking, twill toweling, and towel drills.

Satin and Sateen Weaves.

In basic construction, the satin weave is similar to the twill weave; but the diagonal of the satin weave is not visible because it is purposely interrupted. A continuous diagonal would interfere with the luster and smoothness that are the desired qualities of the satin weave.

The satin weave employs a minimum of five harnesses because a smaller number would simply result in forming a twill weave. The use of five harnesses produces a five-shaft construction; that is, the filling yarn passes over one warp yarn and under four warp yarns. The yarn advances more than one warp yarn on each pick, thus interrupting the diagonal. When more harnesses are used, more filling yarns are interlaced by the warp yarn. The number may run as high as eleven, making what is termed a twelve-shaft construction because one filling yarn interlaces every twelfth warp yarn.

No surface design is visible on satin fabric because the yarns that are to be thrown to the surface are greater in number and finer in count than the yarns that form the undersurface of the fabric.

• *Floating Yarns.* Because the interlacing yarn passes over more yarns than it passes under, long yarns, called *floats,* are exposed on the surface of

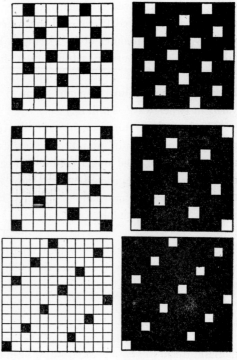

Diagramatic comparisons of satin and sateen constructions. Top left hand: *five-shaft sateen;* top right hand: *five-shaft satin;* center left hand: *eight-shaft sateen;* center right hand: *eight-shaft satin;* lower left hand; *twelve-shaft sateen;* lower right hand: *twelve-shaft satin.*

These drawings show long floats typical of sateen and satin weaves. The left diagram, with the floats in the filling direction, is a five-shaft sateen construction. The right diagram, with the floats in the warp direction, is an eight-shaft satin construction.

the fabric. Since these floats lie compactly on the surface with very little interruption from the yarns going at right angles to them, reflection of light on the floats gives satin fabric its characteristic luster, which is the primary object of the satin weave. When the floats are in the warp, the satin weave produces a warp-faced fabric, and the luster appears in the direction of the warp. When the manner of interlacing is reversed so that the filling yarns are thrown to the surface, a filling-faced fabric is produced, and the luster appears in the direction of the filling. This variation is known as the *sateen weave*. (Sateen is also the name given to a cotton fabric that has floating yarns in either warp or filling.)

The long floats found in the satin weave might be called a disadvantage as they represent a minimum of interlacings, and therefore a potential weakness in the fabric. The longer the float, the greater the chance that the surface of the fabric will snag, roughen, and show signs of wear. On the other hand, the long float gives satin fabric its desired luster and smoothness. The luster makes the fabric suitable for dressy wear; and the smoothness, for use as lining.

Satin-weave fabrics drape well because the weave is heavier than the twill weave, which, in turn, is heavier than the plain weave. More harnesses are employed in the satin weave, thus compressing a greater amount of fine yarn into a given space of cloth. The quality of drapability makes satin fabrics preferable for evening dresses.

Fabrics in Satin Weave. In silk or rayon: slipper satin, merveilleux, damask, duchesse, double-faced satin, satin-faced crepe.

In cotton: damask, lustrine, sateen, ticking, venetian cloth.
In linen: single and double damask.

Designing a Satin Construction. When making a design for a satin construction, the interlacings on successive lines must be separated by a proper interval to avoid forming the contiguous diagonal. When the proper interval for any shaft construction is selected, the design will not repeat itself until the number of successive picks that make up the desired shaft have been interlaced.

In a five-shaft construction, for example, the design begins to repeat on the sixth line; in an eight-shaft, on the ninth line; in a twelve-shaft, on the thirteenth line.

Designing a Sateen Construction. An eight-shaft sateen construction is explained here to illustrate the basic rules that must be followed to select a suitable interval.

1. Arrange in pairs the numbers that will add up to the desired shaft number. For an eight-shaft sateen, the shaft number is 8. The pairs are: 1 and 7, 2 and 6, 3 and 5, 4 and 4.

2. Eliminate the pair that contains the number 1 and the number below the shaft number, which is 7 in this case. A contiguous diagonal would result if these intervals were used, producing the conventional twill weave.

3. Next, eliminate the pairs that have a common divisor and those that are divisible into the shaft number. This step eliminates 2 and 6, 4 and 4. The pair, 3 and 5, remains. These numbers are the only intervals that can be used in an eight-shaft construction. If any of the eliminated numbers were

This drawing illustrates the eight-shaft sateen construction explained in the text. Each of the horizontal lines of blocks represent a filling yarn, or pick. The blocks covered by letters are the points at which the filling yarns interlace the warp yarns on each successive pick. In the eight-shaft satin, the filling is carried across the back, thus creating the float in the warp. The basic idea of the warp-faced satin can be had by turning this diagram sidewise.

used as an interval, the fabric would show no interlacing whatever for one or more warp yarns; in fact, there would be no fabric, as it would fall apart.

Now that the only possible interlacings have been worked out, the design can be constructed. (See the accompanying drawing.) For convenience, here the interlacing begins in the lower left square, at *A*. The horizontal rows of squares represent filling yarns—that is, the successive picks on the loom. The vertical rows represent the warp yarns.

The interval to be used for this particular design could be 3 or 5; in this case, 5 has been selected. As this is to be an eight-shaft construction, the interlacing on the first pick will be 7 squares (warp yarns) apart at *B* and *C*.

To find the warp yarn that will interlace on the second pick, count 5 to the right, beginning with the square above the interlacing that is already started at *A*; thus, the interlacing occurs at *D*. Adjacent interlacing on the same line will be 7 squares apart, at *E*.

To find the warp yarn that will interlace on the third pick, start with the square above *D*. Count 5 to the right, and interlacing *G* is plotted. Adjacent interlacings will be 7 squares apart.

On the fourth pick, interlacing *I* is found by counting 5 to the right of the square above *F*; *J* is found by counting 5 to the right of the square above *G* (or 7 squares from *I*).

This same procedure determines the interlacing points on successive picks, additional interlacings always being 7 squares apart.

On the ninth pick, the design starts to repeat, which proves the accuracy of the construction of an eight-shaft weave.

Where it is not possible to plot subsequent interlacing by continuing to count to the right, because of the small area of the design, interlacings on successive picks can be determined by counting 3 to the left instead of 5 to the right. If the interval 3 had been used to count to the right, 5 would have been used to count to the left.

Fabrics in Sateen Weave. In cotton: damask, sateen, ticking.

In linen: single and double damask.

Pile Weave. The pile weave is a fancy weave that also includes a plain or a twill construction. In contrast to the three basic weaves that produce a flat surface on a fabric, the pile weave introduces a decorative third dimension, creating an effect of depth. Its construction is especially desirable where softness, warmth, and absorbency are desired.

Pile-weave fabrics are also durable if the proper yarns and adequate compact construction are used. In the manufacture of rugs, for example, a strong, tightly twisted staple with compact construction in the base cloth will withstand long wear.

The pile is produced by weaving an additional warp yarn or filling yarn into the basic structure. The additional yarn is drawn away from the surface

This drawing shows the pile weave as it looks after the wires that have raised the filling yarns have been withdrawn.

Cut pile, shown in this drawing, can be produced by using wires equipped with razorlike ends that cut the loops as the wires are withdrawn.

of the fabric by thick wires, which form loops at regular intervals. These loops may be cut or closely sheared, or left uncut if a loop surface is desired, as in Brussels carpet.

When the pile is produced by an extra warp yarn, the result is a warp-pile fabric, of which terry, carpet, and plush are examples. Fabrics are classified as *plush* when the pile is more than ⅛ inch high.

When the pile is produced by an extra filling yarn, the result is a filling-pile fabric, of which velveteen and corduroy are examples.

In certain cut-pile fabrics, the wires used to form the loops are equipped with razorlike ends so that the loops are cut when the wires are withdrawn, thus producing the cut pile exemplified by broadloom carpet.

Cut-pile fabrics are produced economically by constructing double-cloth fabrics, as explained in the following section; then cutting the two cloths apart.

Pile effects can also be created by using varying tension in the warp yarns. In the manufacture of rugs, such as chenille, Wilton, velvet, and tapestry, various processes are used for pile effects, including hand knotting.

Fabrics in Pile Weave. In cotton: chenille, corduroy, duvetyn, frieze, plush, terry (turkish toweling), velour, velveteen.

In wool: frieze, plush, velour, rugs of all kinds.

In silk, rayon, and other filament yarns: chenille, frieze, fur fabrics, plush, transparent velvet, velour, velvets of all kinds.

Linen is seldom made in the pile weave.

Double-Cloth Weave.   In the double-cloth weave, two fabrics are woven on the loom at the same time, one on top of the other. The fabric may have a plain weave on one side and a twill weave on the other. Each of the fabrics

The double-cloth weave can be produced by either of the two methods shown here: the V method in the upper drawing, and the W method in the lower. Cutting the yarn that holds the two cloths together makes two separate cut-pile fabrics.

requires its separate sets of warp and filling yarns. They are combined by interlacing some of the warp or filling yarns, or they may be combined by means of a complete fifth set of stitching yarns.

The surfaces of such fabrics may show different patterns or color on each side by varying the yarns as to color and size. A true double-cloth weave is never a pasted construction.

Because the double-cloth weave produces two pieces of fabric combined into one, fabrics so woven are commonly regarded as strong and warm. Warmth, however, is due primarily to the insulative properties inherent in a fiber; bulk and thickness alone do not give warmth. Also, strength cannot be judged by mere thickness or weight. It cannot be assumed that a double-cloth weave will have the qualities of warmth and strength; on the contrary, the fabric may be heavy, bulky, and needlessly expensive.

Sometimes, this method of construction is chosen in order to use a cheaper material on the reverse side of the fabric, thus reducing the cost of a heavy fabric.

Fabrics in Double-Cloth Weave. In cotton: double-faced blankets, bath-robe blankets.

In wool: polo cloth, steamer rugs, overcoatings.

In silk and other filament yarns: upholstery fabrics of all kinds.

Gauze Weave. The gauze weave must not be confused with the weave used in manufacturing gauze bandages or cheesecloth; these materials are made with the plain weave. The gauze-weave construction produces a fabric very light in weight and with an open-mesh effect. Curtain materials and some cotton dress goods are woven with this weave. Such lightweight fabrics have a strength that could not be provided by the plain weave. In the gauze weave, strength is obtained by the manner in which the yarns are inter-twisted: each filling yarn is encircled by two warp yarns that are twisted about each other.

The gauze weave is sometimes referred to as the *leno weave* because it is made on a leno loom, but the true leno weave is merely a variation of the

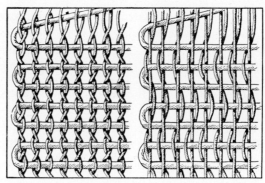

Courtesy U.S. Department of Agriculture

The gauze weave is shown at the left, the leno weave at the right. Note how the filling yarns in the gauze weave are encircled by two warp yarns twisting around each other, a construction that gives strength although the mesh is open. In the leno weave, the second of each of two warp yarns merely passes around the first yarn.

gauze weave. On the leno loom, the action of one warp yarn is similar to the action of the warp in the plain weave. A second warp yarn passes around the first warp simultaneously and alternately over and under the filling yarn. The leno is sometimes used in combination with the plain weave to produce a stripe or figure on a plain background. Generally, the term "leno" is used synonymously with "gauze."

Fabrics in Gauze Weave. In cotton: grenadine, marquisette, mosquito netting, rice net, mesh shirtings.

In silk, rayon, and other filament yarns: bolting cloth, curtain madras, grenadine, marquisette.

Swivel Weave. The swivel weave is the method by which decorative effects, such as dots, circles, or other figures, are interwoven on the surface of a fabric while it is being constructed on the loom. The weaving of the design requires an extra filling yarn and additional small shuttles. A separate shed is made for these shuttles.

While the fabric is being constructed, the row of small shuttles drops across the width of the loom, and each shuttle interweaves its separate design with a circular motion on a small area of the warp. A long thread is carried on the undersurface of the fabric from one design to the next. Different colors may be used in each of the designs because each figure is woven by its own shuttle containing its own miniature bobbin.

The decoration produced by the swivel weave is not considered durable, because the swivel yarns are cut when the fabric is completed and cannot be securely fastened. The cut ends roughen the undersurface of the fabric and may pull out if it is handled carelessly in laundering.

Fabrics in Swivel Weave: dotted swiss, grenadine, curtain madras.

Lappet Weave.   The lappet weave is also used to superimpose a small design on the surface of a fabric while it is being woven. In the lappet weave, the design is stitched into the fabric by needles that operate at right angles to the construction. Thus, the lappet weave is very similar to embroidery.

The lappet design is made with one continuous additional warp yarn, which is carried on the back of the fabric from one design to the next. Only one color is possible. Although the floating threads on the back are cut away when the fabric is completed, the ends are fastened securely and will not pull out easily.

Fabric in the Lappet Weave. Dotted swiss produced by the lappet weave is superior to swivel-weave dotted swiss.

Dobby Weave.   The dobby weave is a patterned weave used to construct designs that cannot be produced by the plain, twill, or satin weaves. The designs are simple, limited in size, and usually geometric in form. They are found in shirtings and tie fabrics.

The dobby weave is created on a plain loom by means of a mechanical attachment, called a dobby or cam, which raises or lowers as many as twenty-four to forty harnesses containing the series of warp yarns that form the pattern. Although a large number of harnesses is used in this construction, the design is always small and does not make use of long floats. The most familiar type of dobby weave is bird's-eye, the small diamond pattern that has an eye in its center.

Fabrics in Dobby Weave. In cotton: bird's-eye, huckaback.
In linen: cretonne, huckaback, mummy cloth.
In wool: granite cloth.

Jacquard Weave.   In any of the weaves that have been described, the number of harnesses determines the construction. For example, two harnesses are required for the plain weave, three or more for the twill, and five to twelve for the satin weave. As many as forty can be manipulated by the special attachment of the dobby. The dobby designs are not intricate, how-

Courtesy Mohawk Carpet Mills, Inc.

*Here is a close-up of Jacquard cards laced together as
they appear on the mechanism at the top of the loom.
As the cards move, needles behind the cards drop
through the perforations and lift strings, which, in
turn, lift heddles.*

ever. They are limited to straight lines, edges, steps, or very small circular
lines.

For curves, swirls, and large-sized figures, it was necessary to devise a
different mechanism that would allow an unlimited range of intricate
designs. This need is met by the Jacquard attachment, named after its inven-
tor, Joseph Marie Jacquard, a Frenchman.

The Jacquard mechanism controls thousands of heddles, which lift one
or more warp yarns independently of others without the use of harnesses.
Its action is similar to that of the player piano, where each note is governed

Courtesy St. Mary's Woolen Manufacturing Co.

This Jacquard loom in operation shows the laced cards at the top of the loom. The long slanting strings control the heddles immediately below the cards. The heddles raise and lower the warp yarns in accordance with the pattern punched on the cards above, the filling yarn making the design as the shuttle passes across the loom.

Courtesy American Viscose Corp.

Damask produced by the
Jacquard.

Brocade produced by the
Jacquard.

by a hole on the music roll and is sounded when the hole passes over a certain opening.

The Jacquard design is first worked out on squared paper. Cards are then perforated to correspond with the design; they are laced together and placed on the Jacquard attachment. The moving cards pass over a battery of needles mounted on top of the loom. Each needle controls a string, which when released picks up the heddle to which it is tied. The perforations on the cards allow the needles to drop through, and lift certain strings, which, in turn, lift single heddles independently of others.

The preparation of a Jacquard weave is the most expensive part of its construction. Setting up the loom may take several weeks or months; but once set, the pattern to be produced can be used and reused for different materials. This is the most expensive form of weaving, and it is chiefly used for linen and for upholstery materials.

Floats are inevitable in the Jacquard weave because of the elaborate designs. As in the satin weave, long floats may affect the wearing quality of the fabric; also, long cotton yarns exposed to friction cause lint. Compact construction of the fabric, however, offsets the tendency to friction and wear; therefore, the consumer should select the better-quality fabrics when purchasing those having the Jacquard weave. This is especially necessary when purchasing linen damask because table linens receive hard wear and repeated washings.

Fabrics in Jacquard Weave. In cotton: matelassé, damask, tapestry.
In linen: single and double damask.
In wool: tapestry.

In silk, rayon, and other filament yarns: brocade, brocatelle, damask, and tapestry.

SUMMARY OF BASIC WEAVES

Weave	Characteristics	Advantages	Limitations
Plain	No distinct design unless yarns have contrasting colors	Maximum yardage; easily produced; inexpensive; strong; adaptable for direct printing and other finishing processes	Sleazy fabric if thread count is low
a. Basket	Basket pattern	Attractive; inexpensive	Not durable for apparel
b. Ribbed	Corded effects	Ornamental	Not serviceable if of inferior construction
Twill	Distinct diagonal design	Strong, firm texture; increased drapability; interesting designs	Requires care to keep clean
Satin	Luster; interrupted diagonal design discernible only with magnifying glass	Beauty contributed by luster; smoothness; maximum drapability	Excessively long floats may snag and roughen fabric

Distinguishing Warp and Filling.   Persons who handle fabrics must be able to identify the warp and the filling yarns, because the direction of the warp determines the way in which the fabric should be cut when a garment is made from it.

In a new piece of yard goods, the direction of the warp is easily distinguished. The length of the fabric indicates the warp yarns. Also, if a piece of the fabric shows part of the selvage, which is the firm edge of the cloth, then the yarns parallel to the selvage are warp yarns. The opposite set of yarns are the filling yarns.

When a sample of fabric contains no selvage, the warp and filling may be identified by observation of the weave.

1. In plain weaves, a greater number of yarns running in one direction indicates the warp.
2. In twill weaves, the filling yarns run in the direction of the diagonal, which may be toward the right or toward the left.
3. In satin weaves, the floating yarns are the warp yarns.

When the name of the fabric is known, its characteristic features aid in distinguishing the warp and filling. For example, the ribs of dimity and of piqué run in the direction of the warp; the ribs of rep, faille, bengaline, and poplin, in the direction of the filling. When colored stripes show in such fabrics as chambray, madras shirtings, and in some dress goods, the direction in which the stripe runs usually indicates the warp.

When the warp and the filling cannot be identified by any of the foregoing aids, the sets of yarns may be examined for some of the following characteristics.

1. Exerting tension on a sample by holding it in both hands and pulling, at the same time pressing with the thumbs and forefingers, will show which set of yarns is stronger. The stronger set will be the warp, because warp yarns have to withstand the tension of the heddles in the weaving process. The filling yarn, which emerges from the bobbin of the shuttle as it crosses the fabric, is under little tension.
2. When one set contains yarns of varying sizes, this set is usually the warp. Filling yarns are usually of the same size.
3. The set of yarns that can be more easily stretched is the filling.
4. Yarns of inferior quality are commonly used as filling in inexpensive fabrics. When both sets of yarns are carefully compared, the inferior yarn is usually the filling.
5. When a yarn has a hard twist, as in serges and overcoatings, that yarn is generally the warp yarn.
6. Yarns with slack twist usually are the filling yarns, because yarns with little twist are used as filling when a soft and lustrous effect is desired.
7. If one set consists of thicker yarns, this indicates the filling, as the bulk produced by large-sized yarns dispenses with the need for a great amount of twist.
8. If ply yarns are used they probably indicate the warp.
9. In a napped fabric, the warp runs in the direction of the napping, because the fabric has been run through the machine in the direction of its length.
10. In light cotton or silk fabrics, a marked evenness between the yarns indicates the warp. This evenness is the result of the mechanical movement of the reed as it battens the filling yarns when the cloth is being constructed. In patterned weaves, such as a herringbone twill, the impact of the battening operation leaves small reed marks that distinguish filling from warp yarns.

► TEST YOURSELF ON THIS CHAPTER

1. Explain why lappet ornamentation is permanent and swivel is not.
2. Why are harnesses not required in the Jacquard weave?
3. Construct a design for one variation of the plain weave.
4. Construct a design for a twill weave.
5. Construct a design for producing a ribbed effect in the warp.
6. Describe the basic operations of the weaving process, naming specific parts of the loom.
7. Compare the pile weave and its uses with the double-cloth weave and its uses.
8. Differentiate between plain weave, ribbed weave, basket weave, and twill. Explain how each is made.
9. Discuss the comparative advantages and disadvantages of the twill and the satin weave. Give an example of a fabric for each.
10. Which of the three basic weaves is: (*a*) The most durable? Why? (*b*) The most beautiful? Why? (*c*) The most inexpensive to produce? Why?
11. What weave would you prefer in a skirt, a suit, curtains? Why?
12. Is it of any advantage to the consumer to know the basic differences between the three foundation weaves? Why?
13. Why was the Jacquard weave somewhat revolutionary in the weaving industry?
14. Contrary to common belief, why does the gauze weave embody strength?
15. How can you differentiate between damask and a fabric made by the dobby weave?
16. Examine the cards on which you mounted small samples of fabrics and identified them as to fiber content and use. Now add the name of the weave pattern used in making each fabric.
17. Wind a piece of yarn or string around a square piece of cardboard, about 4 by 4 inches, so that on each side of the cardboard there are parallel yarns in close rows. These are similar to the warp yarns on a loom. Thread another piece of yarn, of a contrasting color, in a large needle, and insert it through the parallel rows so as to produce the weave pattern of the three foundation weaves.

6 | FINISHING

Appearance and Serviceability

Newly constructed fabric as it comes from the loom does not represent finished consumers' goods. It must pass through various finishing processes that make it suitable for many different purposes. Finishing enhances the appearance of the fabric and also may add to its serviceability and durability, thus increasing its value. Familiarity with finishing processes enables the consumer to recognize and judge quality in fabrics.

The untrained purchaser is influenced too readily by quantity rather than by quality. He is likely to choose the large, the bulky, the heavy. As manufacturers and retailers conduct their businesses to meet existing demand, textile fabrics are finished to a large extent to satisfy this type of purchaser. This explains why many fabrics are "oversized" and others are weighted. If fabric is not properly constructed and if finishing processes are used to conceal inferior construction or to simulate superior quality, the durability of the finished product is questionable.

But this does not mean that all finishing is intended to deceive the consumer, for no type of finish should be labeled as spurious until the purpose of the fabric has been considered. The fact that there is a sustained demand for a particular kind of finished fabric usually explains its continued production.

Converting Gray Goods. Finishing processes have assumed such great importance in the textile industry that this phase of textile manufacturing is undertaken by a highly specialized group of middlemen called *converters*. Conversion of *gray goods,* or goods *in the gray,* includes the various types of finishing processes as well as subsequent dyeing and printing.

The converter contracts for a volume purchase of gray goods and converts this unfinished product into finished consumers' goods in accordance with either solicited demand, which is based on orders taken by his selling force, or with anticipated demand, which is an estimate of the immediate market.

The term *greige goods,* which was originally applied only to unfinished silk fabrics, is also used to denote any undyed, unfinished fabric as it comes from the loom.

Kinds of Finishing Processes.

Finishing may take many forms, for it must be adapted to the kind of fiber and yarn used in the fabric and, most important of all, to its intended purpose. One type of gray goods may emerge from a certain finishing process in a form suitable for curtains, while the identical gray goods put through other finishing processes can be used for dress material.

Even the factor of thread count, so important in the evaluation of a fabric, can be changed by the kind and amount of finishing. Cotton can be given the soft finish required for such fabrics as batiste, nainsook, and lawn, the napped finish required for flannelette and duvetyn, the hard stiffened finish typical of cambric and linene, or the lustrous effect of chintz.

The most common finishing processes are listed here; but the list does not represent a sequence, nor are all the processes mentioned applicable to all kinds of gray goods. Some fabrics must be put through more than one process. Some of the first-named operations are essential preparatory processing for other final finishes, since each fabric is given its own characteristic finishes.

1. Singeing or gassing	14. Ciréing
2. Bleaching	15. Beetling
3. Mercerizing	16. Napping
4. Shrinking	17. Shearing
5. Fulling and other wool-shrinking processes	18. Crepe and crinkled effects
6. Tentering	19. Crease resistance
7. Crabbing	20. Water repellency
8. Decating (or decatizing)	21. Flameproofing
9. Sizing or dressing	22. Mothproofing
10. Weighting	23. Mildewproofing
11. Calendering	24. Milium processing
12. Schreinerizing	25. Slip resistance
13. Moiréing	26. Antiseptic finishes

Singeing or Gassing.

If a fabric is to have a smooth finish, singeing is one of the first essential preparatory processes. It burns off lint and threads, as well as all fuzz and fiber ends, leaving an even surface, which is particularly necessary when a fabric is to pass through the mercerizing process or any printing operation.

Singeing is accomplished by passing gray goods rapidly over rows of gas flames or electrically heated plates at a speed of 100 to 250 yards a minute. After singeing, in the case of cotton fabrics, the cloth is given a bath and is then steeped for several hours in large boiling vats, called kiers, which contain caustic soda, soda ash, and lime. Thorough circulation of these cleansing agents prepares the fabric for the subsequent bleaching operation.

All kinds of fabrics made of short-staple yarns are singed. Singeing may also be done in the yarn stage; for example, lisle yarn, which is made of highly twisted fine cotton staple, is always singed to obtain its characteristic smooth surface.

Bleaching.   If cloth is to be finished white or is to be given surface ornamentation, all natural color must be removed by bleaching. This is also necessary if discoloration or stains have occurred during the previous manufacturing processes. Bleaching can be done in the yarn stage as well as in the constructed fabric. The kind of chemicals to be used depends on whether the fabric or the yarn is composed of vegetable or of animal fibers. When cloth has been bleached for finishing, it is called *bleached goods*.

Cotton or linen fabrics may be bleached by washing only, with subsequent exposure to the sun. Some of the finest Irish linens are bleached in this manner. The slowness of the method eliminates possible overbleaching, which causes deterioration in fabrics.

Chemicals bleach fabrics more quickly than sunshine does; but chemical bleaching requires the utmost care, as too much penetration of the bleaching agent weakens or even decomposes the fibers.

As the use of any strong bleaching agent eventually causes weakness in a fabric, the consumer should select unbleached goods when extreme whiteness is not essential. As there is a general preference for fully bleached white goods, however, additional bleaching is necessary as part of the laundering job; otherwise, white goods eventually take on an unattractive yellowish tinge. If colored goods are selected when possible—for example, in men's underwear —no bleaching is required in laundering, and the garments will consequently last longer.

• *Bleaching Cotton and Linen.* Oxidizing agents, such as chlorinated lime or hypochloric acid, are used for bleaching cotton and linen, the vegetable fibers. A similar bleach can be obtained by diluting a concentrated solution of sodium hypochlorite, which is better known to the consumer by such trade names as Clorox, Rose-X, Dazzle, and the like. Chlorine is an oxidizing agent that bleaches coloring matter in vegetable fibers; but because it is a strong chemical, it also weakens the fabric. Thorough rinsing after immersion in the bleaching agent is therefore imperative.

A commercial preparation, such as Javelle water, can also be used for bleaching cotton or linen. Javelle water can be prepared by mixing ½ pound of washing soda (sodium carbonate) in 1 quart of cold water, adding ¼ pound of chloride of lime. The liquid should be strained through a piece of cloth before using.

Commercial bleaching of cotton and linen fabrics is essentially the same in principle. Gray goods are passed through chlorinated lime or hypochloric acid. The material is then put through a mangle and placed in bleaching bins, where it remains from two to twelve hours, depending on the strength of the bleaching agent and the material. To neutralize the action of the bleach, a mild solution of sulphuric acid is used afterward. The fabric is then rinsed in clear water and dried.

The least injurious chemical bleach used on cotton is hydrogen peroxide. The fabric is also thoroughly rinsed after being treated with this bleach.

Sunlight also may be used to bleach cotton and linen. It is used extensively in Ireland to bleach linen. The gray goods are spread out on the grass and are gradually bleached by the sun. This process is known as *grass bleaching*. The longer the linen remains in the sunlight, the whiter it gets; however, it correspondingly weakens.

• *Bleaching Wool and Silk*. For silk and wool, strong oxidizers cannot be used as they injure animal fibers. White silk and white wool fabrics do not remain white long because exposure to light and air brings back the natural discolorations. In bleaching silk or wool, deoxidizers or reducing agents, such as sulphurous acids or fumes of burning sulphur, are required.

The safest bleach to use is a mild solution of hydrogen peroxide.

• *Bleaching Viscose, Cuprammonium, and Acetate*. Hydrogen peroxide is the only bleach that may be safely used on viscose rayon. Although cuprammonium is also a cellulosic fiber that is very similar to viscose in most respects, hydrogen peroxide should not be used on it. A very mild solution of sodium hypochlorite may be used on cuprammonium rayon. But whenever these fabrics are bleached, they should be thoroughly rinsed immediately.

A characteristic of white acetate is that it remains white; therefore, bleaching should not be necessary. However, if some finish is used to coat the fabric, and the fabric then seems to yellow, a very dilute solution of hydrogen peroxide may be used.

• *Bleaching Nylon*. Nylon is not resistant to bleaches, and therefore should not be bleached.

• *Bleaching Orlon, Acrilan, Dynel, X–51.* These fibers are wholly or partly acrylic. Their reaction to bleaches is very similar. The most effective and safest bleach for all of these is sodium hypochlorite. X–51 may also be bleached with a mild solution of hydrochloric acid.

• *Bleaching Dacron.* Dacron may be bleached by a variety of oxidizing agents. For home use, sodium hypochlorite is recommended.

• *Bleaching Vinyon N and Saran.* These fibers have rather good resistance to bleaches. An oxidizing bleach may be used.

• *Bleaching Fiberglas.* Fiberglas never need be bleached. It always retains its whiteness.

Mercerizing.

Mercerizing is an important preparatory process for cotton fabric. It is also used in the finishing of linen. The fabric is singed before mercerizing, but mercerizing may precede or follow bleaching.

Mercerizing changes the chemical composition of the fiber, strengthening its cellular lines by causing it to swell in diameter and to contract in length; the gain in strength may be as much as 20 per cent. Mercerizing is the simplest chemical method of producing luster in cotton and linen. In addition to increased strength and luster, this process gives fabrics greater absorbency for dyes. Mercerization can also be done in the yarn stage.

Cotton yarn, highly magnified, as it appears
before *gassing and mercerization. Note the dull-
ness of the yarn and the fuzz on its surface.*

Cotton yarn, highly magnified, as it appears after
*gassing and mercerization. Note the smooth, lus-
trous appearance and absence of fuzz.*

Highly mercerized fine cotton yarns can make cotton broadcloth shirting look like silk, and cause cotton damask to be mistaken for linen. When lisle yarn or high-count yarn is mercerized, a silklike luster results that causes the material to be erroneously called "silk lisle."

Gray goods are mercerized by immersion in a specially prepared solution of caustic soda for about ten minutes under conditions of moderate uniform heat and tension. The caustic soda is washed out, and the yarn or fabric is put through a heated acid bath to neutralize the caustic soda. It is then rinsed in clear water and dried. The combined action of the caustic soda, heat, and tension changes and strengthens the fiber cells, thus improving and strengthening the fabric or yarn.

Durene Finish. This is a standardized process of mercerizing that utilizes a fine quality of cotton yarn. Manufacturers who maintain standards established by the Durene Association of America are allowed to label their product "Durene Yarns." These yarns are made of fine long-staple combed cotton and are always of two-ply construction.

Shrinking. When fibers are spun into yarn, they are under constant tension during the weaving process. Their physical condition is changed, but it is not permanently fixed: the fibers will tend to revert to their natural state, causing shrinkage. The yarns are made to assume a final condition by shrinking the fabric in a preparatory finishing process; this minimizes subsequent shrinkage. There are several ways in which this is done.

Some methods comprise immersion in cold water, followed by hot water, steaming, or a chemical treatment. Any such method permits the manufacturer to label his product as preshrunk. But even when textile fabrics are preshrunk, they are liable to further shrinkage when washed. The most that can be expected from manufacturers is some specific information on the label stating the amount of additional shrinkage that may occur after washing.

To realize maximum preshrinkage in finishing, the fabric must be given a preshrinking operation in which no tension is exerted while the fabric is damp. General adoption of such preshrinking methods for all fabrics is not feasible. Additional expense is incurred, and in some cases prized qualities inherent in certain fabrics are sacrificed.

In general, the factors that control shrinkage are the stability of the fiber and the construction of the fabric. Construction is based on the type of weave, the amount of twist in the yarn, the thread count, and the yarn count. The kind of final finishing process also affects shrinkage; for example, a water-repellent quality in a fabric offers resistance to subsequent shrinkage.

If the label on a fabric mentions shrinkage, the fabric must conform to rulings on shrinkage issued by the Federal Trade Commission. One important provision states that if a product is to be labeled preshrunk or shrunk, the label must specifically indicate how much additional shrinkage is to be expected. Formerly, a manufacturer's label reading "fully shrunk" or "will not shrink" or "shrinkproof" did not guarantee that substantially more shrinkage would not take place with continued laundering.

A machine known as a launderometer is used to make washing tests in testing laboratories. A similar, though larger, machine is used for determining shrinkage. Measured distances are marked in indelible ink or with fine threads on unwashed samples of the fabric. The samples are then placed in glass jars containing a washing solution. The jars are sealed and rotated in a tank filled with water that is maintained at a constant temperature. After an interval, the samples are removed, dried, and pressed. By observing any change in the measurements marked on the samples, the amount of shrinkage is determined.

Compressive Shrinkage. Compressive shrinkage is a patented, standardized method that has succeeded in reducing shrinkage in cotton and linens to a practical minimum. The fabric is deliberately shortened in both width and length, resulting in a tighter and closer weave and, consequently, in a higher thread count. Fabrics shrunk by this method are frequently identified as "Sanforized." This term is a registered trade-mark and indicates that the fabric has a residual shrinkage of not more than 1 per cent, and that tests have been made to insure that it conforms to this standard.

The compressive-shrinkage process is carried out on a machine about 65 feet long. The several steps in the process are:

1. Normal shrinkage is determined by subjecting a test sample of the fabric to ordinary washing conditions, using the United States Government wash test.
2. Careful measurements before and after the wash test indicate how much the fabric shrinks in length and width.
3. The compressive-shrinkage machine is set to shrink the fabric to the exact dimensions that the wash test indicated.
4. The fabric is dampened with pure water and live steam, which soften it in preparation for the adjustments to be made in length and width.
5. The width is adjusted by a stretching action, in which the fabric is gripped along its selvages.
6. The fabric is then held firmly against a heavy wool blanket which is under controlled tension.

7. As the tension of the blanket is relaxed to the desired measurements, the fabric shrinks uniformly in length.
8. The fabric is then carried around a heated drum while drying, and the surface finish is restored.
9. A sample is tested again to make certain that additional shrinkage will not exceed 1 per cent.

Perma-sizing. This is a shrinkproofing process developed for, and applied to, knitted cotton goods, which has proved to be effective.

Rigmel Shrinking. Rigmel shrinking is a patented method of mechanical shrinking, somewhat similar to compressive shrinkage, in which a cotton fabric is put through a standard wash test to determine the precise shrinkage in inches per yard, and is subsequently shrunk to planned dimensions that permit anticipation of residual shrinkage.

Sanforsetting. Rayon fabrics may be preshrunk by a process known as Sanforsetting. It will be noted that this term has a resemblance to the term used for preshrinking cotton up to 1 per cent. The process is owned by the same company, Cluett, Peabody & Co., Inc. This process is somewhat similar to the Sanforizing technique. However, Sanforsetting has a residual shrinkage of not more than 2 per cent.

Cylinder Method. This method for shrinking wool uses two perforated cylinders, which steam the fabric as it is rolled off one cylinder and rewound on the other. The steamed fabric is then wound loosely around a wood roller, where it dries and cools slowly and naturally.

London Shrinking. London shrinking is a cold-water process of shrinking wool fabrics. Lengths of wool fabric are retained between wet blankets for about twenty hours. The moisture of the blankets penetrates into the fibers of the cloth. The cloth is then dried slowly and subsequently subjected to a hydraulic pressure of about 3,500 pounds. Cold-water shrinking originated in London. It is considered one of the best methods of preshrinking wool fabrics.

Chlorination Process. This is a chemical method of treating wool so that the fabric will be shrink-resistant. The wool fabric is treated with a dilute solution of calcium or sodium hypochlorite. Some of the scales of the fibers are removed, causing fusion of the outer and inner part of the fibers. As a result, shrinkage decreases. When this protective scaly covering is removed, however, the felting quality is lessened, and the durability of the fabric is affected. But luster and affinity for dyes are increased. Steaming or fulling does not have this result. Chlorinated wool is chiefly used in woolen underwear, socks, and sweaters. Among the trade names for this process are Harriset, Hypol, Kelpie, Kroy, Sanforlan, Schollerizing, and Protonizing.

Resin Treatment. This is also a chemical shrinking process. The wool fabric is treated with an organic resin. The treatment has no harmful effect on the properties or handle of the fabric. There may be a residual shrinkage of not more than 2 per cent. Among the trade names for this process are Lanaset, Pacifixed, and Resloom.

Fulling. The process of fulling, an important operation in the finishing of wool fabrics, actually operates as a preshrinking process for wool. The fibers are cleaned, scoured, and condensed by a combination of moisture, heat, soap, and pressure. Sometimes, chemicals are added to increase the adhesion of the fibers. The condensing is a natural result of the felting property of wool fiber—shrinkage takes place because the fibers are drawn together. As a result, the fabric has a fuller, more compact body.

Tentering. As a fabric passes through various finishing processes, it becomes irregular in width. To restore it to its proper width, the cloth must be stretched in some parts and shrunk in others. This process is called *tentering*. It is done on a machine that grips the fabric along the selvages with movable clips in chain form, so that it can be jerked along its length.

The fabric is fastened on the tentering machine while it is moist, and steam is sprayed from underneath to aid in the stretching and shrinking. Before the fabric leaves the machine, it is dried by heating devices. Occasionally, the tiny holes or marks of the clips are noticeable in the selvages of yard goods.

In properly finished fabrics, the filling threads are at right angles to the

Courtesy H. W. Butterworth & Sons Co.

In the tentering machine, the fabric is restored to its original width.

warp. If the angle varies, the fabric is described as "on the bias." Tentering helps to straighten the warp and filling threads and to smooth the fabric.

Crabbing. In finishing wool fabrics, a stretching process called *crabbing* passes the cloth over rollers into hot water or steam. The fabric is then put into cold water, after which it is pressed.

This process is similar to tentering, as the fabric is stretched or loosened where necessary and finally set at the width at which the warp and filling yarns are in proper relation to each other. Consequently, there is no hidden strain on any portion of the fabric. Crabbing also prevents the formation of creases or other forms of uneven shrinkage in subsequent finishing operations.

Decating (or Decatizing). This finishing process may be applied to wool fabrics. It sets the nap and develops the luster of the fabric. In wet decating, the material is tightly wound on a perforated iron roller and immersed in a trough of hot water which is circulated through the fabric. In dry decating, steam is used instead of hot water.

Decating may also be applied to rayon and other man-made and synthetic fabrics to improve the hand (feel), color, and luster of the fabric. It may also be used to overcome uneven or blotchy dyeing.

Sizing or Dressing. Cotton and linen can be given stiffness, smoothness, weight, and strength by immersion in a solution of starch. This process is commonly known as *sizing*. A small amount of starch in consumers' goods, especially in cotton fabrics, helps to retain freshness while they are on the dealers' shelves. Cotton fabrics that are usually sized are organdy, lawn, voile, and buckram.

Some sizing is acceptable, but the consumer should refrain from purchasing fabrics that have too much sizing because it may conceal inferior construction. Sizing fills in the openings in the constructed cloth, creating an appearance of greater compactness; thus, a low thread count is not immediately discernible at the time of purchase. If a fabric loses body after one or more washings, it has been oversized.

Excessive sizing can be detected by rubbing the fabric between the hands. This causes the sizing to come off in the form of a fine powder. An absolute test can be made by touching the fabric with a drop of weak iodine; if starch is present, a blue color appears.

Other substances used for dressing fabrics are flour, dextrine, glue, shellac, fats, wax, and paraffin. The starches give weight; glue gives stiffness; fats give softness; wax and paraffin produce luster. Starch, baked brown before using, is known as dextrine, or British gum; in this form, it gives a soft dressing to a fabric.

Cotton fabric is sometimes sized with clay chalk, barium sulphate, calcium sulphate, or magnesium sulphate to make it especially heavy and close in texture. Some sizings make cotton fabrics susceptible to mildew, but this tendency can be offset by the addition of zinc chloride to the sizing bath.

• *Glazing.* A stiff polished or glazed surface can be obtained by the application of starch, glue, mucilage, or shellac. The process makes a fabric resistant to dust and spots, and minimizes shrinkage. This finish is found principally on chintz. Everglaze and Vita-glaze are typical trade-marked names for this process.

In recent years, Everglaze has been expanded to include a technique that permits cotton to be so processed that it may look like satin, piqué, or any other fabric. Actually, it is a combination of Everglaze and embossing to give cotton fabric the appearance, luster, or texture of the fabric that it is to resemble. The appearance is permanent, provided it is laundered in lukewarm water with a mild soap and no bleach is used.

• *Permanent Sizing.* Permanent sizing effects can now be achieved without the use of starch. A chemical process changes the cellular structure of the fiber. By this method, sheer and medium-weight cottons are given stiffness, which sometimes lasts throughout the life of the fabric. These processes are known by specific trade names. They vary in method, in the chemicals used, and in the degree of permanency of the final finish. All have the property of making the fabric smoother, and it soils less easily because dirt tends to slide off rather than to cling. As a result, fabrics with permanent sizing usually require less laundering and therefore last longer. Some of these permanent finishes are described here.

Ankord. Ankord, a starchless finish given to cotton and rayon gray goods, increases tensile strength, improves luster, and reduces shrinkage.

Bellmanizing. In the Bellmanizing process, permanent crispness can be given to sheer cottons by sealing the fibers chemically with resinous compounds. The fibers undergo basic structural changes; they become round, stiff, and firm, and thus resistant to untwisting, fraying, and creasing. The chemical compounds do not dissolve in laundering. No starch is used in the process, nor is starch required in subsequent washing. The Bellmanizing process is effective on sheer cottons, such as batistes, lawns, voiles, and organdies.

Clearight. This is a starchless process that imparts lasting crispness. Clearight is generally used on sheer fabrics.

Saylorizing. Saylorizing is a starchless finish similar to the Bellmanizing process. It gives permanent crispness to medium-weight as well as to sheer cottons.

Sheercroft. Sheercroft is a starchless finish that imparts crispness and increases luster, giving cotton a linenlike appearance.

Stabilized. The Stabilized process gives a finish like sizing. It also adds body to spun rayon and to cotton, but the finish is not permanent.

Staze-Right. This finish gives luster and crispness to organdies and marquisettes, and is resistant to washing and dry cleaning.

Basco. This starchless finish increases strength and gives permanent luster and a linenlike appearance to fabrics.

Trubenizing. Trubenizing is a patented process that prevents wilting in collars and cuffs. Fabric made of acetate yarns is used to interline the collars and cuffs, which are then immersed in acetone and pressed with a hot iron; the result is a permanent stiffness that does not require starching. This process also gives rise to the term *fused* collars and cuffs.

Weighting. Fabrics are sometimes weighted to give them additional body. When cotton fabric is weighted with any of the various sizing agents, it is heavier and appears to be closely constructed. Its poor construction becomes apparent after washing, however. The consumer should learn to judge such fabrics for their quality, not for their apparent weight.

Weighted silk fabrics have become acceptable in the textile industry; but if excessive metallic salts are used in the weighting, they eventually weaken the fabric. The Federal Trade Commission has therefore issued specific regulations with respect to kinds of weighting and their proper labeling.

Only low-grade wool fabrics are weighted. As much as 40 per cent additional weight can be obtained by felting extremely short wool fibers into the fabric. These fibers, called *flocks,* are obtained when wool fabrics are washed, brushed, and sheared. The use of an excessive amount of flocks can be detected by brushing and shaking the fabric vigorously. Careful examination of the selvage will also reveal flock particles.

Additional weighting has been gained by treating wool fabric with magnesium chloride, which causes an excessive water content. This spurious practice gave rise to the expression, "watered stock."

Cotton may be weighted by one of two processes. A flat cotton fabric such as sheeting can be heavily starched, and the construction will look and feel very compact. Rubbing the fabric between the hands will cause the dry starch to fall out. The second method is a flocking procedure that is used on napped cottons. These flocks, as with wool, are forced into the fabric under air pressure. They can be detected in the same manner as with wool.

Calendering. Calendering is essentially an ironing process. It presses out folds or creases in the fabric by passing it around a series of heavy, highly polished steam-heated rollers that move at different rates of speed and have varying degrees of heat. Calendering flattens the fabric, removing inequality of surface; it imparts smoothness and luster, but not permanently.

For highly lustrous effects, the fabric is sized before it is run through the calendering machine. The smoothness and the luster are determined by the degrees of heat and the amount of pressure, as well as the amount of sizing, if any is used.

The calendering process varies according to the type of finish desired. Where a light calendering effect is intended, the fabric is passed between cylinders without heat. The pressure alone removes wrinkles and imparts smoothness.

Wool fabrics are sometimes calendered or polished. The process adds a soft luster. Typical of such fabrics are wool broadcloth and sheen gabardine.

Schreinerizing. Schreinerizing is an inexpensive method for imparting luster to low-priced cottons. Steel rollers, finely engraved with lines and exerting a pressure of 4,500 pounds, impress on the fabric diagonal ridges ranging from 125 to 600 to the inch. Reflection of light from these ridges gives the fabric a lustrous effect somewhat similar to that produced by mercerization. But the luster produced by schreinerizing is not permanent because the imprinted ridges disappear with repeated launderings. However, this finish is suitable for lingerie fabrics and for linings and sateens, as the slightly rough surface produced by the diagonal ridges reduces the tendency of fabrics to cling. If the fabric has been mercerized, the additional schreinerizing produces a luster simulating that of silk.

Moiréing. By attaching engraved rollers to the calendering machine, the attractive, lustrous wavy design known as *moiré* can be produced. The best moiré results are obtained on fabrics that have rib effects in the filling. Fine lines are imprinted on the raised filling yarns by hydraulic engraved rollers capable of exerting over 100,000 pounds pressure to the square inch. The luster is produced by the divergent reflection of light on the lines of the design.

A moiré pattern on a rayon fabric is more lasting than the same pattern on a similar silk fabric, because the natural elasticity of silk does not permit the permanent retention of an embossed design. In acetate, moiré is definitely permanent, because acetate fabrics have a melting reaction when subjected

The best moiré results are obtained by imprinting the pattern on ribbed fabrics. Luster is produced by divergent reflections of light on the lines of the design.

Courtesy American Viscose Corp.

to the heat of the moiréing process, thus absorbing and hardening the pattern as the cloth cools. A similar condition can be obtained with nylon because of its tendency to melt and to hold a shape.

An entirely different method of moiréing cotton is obtained by treating the fabric with a chemical and then embossing the cloth. The moiré is permanent provided the fabric is cared for properly. It should be washed with a mild soap in lukewarm water and never should be bleached.

Ciréing. The ciré process may be applied to silk and rayon, usually satins and taffetas. Wax or a similar compound is applied to the fabric. This is then followed by hot calendering. The result is a supergloss almost metallic in appearance.

Beetling. Beetling is a common finishing process for linen. It gives the cloth a firm, flattened, lustrous appearance. All table linen is put through this process, but dress linens are never beetled.

In beetling, the fabric is hammered; the yarns are flattened by the impact of wooden mallets. This hammering actually closes the weave and creates a heavy and compact appearance. Luster is an accompanying result.

Beetling differs from calendering. The smoothness and gloss obtained by the calendering process are the result of horizontal pressing and are not permanent, whereas in beetling the action performed is a vertical impact that permanently flattens the yarns.

Cotton fabrics can be made to simulate linen by beetling, as the process gives cotton the firm feel and lustrous appearance of linen.

Napping. A napped fabric should not be confused with a pile-weave fabric. In the pile weave, the thickness is a true third dimension produced by loops from an extra warp or filling yarn. In the napped fabrics, the

The teasel, a dried flower head with stiff, hooked bracts, is used to produce the fuzzy surface on napped fabrics.

thickness is only a surface fuzziness that is the result of a brushing process. When a fabric is to be napped, the yarns intended for the construction of the cloth are given only a slack twist in the spinning process.

The fuzzy finish produced by napping makes a soft fabric, which provides warmth because of the insulative air cells in the nap. The thicker the nap, the more air cells, and the warmer the fabric. In men's suitings, where long wear is desired, a napped surface acts as a protection against objectionable luster. The fact that stains can be removed easily from a napped surface is an additional advantage. On the other hand, napping may also serve to cover up a sleazy construction as well as weaving imperfections. It is generally considered that excessive napping tends to weaken the fabric, especially where a heavy nap has been produced.

Single napping signifies that both sides of a cloth have been napped in one direction; *double napping* signifies that both surfaces have been napped in opposite directions, which produces greater surface density, increased firmness, and greater warmth. Flannelette, wool flannel, suede cloth, and duvetyn exemplify napped fabrics. Cotton and spun rayon fabrics are napped when a soft, fuzzy surface is desired.

Vegetable burs called *teasels* are used for napping finer grades of wool fabrics. Long cylindrical rollers containing closely set wires, which act like brushes, also perform the teaseling operation. As the brushes slide over the revolving fabric, they pull the top fibers and raise the protruding ends above the surface of the cloth in the form of a fleecelike nap. If a heavy nap is desired, teaseling is repeated several times.

• *Gigging.* Wool fabrics may be napped, or they may be subjected to a raising process called *gigging.* The fabric is first saturated with water. When the fibers of a moist wool fabric are raised, they tend to curl and shrink. They are then brushed in one direction. A smooth and lustrous appearance results.

Shearing. Pile-weave fabrics and fabrics that have been napped are usually sheared to give an attractive smooth surface to the cloth. Shearing levels all surface irregularities caused by the plucking action of the teasels in the

Courtesy National Association of Wool Manufacturers

A rotating spiral blade shears surface irregularities from napped and pile fabrics. A brush (shown in lower part) removes the sheared ends.

napping process. Shearing is done by a cylindrical machine having rotating spiral blades whose action resembles that of a lawn mower. After shearing, the fabric is automatically brushed to remove the sheared ends of the yarns.

Crepe and Crinkled Effects. The permanent types of crepe effects are obtained by the use of hard-twisted yarns in the weaving process, as described in Chapter 5. Crepe surfaces can also be produced by certain finishing processes, but the results are not so satisfactory.

One of the finishing methods imprints a crinkled effect by means of engraved rollers. The effect is similar to that produced when the thumbnail is drawn across tissue paper. The finish disappears with repeated washings, however.

In another finishing method, caustic soda is impressed on the fabric in the form of figures or stripes. The fabric is then washed; the part im-

Courtesy American Viscose Corp.

In seersucker, a crinkled effect is ob-   *In matelassé, a crinkled effect is pro-*
tained by the use of slack warp yarns.   *duced by the Jacquard.*

printed with the soda shrinks, and the other part puckers. A similar effect is obtained by using strips of wax in place of the caustic soda. Plissé crepes are produced by these methods.

The nonpermanency of these crepe effects can be easily detected by pressing the thumb heavily on a portion of the fabric and stretching it sidewise at the same time. The pressed portion will be smoothed; no ripple will be felt on its surface.

A chemical method gives a crepe effect to silk by treating the fabric with concentrated sulphuric acid for a few minutes, followed by rinsing and neutralization with a weak alkali. There is a decrease in luster and a slight loss in strength. This method calls for careful manipulation, because too long an exposure in the acid injures the silk.

A permanent crinkle may be obtained on a fabric that will melt, such as nylon. The fabric is put through a hot roller on which there are raised figurations. The contact of the fabric against the raised hot surfaces causes it to melt and pucker at those points.

All crepe fabrics tend to stretch and shrink when subjected to any wetting operation.

Crease Resistance.

Both silk and wool enjoy a quality of elasticity that makes them resistant to wrinkling, creasing, or crushing. The vegetable fibers do not have such inherent elasticity. Slacks made of cotton, linen, or long-staple rayon, for example, are not so serviceable as wool slacks because the vegetable fibers crush easily. A crease-resistant finish for these fabrics is therefore desirable. Such a finish may be obtained in several ways.

The use of short-staple yarn, particularly in linen and rayon, produces a quality of softness in the fabric that makes it crease-resistant to some degree, but durability is sacrificed.

The soft surface of a napped fabric also gives crease resistance. Fabrics with crepe surfaces possess a real crease-resistant quality, the degree being determined by the process used to produce the crepe surface.

Chemical methods are also used to give cotton and linen fabrics varying degrees of elasticity by impregnating the yarns with synthetic resins and gums. Phenol formaldehyde, urea formaldehyde, and acrylic resins are most commonly used. These produce an elasticity that does not disappear with dry cleaning and washing if the fabric is handled with care. There are several patented processes on the market today.

Anticrease Finish. In the anticrease process, a solution of formaldehyde resins is baked into the cloth, penetrating the fibers and resulting in a softened flexible fabric. Fabrics so treated are not absolutely crease-resistant, but they resist crushing and recover easily. These fabrics also tend to shrink less in laundering. Because of the added weight of the resin, drapability is increased. The process may be used effectively on cotton, linen, rayon, and acetate fabrics.

Perma-Pressed. This is a wrinkle-resistant process that may be applied to cotton fabrics.

Unidure. This finish is applied to spun rayons to avoid excessive wrinkles. Wrinkles that do occur will hang out. Unidure adds body to the fabric and improves the brightness and fastness of color. It also reduces shrinkage and stretch, and is not affected by dampness and wilting weather.

Wat-A-Set. This is a wrinkle-resistant finish for cotton fabrics.

Wrinkl-Shed. This process gives cottons an excellent wrinkle-resistant property. It is difficult to wrinkle such cotton fabrics, and any wrinkles will hang out overnight. The finish does not come out and actually gives the fabric longer life.

Vitalized Finish. The Vitalized finish, also known by its English trade name Tebilized, is a patented crease-resistant process similar to the Anticrease finish. It gives additional "vitality," or elasticity, by the use of synthetic resins. It is applicable to both cotton and linen cloth. Fabrics so treated are heavier and shrink less. Washing or dry cleaning does not affect the Vitalized quality.

Water Repellency. There is only one method of making a fabric permanently waterproof: by coating the surface of the cloth with rubber or with plasticized synthetic resins treated with solvents. The application of either of these solutions, repeated if desired with separate dryings, and subsequent vulcanizing or baking, closes the pores of the fabric, making it permanently impervious to water. But such waterproofing has the disadvantage of giving excess weight to the fabric and eliminating porosity, so important for health and comfort. When rubber solvent is used, cracks eventually appear in the surface coating.

Consumers have preferred garments that have been made repellent to water rather than absolutely waterproof. Water-repellent fabrics are sprayed or brushed with resins, waxes, metallic soaps, or linseed oil. These substances impregnate the fibers of the cloth and fill in the spaces between the yarns, giving the fabric a water-repellent quality. Water-repellent fabrics must not be confused with waterproof fabrics. A water-repellent treatment does not affect the natural characteristics of a fabric, including its porosity.

The protective coatings used in some of these processes tend to disappear when exposed to friction and wear. However, a water-repellent quality can always be restored to a fabric.

Silk can be made water-repellent by treatment with oil, both sides of the cloth being coated with linseed oil varnish. This method changes the original appearance of the fabric: it produces a smooth hard surface and a quality of translucency. Oiled silk is popular for shower curtains and light raincoats for women.

Wool fabric has a natural water repellency that makes this fiber suitable for raincoats that are used in a light rain. Napped surfaces and fabrics with high thread count have natural water repellency. When fine, highly twisted yarns are constructed into fabrics having a high thread count, the garment is sometimes windproof as well as water-repellent.

Any fabric can be made water-repellent by spraying it with a solution of paraffin in benzine; a fine coating of paraffin is produced on the cloth. This finish is not permanent.

Many patented processes have water-repellent features; some of these are: Cravenetting, Zelan, Aradex, Impregnole, Koroseal, Neva-Wet, Aquasec, Bandri, Hydrovised, Rainfoe, Repel-o-tex, Sayles Storm King, Wat-A-Tite.

Cravenetting. In this patented process, the fabric to be made moisture-repellent is placed in a solution of aluminum stearate, pressed until dry, and then passed through a tallow soap solution. The aluminum stearate is precipitated on the fabric. With continued wear, fabrics so treated may lose some of their rainproof quality, as dry cleaning and high temperature tend to decompose the aluminum stearate coating.

Zelan. The Du Pont Company has patented the Zelan process, which gives a water-repellent finish to cotton, linen, and viscose rayon. This finish can be applied to fabrics only under carefully controlled conditions, and therefore must be given to the unfinished cloth at a finishing plant.

To be effective, the Zelan finish must be applied after mercerization, but before any other finishing agent, such as soap, salt, oil, gum, or starch, is used. The treatment contains no rubber, wax, or insoluble soap. It does not coat the fabric but permeates and becomes a part of the fiber without impairing the natural porosity of the fabric.

Zelan is regarded as a permanent finish because its water-repellent quality endures repeated washings as well as dry cleanings. Other advantages that may be claimed for fabrics treated with Zelan are that stains and spots can be sponged off with a damp cloth, and that the fabrics resist perspiration and wrinkling, manifesting a softness of texture that improves appearance.

Aradex. The Aradex treatment, which is somewhat similar to the Zelan finish, uses a chemical emulsion that imparts qualities of water repellency, spot and stain resistance, and improved crease resistance. In contrast, the Aradex finish is not permanent, since it is affected by laundering and dry cleaning; but the finish can be restored after cleaning. Aradex does not coat the cloth, and thus permits the normal circulation of air. The appearance and feel of the fabric are not impaired.

Impregnole. In the Impregnole process, a fatty emulsion is used that contains paraffin hydrocarbons and aluminum salts. This process makes cotton and wool fabrics water-repellent as well as resistant to spots, stains, perspiration, and wrinkles. One immersion is sufficient, and the emulsion is easily applied. Washing and dry cleaning remove this water-repellent quality, but the finish can be restored.

Koroseal. The Koroseal process can be applied to any finished fabric except acetate. It makes fabrics impervious to water, wind, moths, and mildew, and resistant to acid, grease, sunlight, perspiration, and stains. Koroseal fabrics do not contain any rubber or oil; consequently, they will not deteriorate by cracking, sticking, or peeling, and therefore serve a multitude of uses. The coating applied to the surface of the fabric is plasticized white powder, polyvinyl chloride, which is obtained by compressing two gases—acetylene from coal and limestone, and hydrogen chloride from salt. The result is a tough, stretchable plastic coating having unusual properties.

Flameproofing. Only mineral, asbestos, glass, or metal substances are really fireproof. Textile fabrics cannot be made absolutely fireproof, but they can be chemically treated to retard inflammability. Fabrics so treated may be regarded as flameproof, which means that they will not flame or burn actively. Flameproofing is a practical form of fire protection where a fire-resistant quality is desirable, as in fabrics used for awnings, mattresses, work clothes, or draperies.

The objection to most fire-retardant compounds is that the fabric so treated loses this quality in washing or in dry cleaning. Also, such compounds sometimes affect the feel of a fabric, causing it to lose softness and flexibility. Where the fire-retardant quality is lost in washing or in dry cleaning, it can be easily restored by reprocessing with any of the commercial fire-retardant compounds.

Some of the trade-marked names that indicate a fire-retardant quality are Du Pont, Fire-Retardant, Saniflame, Neva-Flame. These processes are applicable to all fabrics except acetate.

A more recent flameproof compound, called Permaproof 300, has been described as the first finish that permits cloth to be laundered repeatedly without losing its fire-retardant properties.

Among the most effective flameproofing compounds is one that uses ammonium sulphamate; it makes a fabric fire-resistant without imparting a harsh quality. The fabric must be reprocessed after washing, but this is not necessary after dry cleaning, as the ammonium sulphamate finish is fast to dry-cleaning solvents.

Textile fabrics may be given a fire-resistant quality by a simple home method of immersing them in a solution of 70 per cent borax and 30 per cent boric acid. If the fabric to be treated is already water-repellent, soap should be added to the solution so that an even wetness and absorbency will be obtained. This method does not alter the appearance of the fabric, but the treatment must be repeated after every washing.

Mothproofing. Wool fabrics are sometimes mothproofed as one of the finishing operations to the cloth by impregnating the yarns with a chemical. Of all these preparations, tests seem to indicate that the most effective are Mitin F F, Eulan C N, and Lanoc C N. These are fast to other finishing processes as well as dry cleaning, but are only moderately fast to washing.

Simple home methods of moth damage prevention comprise daily brushing of apparel after wearing, frequent exposure to sunlight, and dry cleaning before placing the garments in airtight storage and cold storage at a maximum temperature of 40 degrees Fahrenheit. For additional protection, various commercial compounds are available for use in the home. Among these are naphthalene and paradichlorobenzene (moth balls, flakes, and cakes). These do not act as a repellent, as is commonly thought. They will actually kill the moth, eggs, and larvae, provided the closet, chest, or package containing the wool fabrics is airtight. The atmosphere must be thoroughly saturated for these substances to be effective. Incidentally, since the vapor emitted is heavy, the container should be hung above the clothes so that the vapor will flow down over them.

Many sprays are also available. Some of these, such as Atomoth, Berlou, Boconize, Larvex, and Ya-De, contain either a fluoride or silicofluoride. These are very stable to exposure to light and air and are not removed by dry cleaning. However, they are water-soluble and also may give rise to white markings when the fabric is rubbed. They also may cause a harshening of the fabric's handle. Other products containing carbon tetrachloride, such as Moth Gas, are also effective but are inflammable. And others containing arsenic, such as Per Mo, are poisonous to humans as well as to moth larvae.

Products containing DDT in concentrations of at least 5 per cent kill moth grubs quickly. These sprays are sold under such proprietary names as Black Flag, Gulf Trak, and SLA. However, DDT has the disadvantage of dry-cleaning and washing out.

Mildewproofing.

The use of sizing in finishing makes a fabric susceptible to mildew if it is later exposed to moisture and warmth.

To prevent mildew, inorganic salts, such as magnesium chloride, calcium chloride, and zinc chloride, are used as warp sizing. Washing, however, tends to remove the mildewproof quality. Among recent developments has been the use of turpentine and formaldehyde as preventives. One compound that is not easily washed out is a 1–2000 solution of phenyl mercuric acetate in water. This is one of the most effective mildewproofing agents.

Shower curtains or other cotton fabrics may be mildewproofed in the home by soaking the material in very soapy water, then, without rinsing, dipping it into a solution of copper sulphate.

Various antiseptics, such as boric acid and carbolic acid, also prevent rapid growth of the mildew fungus.

Milium.

This is a process of adding a coating of metallic particles on one side of a fabric to give remarkable warmth-retentive properties. Any fabric that is to be used as a lining can be coated with this resinated metal (usually aluminum) spray, which adds less than an ounce to the weight of the lining and does not interfere with the porosity or pliability of the fabric. The process operates on the principle that the metal will prevent body heat from radiating outward through the garment by reflecting the heat back toward the wearer. Tests using a wind velocity of 15 miles an hour have shown that a wool outer fabric with a milium satin lining is approximately equal in warmth to an untreated satin lining plus an 8½-ounce wool interlining with the same outer fabric.

Slippage at the seams may be the result of low thread count as well as poor construction of the fabric.

Courtesy U.S. Department of Agriculture

Slip Resistance. In fabrics that have a low thread count, the warp yarns sometimes slip along the filling yarns. This action is known as *slipping*. Unusual wear or strain on some part of a fabric may also cause the same action. It is not frequent with rough-surfaced fabrics made of hard-twisted yarns.

Permanent firmness can be given to fabrics by immersing them in synthetic resins, then stretching and drying them under tension. The deposit of resin at the points of interlacing in the weave prevents the yarns from slipping. This treatment is particularly advantageous for smooth-surfaced rayons, as the smoothness of the synthetic yarn causes it to slip and fray.

Fabrics labeled "slip-resistant" should be examined closely for thread count, as the resinous coating may be used to create an effect of compactness in construction.

Antiseptic Finishes. Chemical antiseptic finishes impart a self-sterilizing quality to a fabric. The appearance and the feel of the fabric are unchanged, and no chemical odor remains. Dry cleaning does not impair the finish. Sanitized, Hygienized, Sani-Age, and Vita-Fresh are trade-marked names exemplifying these finishes.

▶ TEST YOURSELF ON THIS CHAPTER

1. Describe one important preparatory finishing process for smooth-surfaced fabrics.

2. Name six finishing processes for producing luster.
3. In each pair of the following finishes, which type is preferable and why? (*a*) Waterproof or water-repellent; (*b*) fireproof or flame-resistant?
4. What is the purpose of weighting? Why would it be unwise to buy a heavily weighted silk garment?
5. Explain two finishing methods by which a crinkled effect is achieved.
6. What is the result of the beetling process? How does it compare with schreinerizing?
7. How is starch used in finishing fabrics?
8. Explain the following processes: singeing, mercerizing, calendering.
9. How may a finishing process deceive the consumer?
10. Discuss shrinkage, telling (*a*) why it occurs, (*b*) whether it can be prevented entirely, (*c*) what methods are preferable for cotton, (*d*) what methods are preferable for wool.
11. Discuss the advantages of napping. Name the disadvantages, if any.
12. What fabrics are naturally crease-resistant? How can this quality be produced in other fabrics?
13. What method of bleaching is preferable? Is there any advantage in buying unbleached fabrics?
14. Why are finishing processes necessary?
15. Explain tentering and crabbing.
16. Add the name of the finishing process that was used for each of the sample fabrics you have obtained. If this is not readily discernible, visit the yard goods department of any large retail store, and examine the finish used for ten different fabrics. Obtain the names of these fabrics from the salesperson or by noting the label. List them on a sheet of paper, and explain each.

7 | DYEING

Finishing with Color

As the textile fibers have been examined and tested for their differential qualities, and as the spinning and weaving processes have been explained, the qualities of durability and serviceability have been constantly stressed. When the yarn is woven into fabric, the interesting and intricate designs of weaves begin to add beauty of appearance as well as serviceability. The various finishing processes suggest additional means of enhancing the appearance of the newly formed fabric.

It remains for the dyeing and printing processes to provide lasting beauty and delight to the eye; for both these processes add color to fabrics, and color delights by stimulating or soothing. Dyeing and printing differ in the method by which color is applied to fabric. In the dyeing process, fiber, yarn, or fabric is immersed in a solution of dyestuff, and is thus saturated with the dye. In printing (to be described in the following chapter), a pattern or a design is imprinted on the fabric in one or more colors by using dyes in paste form.

Selection of Dye. To select the proper dye for a fiber, it is necessary to know which dyes have an affinity for the vegetable, animal, man-made, or synthetic fibers. In general, the dyes used for cotton and linen may be used for viscose and cuprammonium rayons; but it was necessary to produce a special class of dyes for acetate.

When a dye colors fabric directly with one simple operation of immersion, without the aid of an affixing agent, the dye is said to be a direct dye for that fiber. Direct dyes are the easiest to produce, the simplest to apply, and the cheapest in their initial cost as well as in application. They are the most fugitive, however; that is, they are not fast to washing or to light. The term *bleeding* describes dyes that run in washing. If dye rubs off a fabric when the fabric is exposed to the friction of wear, the action is termed *crocking.*

Requirements for colorfastness differ. Fastness to *light* is important in draperies, for example, as they must stand strong light daily but do not need to be washed frequently. Fastness to *washing* is important in dress fabric and household linens because they must undergo frequent washings.

Therefore, both the kind of fiber to be dyed and the intended use for the fabric enter into the selection of the dye.

Mordants. A dye that has an affinity for one type of fiber may not adhere to other types of fibers; but it is possible to dye finished fabric containing a mixture of fibers by using a mordant in the dye bath. Salts of metals and tannic acid are typical examples of such chemical agents. The mordant adheres to the fiber for which the dye has no affinity, and the dye adheres to the mordant. Dyes that are used with a mordant are called *mordant* or *adjective* dyes.

Natural Dyes. Primitive man obtained dyes from flowers, nuts, berries and other forms of vegetable and plant life, as well as from mineral and animal sources. These same sources have provided what are termed "natural dyes" throughout the succeeding years of civilization.

The principal vegetable dyes are: fustic, sumac, catechu or cutch, madder, henna, saffron, logwood, indigo, and alizarin. Animal dyes, such as cochineal, squid sepia, lac, and Tyrian purple, are obtained from species of fish and small insects; minerals provide such dyes as Prussian blue, chrome yellow, and iron buff.

Natural dyes are no longer used in quantity by the dyeing industry, but they are still used in Oriental countries to a certain extent for rug dyeing and in many parts of the world for native handicraft.

Artificial Dyes. Although artificial dyes were first derived from coal tar in 1856, they were not developed in the United States to any great extent until World War I, when the supply of imported synthetic dyes was cut off. Since then, the United States has built up a dye industry that is unsurpassed. Innumerable dye compounds made from coal tar have now supplanted natural dyes. These artificial or synthetic dyes are constantly being improved as to beauty of color and colorfastness.

Lasting beauty of color is an important factor in consumers' finished goods. Durability of color depends on: (1) selection of the proper dye for the fiber to be dyed; (2) selection of the method of dyeing the fiber, yarn or fabric.

Classification of Synthetic Dyes. The synthetic dyes are classified as (1) acid, (2) basic or alkali, (3) neutral or substantive. The acid dyes are used chiefly for wool, and the basic dyes chiefly for silk. The substantive dyes are a new class especially adapted for cotton, linen, and rayons. For this reason, they are called direct cotton dyes. They are also known by the specific names that describe their method of application: direct or salt dyes, developed dyes, sulphur dyes, vat dyes, and naphthol or azoic dyes.

Acid Dyes. In the textile industry, acid dyes are known as *commercial colors.* They are used as direct dyes for wool and Vicara; they are also used when delicate tints are required for silk. Acid dyes also may be used on Orlon, Acrilan, Dynel, and X–51. They can be applied with some difficulty to nylon and Vinyon N.

Acid dyes are inexpensive and fairly fast to light, but they are not fast to washing. Acetic acid or sulphuric acid, and sometimes Glauber's salt (sodium sulphate), is used in the dye bath.

Wool may be given increased fastness to both light and washing by boiling the fabric in a chromate solution after the first dye bath. This is called *afterchroming.* A special group of acid dyes known as *chrome dyes* is used for this purpose.

Basic Dyes. Basic dyes are direct dyes and have been used chiefly for silk because they give brilliant, full colors. They can also be used with a mordant for cotton, linen, nylon, and X–51. Basic dyes are not fast to light, washing, perspiration, or atmospheric influences; they tend to bleed or crock. These dyes are frequently used as an aftertreatment for fabrics that have been previously dyed with acid colors.

Direct or Salt Dyes. Direct dyes for cotton and linen, and viscose and cuprammonium rayons are known as *direct cotton dyes* because they achieve very bright, full colors for that fabric. They are sometimes used for reclaimed wool and for inferior grades of wool. When so used, a small amount of acid must be used. Direct dyes may also be used for nylon, Vicara, X–51, Dynel, and Vinyon N.

Because sodium chloride (household salt) is included in the dye solution, direct cotton dyes are also known as *salt dyes;* the salt helps to drive the color into the fabric by lessening the solubility of the dye in water. The process is one of simple immersion and absorption rather than one requiring affixing chemical agents or compounds. When direct dyes are used for cotton fabrics, they do not need to be bleached, except when a half bleach is necessary to prepare the fabric for light shades.

Direct dyes are not fast to washing. An aftertreatment with potassium bichromate or formaldehyde gives an additional degree of fastness in washing; a similar treatment with copper sulphate increases fastness to light. More expensive operations, such as are used in developed, sulphur, vat, and naphthol or azoic dyes, are designed to produce additional degrees of color-fastness.

• *Developed Dyes.* Developed dyes are used for cotton, linen, and viscose rayon. The color is developed by additional treatments, which also make the dye fast to washing. But developed dyes are not fast to light. As these dyes do not bleed, they are called *tub-fast colors,* and are used for women's apparel that must withstand frequent washings.

Developed dyes cost more because of extra operations. After the fabric has been immersed in a suitable dye bath and rinsed, it is dipped in a cold acid solution of sodium nitrite; this process is known as *diazotizing.* The original dye is transformed into an active chemical, which is combined with a developer (beta naphthol) in another cold bath. This third treatment develops a new color that is insoluble in water and therefore fast to washing. Developed dyes are also fast to acids and alkalies.

• *Sulphur Dyes.* Sulphur dyes are used for cotton, linen, and viscose rayon. These dyes are fast to washing, light, and perspiration. They have one weakness: excessive chlorine bleaching will strip the color. Sulphur dyes are more expensive than direct dyes because of the unusual care required in the extra operations.

Sulphur is insoluble in water, but it is made soluble with the aid of sodium sulphide and soda ash. The dyeing is done at high temperature and with a large quantity of salt, which helps to drive the color into the fabric. After immersion in the dye bath, followed by rinsing, the fabric is oxidized to the desired shade by exposure to the air or, chemically, by the use of potassium bichromate and acetic acid. The oxidizing process must be carefully controlled because penetration of the dye is retarded by premature oxidation. Also, oxidation changes sulphur to sulphuric acid, which may be harmful to the fabric. Excess chemicals and excess dye must be completely removed by thorough washing.

Sulphur dyes penetrate more thoroughly than any other dye because of the high temperature and the alkalinity of the dye bath. They are excellent for khaki and for the heavy piece goods used in work cloth. Sulphur dyes produce dull colors, such as navy, brown, and black. They are used for black more than any other dye. If stored for a great length of time, sulphur-dyed fabrics become tender.

• *Vat Dyes.* Vat dyes are the fastest dyes for cotton, linen, and viscose and cuprammonium rayons. They also may be applied to nylon, Orlon, Acrilan, X–51, Dynel, Dacron, Vicara, and Vinyon N with the use of a mordant. Vat dyes are not only resistant to light and to acids and alkalies, but they are equally resistant to the strong oxidizing bleaches used in commercial laundries. In this respect, vat dyes excel sulphur dyes, which are not fast to chlorine washing. In reds and pinks, however, absolute colorfastness is sacrificed for brilliancy of dye. Consequently, a label stating that a garment is vat-dyed is not a guarantee that the fabric is absolutely fast to washing if it is of brilliant color.

The name "Indanthrene" on labels indicates that a special type of dye has been used that is particularly fast to light and to washing. This type was among the first of the synthetic vat dyes.

The old-fashioned method of fermenting and steeping indigo in a vat gave vat dyes their name. They are prepared today on the same principle, but they are chemically purer and the process is shorter. Vat dyes are expensive because of the initial cost as well as the method of application. They are insoluble pigments; but they are made soluble in water by the use of a strong reducing agent, such as hydrosulphite dissolved in the alkali, sodium hydroxide. The fabric is immersed in this solution. Subsequent exposure to air or immersion in an oxidizing bath (bichromate) restores the dye to its insoluble form as a part of the fiber.

Naphthol or Azoic Dyes. Naphthol or azoic dyes are as satisfactory as vat dyes in their fastness to washing and to strong bleaching agents, but not in fastness to light. When a bright red that will be fast to washing and to light is desired for cotton or rayon, a naphthol red dye is used. Azoic dyes also may be used for nylon, Acrilan, Dacron, and Vicara.

The method of applying these dyes is somewhat similar to that of developed dyes, as it involves diazotizing. The fabric is first immersed in naphthol, which impregnates the fibers; it is then dipped into the diazotized color bath. The dyeing is followed by thorough soaping and rinsing. Naphthol or azoic dyes are sometimes referred to as *ice dyes* because ice is frequently used to bring the dyes to a low temperature.

• *AZO Dyes.* A large single group of dyes that, in recent years, has accounted for almost half the total production of dyes are sulphonic acids. These are used as acid dyes. In the use of AZO dyes, the fiber may be treated with a chroming solution that deepens the color and produces a greater fastness on the fiber.

Acetate Dyes. When acetate was first made, it could not be colored with dyes that were available at that time; but special acetate dyes were produced after experimentation. These dyes do not have affinity for any of the natural fibers or for viscose and cuprammonium rayons. They will dye nylon, but the final shade of the color will not be the same as the acetate shade. Acetate dyes may be used on all the man-made and synthetic fibers with varying degrees of success.

Two groups of acetate dyes are now used: (1) those that dye directly, and (2) those that require diazotizing and affixing agents in developing the color. Some of the earliest acetate dyes are known as S.R.A. dyes. This name was derived from "sulphoricinoleic," the acid that is required to make the dyes soluble in water.

Selection of Method of Dyeing.

Textiles may be dyed at any of the stages of their development from fiber into fabric. The methods are summarized as follows:

1. Stock dyeing, in the fiber stage.
2. Yarn dyeing, after the fiber has been spun into yarn.
3. Piece dyeing, after the yarn has been constructed into fabric.
4. Cross dyeing, a combination of either stock dyeing or yarn dyeing with subsequent piece dyeing.
5. Solution pigmenting or dyeing, before the man-made or synthetic fiber is extruded through the spinneret.

In stock dyeing, a mass of fiber is immersed in the dye bath.

Courtesy Cleveland Crane Engineering Co.

Stock Dyeing. In stock dyeing, the fibers are immersed in a dye bath, and the dyestuff is allowed to penetrate them. This method is considered most desirable because maximum penetration may be expected when material is in this form. A dye that penetrates to the center of a fiber will resist rubbing; therefore, stock-dyed fabrics are likely to be colorfast.

Yarns spun from dyed fibers are uniformly colored; if there is any irregularity of color, it is evened up in the subsequent carding, drawing-out, and spinning operations. Dyed fibers are more difficult to spin than undyed ones, however, because a degree of flexibility is lost in the dyeing process.

Woolens are often stock-dyed. The completeness of this method of dyeing is reflected in the expression, "dyed in the wool," which is used to attribute the quality of thoroughness.

Stock dyeing produces mixture effects and color blends, of which oxford suitings and tweed homespuns are examples.

Yarn Dyeing. When dyeing is done after the fiber has been spun into yarn, the fabric is described as yarn-dyed. This method is also sometimes referred to as *skein dyeing*; the yarn is on spools or is in the form of skeins when immersed in the dye bath. The dyestuff has a chance to penetrate to

Courtesy Bibb Manufacturing Co.

In package dyeing (a form of yarn dyeing), bobbins or cones of yarn on a single large rack (at left in picture) are immersed at one time in a huge vat.

Plaids and ginghams are constructed of yarns dyed in the yarn stage.

Courtesy National Association of Wool Manufacturers

the core of the yarn, similar to the penetration of the fiber in stock dyeing. Yarn-dyed fabrics are usually deeper and richer in color, and tend to be more colorfast than when the fabric is dyed after it is woven.

When yarns have been dyed separately, interesting color effects can be introduced into the weaving process by combining yarns of different colors. In such fabrics, the warp yarn is usually one color and the filling another color. Examples of combinations of different-colored yarns are: checked gingham, striped percale, shepherd's check, plaid, chambray, seersucker, and heather mixtures.

Piece Dyeing.   When cloth is dyed after it is woven, the process is called *piece dyeing,* sometimes *dip dyeing.* In piece-dyed fabrics, the dye does not penetrate and envelop the fibers or yarns as in stock dyeing or yarn dyeing. But this method is advantageous to the manufacturer because it permits him to keep his production close to changing fashion demands. When fabric is to be piece-dyed, it is woven "in the gray," and can be subsequently dyed to supply any current seasonal color. This method is also economical because less dyestuff is required. It is commonly used for the less expensive fabrics.

Piece dyeing is limited to the production of solid colors, but two-color effects may be obtained by constructing the fabric of fibers or yarns that have been specially treated so as to take a deeper color, or to absorb no color at all.

From the point of view of the consumer, piece dyeing is the least desirable process because complete penetration does not take place, and the fabric may fade. When light spots show at frequent intervals, this is an indication that the fabric was piece-dyed; in this case, only the surface of the yarns took the dye. The consumer can generally detect piece dyeing by raveling and

Courtesy St. Mary's Woolen Manufacturing Co.

Piece dyeing in a modern stainless-steel dye vat.

untwisting a single yarn, and examining the innermost part to see whether the dye has penetrated.

Piece dyeing is used for a wide variety of fabrics. Linens, silk crepes, and sheer cottons such as organdy and voile are piece-dyed.

Cross Dyeing.

Cross dyeing is a combination of stock dyeing or of yarn dyeing with subsequent piece dyeing. Cross dyeing produces varied effects. For instance, either the warp or the filling yarns may be stock-dyed or yarn-dyed, one set of yarns being left undyed. The fabric is piece-dyed after weaving; thus, color is given to the undyed yarn in a second dye bath, and the yarns that were originally stock-dyed or yarn-dyed acquire some additional coloring, which blends with the piece-dyed portion of the fabric.

If yarns of vegetable fibers have been combined with yarns of animal fibers in a fabric that is to be piece-dyed, two separate dye baths must be used. The fabric must be dipped into both solutions, each of which affects the fiber for which it has an affinity. This affords a good opportunity for colorful effects.

A mordant can be included in a single dye bath to cause the dye to adhere to the fiber for which it does not have an affinity. Thus, the more expensive method of cross dyeing, requiring two dye baths, need not be used.

Still another method of cross dyeing is to immerse a fabric composed of two different types of fibers into one dye bath containing two different dyes, one specific for each of the fibers. For example, a fabric composed of viscose rayon and acetate yarns may be cross-dyed in this manner. When the fabric is removed from the dye bath, the viscose rayon yarns will be one color, and the acetate yarns will be another color.

Solution Pigmenting or Dyeing. In producing man-made or synthetic fibers, a great deal of time and money can be saved if the dye is added to the solution before it is extruded through the spinnerets into filaments. This method also gives a greater degree of colorfastness.

A process called solution pigmenting or dyeing has been used with varying degrees of success for man-made and synthetic fibers ranging from rayon through saran and Fiberglas. Some effective results have been obtained.

Two outstanding examples of the solution-pigmenting process for acetate fiber are *Chromspun* and *Celaperm*. The former is the trade name for the process developed by the Tennessee Eastman Company; the latter is the trade name for a similar process developed by the Celanese Corporation of America. These solution-pigmenting processes were developed to overcome two problems in dyeing acetate yarns and fabrics: inability to absorb dyes well and evenly, and the tendency to fade, particularly gas-fade. Chromspun and Celaperm insure uniform color and colorfastness to gas, light, perspiration, salt (sea) water, washing, and dry cleaning.

Tests to Determine Colorfastness. Beauty of color in any fabric is of no value to the consumer unless the dye may be considered fast under the conditions in which the fabric will be used. Color must meet such tests as washing, ironing, steaming, perspiration, strong light, and dry cleaning.

The United States Government tests fabrics for colorfastness to maintain and enforce trade standards. Retail stores often have laboratories for testing consumers' goods to maintain merchandise standards for their own protection as well as to give their customers proper value for the price paid.

The consumer may also test fabrics for colorfastness at home. Some of the simple tests are well worth while, as garments will give additional wear and retain a fresh, new appearance if samples of the fabrics are tested before the garments are subjected to cleaning at home or at commercial laundries or dry cleaners.

• *Fastness to Washing*. The usual method for determining fastness to washing is to wash a sample of the fabric, and to iron the sample while it is still wet under a white cloth. If the dye bleeds on the white cloth, the color cannot be considered fast. Home washing is not a rigorous enough test for fabrics that will be washed in commercial laundries. For such, a more adequate test is to immerse the sample in water containing a bleach, such as Clorox, or in Javelle water, because similar strong compounds are used in the laundries.

• *Fastness to Ironing*. To test for fastness to ironing, iron the sample with a very hot iron. After the sample has cooled, compare it with the original fabric. If the color is unchanged, the fabric is fast to ironing.

• *Fastness to Steaming*. To test for fastness to steaming, place a sample between the folds of a white cloth, and steam it over a teakettle. If the color is fast, it should be unchanged, and no dye will show on the white cloth.

• *Fastness to Light*. To test for fastness to light, cover half of a sample of fabric with opaque paper, and expose the sample to outdoor light for perhaps twenty days; then compare both halves. If the exposed portion shows a perceptible fading, the fabric is not fast to light. It is not possible to give a more specific period of time for exposure because the intensity of sunlight varies in different localities. Usually, resistance to an exposure of twenty days is considered good.

This test is performed in a much shorter time in textile testing laboratories by the use of the Fade-Ometer, an apparatus having very strong electric lamps or a special carbon arc light. If a fabric can withstand an exposure of forty hours in this machine with no perceptible loss of color, it is said to have superlative fastness to light. A fabric has good fastness to light if it withstands an exposure of thirty hours.

• *Fastness to Perspiration*. To test for fastness to perspiration, soak a sample of the dyed fabric for ten minutes in a weak acid, such as a dilute acetic acid solution. Do not rinse. Roll the sample in a piece of undyed cloth. Permit gradual drying, and leave the material rolled for a few days. If comparison with the original color shows that the shade of the dyed fabric has changed, or if the dye appears on the cloth in which the sample was rolled, the color is not fast to perspiration.

The effects of both acid and alkaline perspiration can be determined by the standard Government test, which recommends the use of two solutions. *For acid perspiration:* 10 grams sodium chloride; 1 gram lactic acid, U.S.P. 85 per cent; 1 gram disodium orthophosphate, anhydrous. Make up to 1 liter with water. *For alkaline perspiration:* 10 grams sodium chloride; 4 grams

Courtesy American Viscose Corp.

The Fade-Ometer is used for testing colorfastness to sunlight. Samples of fabric are placed between slides and are exposed to the rays of a sun lamp for a period of hours or days. After removal, the samples are compared with an unexposed piece of fabric to determine the extent of loss of color.

ammonium carbonate, U.S.P.; 1 gram disodium orthophosphate, anhydrous. Make up to 1 liter with water.

Samples of the dyed fabric are placed against pieces of undyed cloth and left for a few days in each solution. The pieces of dyed fabric and undyed cloth are then squeezed and allowed to dry. Any indication of staining denotes poor fastness to perspiration.

• *Fastness to Crocking.* To test for fastness to crocking, rub a dry sample against a white cloth; make the same test with a wet sample. If the color does not rub off on the white cloth, the color is fast to rubbing or crocking.

• *Fastness to Gas Fading.* Flames from heating appliances cause nitrogen in the atmosphere to unite with oxygen, forming nitrogenous compounds that cause some acetate dyes to lose color if the fumes come in contact with the fabric. This is known as gas fading or acid fading in acetate; blue is especially susceptible. An antifume finish of an alkaline nature can be

ARTIFICIAL DYES RANKED BY COST
AND DEGREE OF FASTNESS[1]

Type of Dye	Home Washing	Commercial Laundry	Light	Slashing	Bleaching (Chlorine)	Cross Dyeing	Mercerizing
Direct	Good in light shades; poor in heavy shades	Poor	Some poor, some good	Good in light shades; heavy shades require care	Bad	Bad	Some good
Basic	Poor	Bad	Bad	Require extreme care	Bad	Bad	Bad
Sulphur	Good	Fair to poor	Good	Excellent	Bad	Good	Good
Developed	Good	Fair to poor	Poor	Excellent	Bad	Good	Good
Naphthol	Excellent	Excellent	Very good	Excellent	Excellent (not good to peroxide)	Excellent	Excellent
Vat	Excellent	Excellent	Excellent	Excellent	Excellent	Excellent	Excellent

[1] Courtesy Franklin Process Company. The sequence runs from the less expensive direct dyes to the more expensive vat dyes.

applied to a fabric to minimize gas fading. This is accomplished by the use of an inhibiter in the dye.

Fabrics can be tested to determine the permanency of their antifume finish by exposure for about twenty hours in a chamber containing the combustible fumes of a gas burner.

▶ TEST YOURSELF ON THIS CHAPTER

1. What are the essential differences between stock, yarn, and piece dyeing?
2. Explain the importance of dyeing from the consumer's point of view.

3. What is vat dyeing? When would it be used?

4. Discuss both the limitations and the advantages of direct dyes.

5. Discuss the advantages and the limitations of acid dyes.

6. When is cross dyeing used?

7. Explain the following terms: fugitive, crocking, bleeding, gas fading.

8. What is a mordant? Explain how this can be used to replace one method of dyeing.

9. Why are warp yarns dyed in the fiber stage or in the yarn stage instead of using the piece-dyeing method entirely?

10. What two factors enter into the selection of a dye?

11. What type of fabrics need to be colorfast to washing? To light? To perspiration?

12. What kinds of dyes are used for the animal fibers? For the vegetable fibers? For man-made and synthetic fibers?

13. Why is salt often put into a dye bath?

14. What happens to sulphur-dyed fabrics if they are stored for a great length of time?

15. Why are direct dyes the least desirable for the general consumer?

16. Why are vat-dyed fabrics the most desirable for the general consumer?

17. What is solution dyeing? What are its advantages?

18. What characteristic is common to yarn dyeing and skein dyeing?

19. What factors determine the durability of a dye?

20. Explain the difference between dyeing and printing.

21. Describe briefly the methods and stages of dyeing.

22. Explain how to test colorfastness to: (*a*) light, (*b*) washing, (*c*) crocking.

23. Obtain small samples of colored fabrics, and test them for colorfastness. Report the procedure used in your test and your findings.

24. Examine the labels on three pieces of apparel or household furnishings. Copy each label on a sheet of paper, and write your interpretation of each label in terms of the textile information that you have acquired.

8 | DECORATION

With Color Design

The spinning process produces yarns of varying sizes—linenlike yarns with nubby effects, slub yarns, and a variety of complex yarns, such as bouclé and ratiné. All these yarns are used to create some form of decoration in the fabric. Later, in the weaving process, decoration is also obtained by the pattern of the weave. The checkerboard pattern of the plain weave, the variations of the basket construction, the diagonal of the twill weave, and the luster of the satin weave produce simple designs. This type of decoration becomes more elaborate as fabric construction advances to the use of the third dimension in the pile weave, to the open-mesh lacelike effect of the lappet weave, and to the intricate effects of the Jacquard weave as seen in damask, brocade, and brocatelle fabrics.

When fabric passes through finishing operations, it is given lustrous effects by mercerizing, sizing, schreinerizing, calendering, beetling, or moiréing, all of which contribute something to its final appearance. Other finishing processes create the additional effects of soft napped surfaces and the crinkled designs seen in seersucker, matelassé, and similar crepes.

Dyeing makes an important contribution to fabric decoration by the many beautiful colors it produces and the color harmonies that may be obtained by combinations of the various dyeing methods.

All the foregoing decorative effects are obtained at various stages of construction of the fabric—some at the fiber stage, others during the spinning and weaving processes, still others during the finishing and dyeing processes.

Methods of Decoration with Color. Decoration in the form of color can be applied after the fabric has been otherwise finished. One such form of decoration is called *printing*. Fabric that is to be printed must be singed, bleached, and cleaned.

The methods of decoration that produce color designs are:

1. Block printing
2. Roller printing
3. Duplex printing
4. Discharge or extract printing

Courtesy Celanese Corp. of America

Machine-printed fabrics.

5. Resist printing   10. Batik dyeing
6. Stencil printing   11. Tie dyeing
7. Screen printing   12. Composition or paste designs
8. Warp printing   13. Spray painting
9. Photo printing

In most of these methods, the dye is imprinted on the fabric in paste form, and any desired pattern may be produced. Paste dyes require a sizing, such as cornstarch or wheat starch, which acts as a binder. In this method of applying color, thorough penetration of the dye is not necessary.

Distinguishing Printing from Dyeing. When the consumer wants to know whether a fabric has been dyed by immersion or whether the color has merely been printed on the cloth, he should examine the outline of the design. On a printed fabric, the outline or edges of the design are sharply defined on the right side, and the entire design seldom penetrates to the wrong side.

On sheer fabrics, the design may show up favorably on the wrong side because dyestuffs will penetrate sheer construction. Such fabrics may intentionally simulate woven designs, which use yarn-dyed warp and filling; therefore, the consumer should examine some of the raveled yarns. If the design has been imprinted, the yarns will show areas on which the color is not equally distributed.

Block Printing. The oldest method of printing designs on fabric is the hand method called block printing. This method is not commercially important because it is too slow—printed fabric cannot be produced inexpensively in large enough quantities by the hand-blocked method. Block printing has usually been done in countries where labor is less costly than in the United States. Today, fabric is block-printed only in comparatively short lengths of material. Block printing is found chiefly in decorative pieces for the home or in expensive linens for upholstery purposes.

To make hand-blocked prints, the design must first be carved on a wooden or metal block. The dyestuff is applied in paste form to the design on the face of the block. The block is pressed down firmly by hand on selected portions of the surface of the fabric, imprinting the carved design as many times as desired on a specific length of cloth.

To obtain variation of color in the same design, as many additional blocks must be carved as there will be additional colors; the portions of the design that will appear in different colors must be separately imprinted by hand before each design is complete. The more colors used, the more valuable and expensive the hand-blocked print will be, because of the enhanced beauty of design as well as the labor involved in the hand printing.

The consumer can recognize hand-blocked prints by noting slight irregularities in the detail and in the repetition of the design and by comparing areas for slight variations in color. These irregularities are imitated by machine printing, however, to give machine prints the characteristic appearance of expensive hand-blocked prints.

Roller Printing. The machine method of printing designs on cloth turns out color-designed fabrics in vast quantities at the rate of thousands of yards an hour. This method of producing attractive designs is relatively inexpensive when compared with any hand method. It is a machine counterpart of block printing.

In roller printing, engraved copper cylinders or rollers take the place of the hand-carved blocks. Just as there must be a separate block for each color in block printing, so must there be as many engraved rollers in machine printing as there are colors in the design to be imprinted.

Each of the engraved rollers first comes in contact with a companion roller that has been submerged in the dye paste to be used for its part of the design. A sharp blade, called the doctor blade, scrapes the dye from the part of the roller upon which there is no design, so that other portions of the fabric will not come in contact with the dyestuff. As the fabric passes between the engraved rollers, the design is imprinted on it. A mordant is generally used in the dye paste to fix the color.

Duplex Printing. Duplex printing simulates a woven pattern by printing the fabric on both sides. To accomplish this, the fabric may be passed through the roller printing machine in two separate operations, or through a duplex printing machine in a single operation. Duplex printing produces an equally clear outline on both sides of the fabric. The design is applied so skillfully by careful registration of the printing cylinders that the result may be mistaken for a woven design. But the difference can be detected by raveling a yarn.

• *Blotch Prints*. Blotch prints may have a colored background as well as a colored design. Both may be printed at the same time. This method is used chiefly for cottons and linens.

Discharge or Extract Printing. The discharge or extract method of printing cloth receives its name from the fact that color is discharged or extracted from fabric that has first been piece-dyed. Because of the intention to extract the color, basic or direct dyes, which can be easily removed, are used. The chemical that discharges the dye tends to weaken the fabric, however, in the area of the design.

Because the background dye is not fast and the construction may be weak in parts, the consumer should not buy fabrics that have been printed by the discharge method if he wants serviceability and durability. Discharge prints are found in cottons and rayons, and in some patterned silks with dark backgrounds.

In extract printing, the cloth is put through rollers that exude a bleaching agent, such as zinc oxide paste or hydrosulphite, in the form of a small

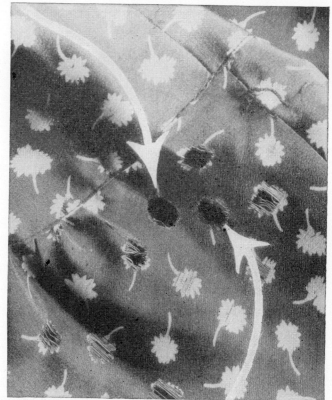

Courtesy U.S. Department of Agriculture

*This fabric was discharge-printed. The chemical used
to bleach the design on the fabric was too strong, causing the design area to deteriorate.*

pattern, reproducing it on the fabric by bleaching the dye. This method is
chiefly employed where a light design is required against a dark background,
because the bleaching produces an off-white color in the design. A light
polka-dot pattern on a dark ground is an example of discharge printing.

Resist Printing. In resist printing, bleached goods are run through cylinders that stamp a pattern on the fabric in the form of a resist paste, a resinous
substance that cannot be penetrated when the fabric is subsequently immersed in a dye. The dye will affect only the parts that are not covered by the
resist paste. After the fabric has passed through a subsequent dyeing process,
the resist paste is removed, leaving a pattern on a dark ground.

In the discharge method, fabric is first dyed, and the color is then extracted by an imprinted chemical; in the resist method, a resist paste is first imprinted, and the fabric is then dyed. The durability of the fabric is not affected by the resist method.

Stencil Printing. Stencil printing originated in Japan. Its high cost limits its use and importance in the United States. In stencil printing, the design must first be cut in cardboard, wood, or metal. The stencil may have a fine, delicate design, or there may be large spaces through which a great amount of color can be applied. A stencil design is usually limited to the application of only one color and is generally used for narrow widths of fabric.

Screen Printing. The chief advantage of screen printing is individuality of design. The method is especially adapted for printing large designs having elaborate effects. The expense of the process limits its use to the printing of comparatively short yardages. The process is not used for mass production.

In screen printing, the design is drawn on an intermediary cloth or screen, which serves as a stencil. A lacquer coating is applied to all parts of the underside of the screen on which the design does not appear. The fabric is spread

Courtesy Owens-Corning Fiberglas Corp.

In screen printing, the dye is forced through the screen with a squeegee. A different screen is used for each color of the pattern.

on a long table, sometimes several hundred feet long. The screen is placed on a small portion of the fabric. The printing paste or dye is poured on and forced through the unlacquered portion of the screen onto the fabric with a wooden or rubber paddle or squeegee. The frame is then raised and placed on the next section of the fabric, and the operation repeated until the entire length of the cloth is printed with that one color. This process must be repeated for each color to be used in the design.

In screen printing, it is possible to have designs consisting of squares, circles, and ovals because the areas not to receive the dye are painted out by the lacquer. If clearly defined geometric designs were attempted in cardboard or metal stencils, obviously, the cut area would fall away.

On a knitted fabric, such as jersey, screen printing is the only printing method that can be used; other methods smear the dye, as a knitted fabric stretches when it receives the impact of the rollers.

Warp Printing. Warp printing is roller printing applied to warp yarns before they are woven into fabric. White or neutral-colored filling threads are then used in the weaving process. This method produces designs with soft, nebulous, but striking, effects. Fine filling yarns are generally used so that the design on the warp will not be obscured. Great care must be taken to keep the warp yarns in their proper position so the outline of the design will be preserved. Warp printing is used for expensive cretonnes and upholstery fabrics.

Photo Printing. In this process, the fabric is coated with a chemical that is sensitive to light. Any photograph then may be printed on the fabric. The results are the same as obtained when printing photographs on paper. All the details can be reproduced if the photographer and the technician are careful.

Batik Dyeing. The hand method of producing designs known as batik originated in Java. It enjoys frequent renewal of popularity in the United States. Batik is somewhat similar to the machine method of resist printing.

The design is drawn on the fabric, and beeswax containing paraffin is deposited through a small cup-shaped instrument on the areas that are not to be colored. The fabric is then immersed in a tepid dye bath, and the wax resists penetration of the dye. After the fabric is dried, the wax is removed by applying heat or benzine. The result is a silhouette design on a dyed background. The process is repeated if additional colors are to be added.

Sometimes, in the last application of color, the wax is permitted to crack, and the last dyestuff partially penetrates the other dyed portions, producing the multicolored design characteristic of batik. The American method differs from the Oriental in that light colors are applied first, followed by the wax; then the deeper shades are built in. In the Oriental method, the dark shades are applied first, and the portions to be kept light are waxed.

Tie Dyeing.   The results of tie dyeing are similar to batik, but the designs can be only circular in form, as the dye is resisted by knots that are tied in

DECORATION OF FABRIC BY PRINTING AND DYEING

Type of Decoration	Hand Method	Machine Method
Block printing	Design carved on blocks; dye applied to block; block pressed on fabric	
Roller printing		Design etched on roller; companion roller transmits dye to etched roller, which transmits it to fabric
Discharge printing		Bleached goods first dyed; chemical bleach printed on fabric; color discharged
Resist printing		Resist paste put on fabric; fabric dyed; paste removed
Stencil printing	Design cut in stencil; color applied over stencil	
Screen printing	Design sketched on sheer silk or nylon for screen; lacquer applied to background of design; color applied to screen as stencil; color forced through screen	

the cloth before it is immersed in the dye bath. The outside of the knotted portion is dyed, but the inside is not penetrated if the knot is firmly tied.

Partial penetration occurs when the knot is not tight, causing gradations and irregularities of color that produce indistinct but attractive designs. The process is repeated as many times as desired by making new knots in other parts of the cloth and immersing the fabric in additional dye baths. This gives a characteristic blurred or mottled effect, which is the result of the dyes running into each other.

Like other hand methods of decorating cloth, tie dyeing is expensive.

DECORATION OF FABRIC BY PRINTING AND DYEING

Type of Decoration	Hand Method	Machine Method
Warp printing		Engraved rollers print design only on warp yarns; fabric then woven, using white or neutral filling yarn
Duplex printing		Design printed back to back on both sides of fabric; gives effect of woven pattern
Photo printing	Photographs printed on sensitized fabric	
Batik dyeing	Design put on fabric; wax deposited on background of design; fabric dyed; wax removed	
Tie dyeing	Fabric knotted or tied in parts with string; dipped into dye; fabric untied	
Composition or paste designs		Lacquer figures or colored paste glued or baked on surface of fabric
Spray painting	Mechanized airbrush applies surface coating	

Pasted designs, like the dots in this fabric, may disappear in laundering.

Courtesy U.S. Department of Agriculture

Because the method creates interesting designs, the patterns are duplicated in roller printing.

Composition or Pasted Designs.   The rollers or cylinders that are used to imprint color by means of dyes, chemicals, or resist pastes can also apply lacquer or colored paste to fabric as small designs, called *flocked dots*. Considering that the dots are only glued on, this method is surprisingly lasting. It is not used on fabrics that are expected to withstand laundering, however. Even for the dry cleaner, it presents a problem.

Substances that can be baked into the fabric are also used for this decorative effect. When this is done, the designs become so much a part of the cloth that they may be considered permanent, seldom being destroyed by washing or dry cleaning.

Spray Painting.   Designs may be hand-painted on fabric, or the dye may be applied with a mechanized airbrush, which blows or sprays color on the fabric. Spray painting is used when surface coloring is to be done quickly and economically: for example, designs on tablecloths. The type of dyestuff used may be direct, acid, or vat dyes dissolved in water, alcohol, or other organic solvent.

▶ **TEST YOURSELF ON THIS CHAPTER**

1. Explain roller printing and duplex printing.
2. Differentiate between discharge and resist printing.

3. Describe warp printing and its result.
4. Compare and contrast the batik method and the resist method of decoration.
5. Describe tie dyeing, and explain why it is expensive.
6. What is meant by block printing?
7. What are the several methods of hand decoration with color?
8. Why are most fabrics machine-printed?
9. How could one determine whether a color design is printed or woven?
10. Name and describe five types of printing on fabrics.
11. How do screen printing and stenciling differ?
12. What are the characteristics of a well-printed fabric?
13. How can spinning and weaving processes produce decoration in fabrics? Finishing processes?
14. Why is the discharge-printed fabric the least desirable?
15. What is the difference between a blotch and a duplex print?

9 | COTTON

Universal and Economical

Ancient historical records show that cotton was first cultivated in Oriental countries at least three thousand years ago. India is believed to be the oldest cotton-growing country. Cotton was known and used in all the Mediterranean countries, being introduced into Italy by the Arabs and into other parts of Europe by the Crusaders. The use of cotton in England is mentioned in writings of the thirteenth century, although its use did not become general until the first half of the sixteenth century.

In the United States, cotton was cultivated in the early seventeenth century. The impetus of the Industrial Revolution, represented in the cotton industry by the invention of the spinning frame and the spinning mule in England, and by the invention of the cotton gin in the United States, resulted in vastly increased cotton production and manufacturing. Today cotton fields extend across the southern section of the United States from Virginia to California.

Cotton fabrics have been so well known and so extensively used throughout the world for hundreds of years that the spinning of the cotton fiber into yarn, the weaving of cotton yarn into fabric, and many of the finishing processes used for cotton goods come first to mind, and naturally serve as foremost examples, in a study of fiber and fabric.

Cotton has been of service to mankind for so long that its versatility almost unlimited. New uses for cotton are constantly being discovered. Cotton is considered nature's most economical fiber; it is low-priced as raw material and as a finished product. It can be depended on to serve many purposes. Not only is cotton a textile fabric in its own right but its by-products form the base for some of the man-made textile fibers.

Cultivation of Cotton. Cotton can be cultivated only in warm places which, of course, is the reason for its cultivation in the southern part of the United States. Cotton requires about two hundred days of continuous warm

138

Courtesy Deere & Company

This mechanical cotton picker can pick cotton bolls from two rows of cotton plants at one time. Upper left: *cotton bolls;* upper right: *baled cotton.*

weather with adequate moisture and sunlight; frost is harmful to the plant. The ground must be thoroughly plowed, and the soil pulverized.

In the United States, usually in March or April, carefully selected cotton seeds are planted in rows. Approximately thirty-five days pass before the seeds develop. The plants require careful fertilization. When they are about 3 inches high, they are weeded and thinned out.

The cotton plant begins to bloom in June or July, about four months after planting. Creamy white blossoms appear first. These change to a reddish purple in about two days and fall off, leaving seed pods that grow to full size by August or September, a month or more after blossoms first appeared. Before maturing, the cotton bolls must be protected against the boll weevil, which is attracted to the plant at this stage.

When fully grown, the cotton plant may be from 3 to 6 feet in height. Its wide green leaves conceal some of the bolls, which begin to burst with fleecy white cotton fiber. This indicates that the cotton is ready for harvesting.

• *Harvesting*. Not all cotton bolls open at the same time. Only those that

Cotton fiber, which has entered the top of the cotton gin from a pneumatic conveyor, is here seen falling on covered gin saws after sand and coarse soil have been removed. The saws separate the seeds from the fiber. The fiber is removed from the saw teeth by a blast of air and is whisked toward the back. The seed falls into a conveyor at the bottom of the machine.

burst, thus exposing the fiber, are ready for picking. A cotton field must be gone over several times. Consequently, harvesting the cotton fiber requires a large amount of labor as picking is mainly done by hand. The picking is the most expensive operation in cotton production.

A machine picker has been developed that can pick cotton from plants 2 to 4½ feet in height. The mechanical picker, however, represents a large capital investment for the owner of a comparatively small cotton tract. Co-operatively owned mechanical pickers might be economical.

Ginning and Baling.   When the raw cotton is harvested, it contains seeds, leaf fragments, dirt, and other material that must be removed before the fiber can be baled. Cotton seeds alone constitute approximately two-thirds of the weight of the raw cotton when first picked. The seeds are removed by the cotton gin, a machine having rows of revolving saw-toothed bands that

1. SEED COTTON

This drawing shows the basic principle of operation of the cotton gin. (1) Seed cotton enters gin. (2) Roll throws seed cotton against fast-turning saws. (3) Saw teeth take cotton up and against bars. (4) Bars near saws on both sides let lint pass through but hold back seed. (5) Seed falls into conveyor. (6) Lint on saw teeth is struck by blast of air and blown into (7) lint cotton conveyor pipe.

Courtesy Bibb Manufacturing Co.

pull the fiber away from the seeds as well as remove other extraneous material. The cotton seeds are one of the valued by-products.

The cotton fiber is compressed into rectangular bales, which are then covered with jute bagging and bound with iron bands. These bales weigh about 500 pounds each.

By-products of Cotton. The raw cotton passes through several cleaning processes before it is baled as well as after it is unbaled at the cotton mill. As a result, the grower obtains valuable by-products that amount approximately to one-sixth of the entire income derived from the cotton plant. Cotton is therefore important because of its contributions to other industries as well as to the textile industry.

• *Cotton Linters.* Linters are the short, fuzzy, hairlike fibers that remain on the seeds after they have been separated from the fiber in the cotton gin. The cotton linters are removed from the seeds by a second ginning process. They serve as raw material for the manufacture of rayon, other synthetics, plastics, shatterproof glass, guncotton, photographic film, fast-drying lacquers, and for various other purposes.

• *Hulls.* The hulls, which are the outside portion of the cotton seeds, are obtained after the linters have been removed. The hulls are used as fertilizer, because they are rich in nitrogen, an important plant food. They are also used in the manufacture of paper, plastics, cattle feed, and as a base for explosives.

• *Inner Seeds.* The meat of the seed inside the hull yields cottonseed oil, which is used in cooking oils and compounds and in the manufacture of soap. The residue of the inner seed becomes cattle feed.

Varieties of Cotton. Soil and climatic conditions affect the length and the character of cotton fibers. The relative fineness of the fiber seems to vary directly with the length of staple, the shortest staple being the coarsest type. The names of countries or of sections of countries where cotton is produced usually indicate the quality and the kind of cotton; these varieties may be used as a general classification.

Cottons of high quality have been successfully transplanted; the name of the country or section in which they originated is usually retained. The better-known cottons that are of importance in the United States are described here according to their rank.

• *Sea Island Cotton.* Sea Island cotton received its name from Sea Island off the coast of Georgia. This cotton is now successfully grown on other islands off the southern coast of the United States as well as along the seacoast of the mainland. As nearness to the ocean provides the moisture so necessary to the proper development of good-quality cotton, Sea Island cotton has an extremely fine long staple, ranging from 1½ to 2½ inches in length. Wherever this variety has been successfully transplanted, it has produced the finest and the longest staple of all cotton fibers. Sea Island cotton is used for the highest-quality cotton fabrics, including laces, fine sewing thread, and imitations of silk.

• *Sakel (Sakellaridis).* This is the best variety of Egyptian cotton. It is a lustrous, light-cream-colored, fine fiber with a length of 1⅜ to 1 17/32 inches. Its fineness and strength permit the spinning of Sakel into yarns of 200s, which can be used for the manufacture of the very best sheerest cotton fabrics. It is also used for fine-quality white-on-white and broadcloth. Through crossbreeding, Sakel has given rise to the best American Egyptian cottons, which are used in making the finest cotton goods today.

However, due to its low yield per acre, its low resistance to wilt disease and boll damage, the production of Sakel is only about 1.5 per cent of the entire cotton crop of Egypt. There are two other varieties of Egyptian cotton however, that are very good. But the label "Egyptian Cotton" does not necessarily indicate superiority, since there are many varieties of Egyptian cottons. Some of these are excellent to very good. Others are only average quality.

• *Pima.* The true designation for this variety of cotton is Pima 32. It is the result of a series of crossbreeding of original Sakel and Pima (an American cotton). It is grown in the Upper Rio Grande Valley in Texas and New Mexico and in Arizona. Pima is a fine, lustrous, almost white fiber with a length of 1 7/16 to 1 9/16 inches and is very strong. Since there is more Pima cotton available than either the Sea Island or Sakel cottons, it is more commonly known and more popular. Pima cotton is used for high-quality white-on-white, and for broadcloth and other fabrics.

• *Amsak.* Amsak, another variety of American Egyptian cotton, is the result of a series of crossbreeding involving Sakel and a strain of Pima. It is a very good quality of cotton about 1½ inches in length.

• *Malaki.* Malaki owes its origin to crossbreeding between Sakel and Sea Island. Its fineness and strength are in close competition to that of Sakel. However, it is dark brown in color, a serious disadvantage since strong bleaching is required. The fiber length is 1 7/16 to 1 21/32 inches. Malaki represents about 8 per cent of the total Egyptian cotton acreage. It is used for a wide variety of cotton fabrics.

• *Karnak.* The largest acreage in Egypt is given to Karnak, a long-staple cotton. It also has the third largest acreage of the Egyptian cottons. Karnak is about as fine as Sakel and is 1⅜ to 1⅝ inches in length. It is light brown in color and therefore must be thoroughly bleached to obtain the desired white.

• *Acala.* Varieties of Acala are grown in the Upper Rio Grande Valley in Texas and New Mexico and in the San Joaquin Valley in California. Acala is one of the stronger American cottons, having a fiber length of about 1 1/16 to 1 3/32 inches. Its color is light cream to white. It is used for a wide variety of cotton fabrics.

• *Peeler.* This cotton is grown in the Mississippi Delta and in the low wet portions of the southern states. It is valued because of its fairly long length of 1⅛ to 1¼ inches and is considered as the best of the varieties of cotton grown in the states east of the Mississippi River. Peeler cotton is used for better-quality sheer fabrics and for broadcloth.

• *Upland.* American Upland cotton supplies the bulk of the United States cotton crop. It yields a soft, fairly strong fiber and has a staple length of ¾ to 1 1/16 inches. Upland is used for most popular-priced cotton fabrics.

• *Peruvian Cotton.* Peruvian cotton is harsh and wiry; its staple is from

1 to 1¼ inches in length. Its rough, crimpy texture makes it resemble wool and it is sometimes mixed with wool for the purpose of adulteration. Peru also produces cotton of finer quality.

• *Asiatic Cotton.* Cotton grown in India, China, Asia Minor, Iran, Indo China, and Japan is called Asiatic cotton. It is of relatively short staple nearly all being less than 1 inch in length. Its use is therefore limited to low grade cotton goods.

Manufacturing Processes of Cotton.

Because cotton is such a universal fiber, its manufacture into yarn was used in Chapter 4 to illustrate the spinning process.

Cotton fabrics may be produced in any weave. In the finishing processes they may be given:

> Full bleaching—for clear whiteness
> Mercerizing—for strength, luster, and affinity for dyes
> Singeing—for smoothness
> Sizing—for stiffness, smoothness, and body
> Weighting—for bulk
> Preshrinking—for serviceability
> Sanforizing—for maximum preshrinking
> Calendering—for luster
> Schreinerizing—for luster
> Beetling—for flattened effects
> Napping—for softness, warmth, and absorbency
> Crepe effects—for wrinkle resistance
> Water repellency—for resistance to water and rain

The types of dyes used for cotton and their degree of fastness to light and to washing were explained in Chapter 7.

• *Simulating Linen.* Cotton yarn can be spun to simulate the irregularitie characteristic of linen fiber. The fabric is woven in the damask and other pat terns usually associated with linen fabrics and is then sized, beetled, and calendered similarly to linen.

• *Simulating Wool.* Cotton fibers can be treated with chemicals to give them the roughness characteristic of wool fibers. The fibers are spun into thick yarns to increase the similarity. The finished fabric is napped or roughened to produce a wool-like surface. Because Peruvian cotton fiber has crimp, an inherent similarity to wool fiber, it is sometimes mixed with American Upland cotton to simulate wool.

• *Simulating Silk.* The highest quality of cotton fiber, when spun to a high yarn count and then mercerized, simulates silk. The use of the satin weave in spinning produces a silklike luster. The cotton fabric may be singed and calendered to smooth its surface and to increase the luster. Cotton fabrics are frequently schreinerized to obtain an added lustrous effect.

Judging Cotton Fabrics. Many manufacturers now place labels on finished consumers' goods to give such information as the thread count, fiber content, shrinkage to be expected, permanency of crispness (if any), and fastness of dye to strong light, washing, and dry cleaning, with general instructions on the maintenance and care of the fabric.

Such labels are designed to protect the consumer. If he understands them, he will know how long the fabric or garment that he is purchasing may be expected to give good wear. These labels also protect the manufacturer from the consumer's possible misunderstanding of the quality and durability of a fabric and from complaint if it is improperly handled when washed or dry-cleaned.

It should be of interest to the reader to observe how the information gained in the first chapters of this book concerning the essential qualities of the fibers and their spinning into yarn and weaving into fabric can now be applied to the actual purchase of consumers' goods. Proper evaluation is based on the following summary.

• *Strength.* Compact construction, represented by high thread count, helps a fabric keep its shape and give longer wear. Strength is also judged by the character of the cotton yarns, which should be of long staple and tightly twisted. A sample of the fabric may be tested for strength by holding it in both hands and pressing down firmly with the thumbs while pulling. If the cloth gives easily, it will not stand the strain of wear.

• *Amount of Sizing.* If a cotton fabric is oversized, rubbing or tearing a sample swatch will cause shedding of excess starch. Holding the fabric to the light will reveal defects in construction that may have been concealed by sizing. Washing a sample will remove excess sizing, showing sleazy construction. An absolute test for starch is made by dipping a sample in a very dilute iodine solution; a dark-blue color indicates starch.

• *Crease Resistance.* The tendency of cotton fabrics to wrinkle easily may be offset by finishing processes that give a crease-resistant quality.

• *Heat Conductivity.* Cotton fabrics make excellent summer clothing because cotton is a good conductor of heat. Crisp, clean, fine cotton fabrics look cool as well as feel cool. Napped or pile-weave cotton fabric has a warmth-giving quality.

• *Absorbency.* Cotton is not a naturally absorbent fiber, but certain finishing processes, such as kiering, mercerizing, and napping, increase the absorbency of cotton fiber and fabric.

• *Cleanliness and Washability.* Although cotton attracts dirt particles because of its roughness, this disadvantage is offset by the washability of the fiber. Cotton fabrics are not injured even in strong, hot solutions of alkalies; therefore, they can stand laundering with strong soap. They withstand rough handling and considerable heat in ironing. Because of low resistance to acids, cotton deteriorates when exposed to perspiration. Mercerizing and new types of finishes, however, in many cases offset this.

• *Shrinkage.* A great amount of shrinkage will occur if cotton fabric is loosely woven and stiffened with starch, which is usually lost in washing. Preshrinking finishing processes minimize shrinkage in cotton fabrics.

• *Fastness of Color.* Fastness of dye to washing can be tested by washing a sample in hot water. Fastness to light can be tested by exposing a sample to light for a week or more. Penetration or thoroughness of dye can be tested by raveling a yarn and examining its unexposed surfaces.

• *Resistance to Mildew.* Cotton fabrics, especially sized fabrics, mildew readily when permitted to remain in a damp condition. New processes, in many cases, offset this tendency to mildew.

• *Resistance to Moths.* Cotton is not digestible to moth larvae. Cotton fabrics, therefore, will not be attacked by moths. However, fabrics containing cotton and wool may be attacked, the larvae damaging the cotton to get at the wool.

• *Reaction to Alkalies.* Cotton is not harmed by alkalies. In fact, a solution of sodium hydroxide is used to mercerize cotton, making it stronger, smoother, and more lustrous.

• *Reaction to Acids.* Although unaffected by cold weak solutions, cotton is quickly damaged by hot dilute or cold concentrated acids.

Construction of Sheets.   As sheets are an important item in the budget of the American family, the labeling of sheets is explained here. It affords an excellent example of consumer guidance.

• *Thread Count.* Sheets are labeled as belonging to one of seven types: backfilled, 112, 128, 140, 180 carded, 180 combed, and 200. The figures are obtained by adding the number of warp and filling yarns to the square inch, which represents the thread count. The higher the count, the closer and more uniform the weave; the more compact the weave, the greater the resistance to wear.

Types including backfilled, 112, 128, and 140 are known as *muslin.*

SUMMARY OF TYPES OF MUSLIN AND PERCALE SHEETS

	Grade	Weave or Thread Count	Points to Consider in Buying	Price
	Back-filled muslin	Woven with less than 112 threads to each square inch	Loosely woven; excess starch washes out, leaves sheets sleazy	Lowest
	Light-weight muslin	Woven with not less than 112 threads to each square inch	Wears well considering low price. For limited household service	Low
	Medium-weight muslin	Woven with not less than 128 threads to each square inch	Strong; gives satisfactory wear. Widely used for everyday household service	Medium
	Heavy-weight muslin	Woven with not less than 140 threads to each square inch	Sturdy; longest wearing muslin. Used where durability is prime consideration, as in hospitals, many hotels, etc.	Highest price muslin
	Percale (carded)	Woven with carded yarns not less than 180 threads to each square inch	Lightweight; durable. Smooth, pleasant to sleep on. Easy and economical to launder	Medium
	Percale (combed)	Woven with all combed yarns. Not less than 180 threads to each square inch	Lightweight, extremely strong and durable. Soft and unusually smooth. Easy and economical to launder	Medium
	Finest quality percale	Not less than 200 threads to each square inch	The finest, most luxurious sheets available. Light, fine, soft texture, beautiful appearance. Made of finest all combed yarns	Highest price percale

Courtesy Cannon Mills, Inc.

Muslin is made from cotton yarns that have been carded but not combed. Of the four muslin types, 140 represents the best quality, because such sheets are made from good-quality carded cotton yarns that are coarser and heavier and more compactly constructed than the first three types. As heavier yarn gives greater durability, preference is for type 140. Heavy muslin sheets are practical and economical because they are moderately priced and withstand wear longest, particularly when subjected to hard laundering.

Types including 180 carded, 180 combed, and 200 are known as *percale*. Percale is woven from fine-quality long-staple cotton yarns. In the case of 180 carded percale, the sheet is woven with 180 carded threads to the square inch. The 180 combed percale is woven with 180 combed threads to the square inch. Combed yarns are smoother, more lustrous, and stronger than yarns that are merely carded. The 180 combed percale is therefore superior and a little more expensive than the 180 carded percale. The 200 percale is woven with 200 combed threads to the square inch. It is constructed of the finest cotton yarn and is considered the most luxurious of sheets. The thread count is high in all the percale sheets because of the fineness of the yarns and their compact construction. Such yarns make lightweight sheets of fine texture; they are desirable for summer use. There is a gain in luxury but a slight sacrifice in durability because, all other conditions being equal, the heavier fabric gives the longer wear.

Sheets are generally labeled as to type. However, the consumer can always examine the sheet itself for quality. By holding the sheet up to the light, it can be determined whether the sheet is firmly, closely, and uniformly woven. It should look smooth; the lengthwise and crosswise threads should be of the same thickness. The yarns should be even rather than thick or thin in spots; there should not be any weak places, knots, or slubs, and the yarns should run straight and unbroken.

• *Selvage.* Sheets should be made with a tape selvage in which extra threads are woven. The selvage should be firm and strong, clean, neat, and with no loose threads.

• *Weight.* Many weights of sheets are available, varying from $3\frac{1}{4}$ to $5\frac{1}{4}$ ounces per yard. But good weight should be the result of compact construction, not of excessive sizing. Government regulations on sheets permit a certain amount of sizing depending on the grade of the sheet. In the lowest grade of sheet, an excessive amount of sizing may be used to give the material greater body. Since this washes out, leaving the sheet thin and sleazy, it is advisable for the consumer to test sheets for sizing by rubbing parts of the sheet together over a dark surface. If much of a white powdery substance comes out, the sheet is "loaded" or sized. Sometimes, sheets are labeled "no weighting," which indicates that no overdose of sizing has been used.

• *Length and Width.* Sheets should always be long enough and wide enough to tuck underneath a mattress at least 6 inches on all sides. The better grades of sheets are torn to size to make certain that the length is absolutely even; therefore, the size is given as a torn size, which means before hemming. After hemming, sheets are shorter; top hems are usually 3 inches wide on muslin, 4 inches wide on percale sheets; bottom hems are 1 inch wide. After washing, there is another decrease in length of approximately 5 inches, or 5 per cent, due to shrinkage.

Sheets 108 inches long should be selected. As about 10 inches must be deducted from the stated torn size for hems and shrinkage allowance, 98 inches remain for use. The average mattress is 74 inches long and 6 inches thick. Thus, 6 inches will be left for tucking under when a sheet is used to cover the mattress directly, and when used as an upper sheet, there will be a sufficiently wide turnover to protect blankets.

Careful consideration should be given also to the width of sheets. For a double bed, a sheet should be 81 to 90 inches wide. A three-quarter bed requires a sheet 72 inches wide; and a single bed, a width of 63 to 72 inches.

There are also mortised sheets, the corners of which conform to the shape and size of the mattress. When buying sheets of this type, it is not necessary to be concerned about the size of hems, the amount needed for tucking, and the like. One needs to know only the size of the mattress, that is, whether the sheet is for a single, three-quarter, or double bed. The sheet will conform to the length, width, and thickness of the mattress.

Construction of Terry Towels.

The primary function of a terry towel is to absorb moisture from wet skin. However, it must be strong enough to withstand the strain of the rubbing and pulling, twisting and tugging of the user and of constant laundering. Therefore, a terry towel should be constructed of an uncut pile with a sound underweave. One cannot purchase towels merely by a brand name because the name identifies only the manufacturer, not a particular quality. A company may manufacture many different grades and qualities of towels under the same brand name.

• *Weave.* The underweave, which supplies the strength of the towel, should be firm, close, and tight, preferably of a twill weave. It is difficult to examine the weave because the loops hide it. It can be more readily seen

Loops do the drying.   *Ground weave does the wearing.*

in the plain portion or near the hem or selvage of the towel. To examine the weave better, the towel should be held up to the light. If light shows through in tiny and regular pin points, the weave is uniform and good; if the light shows loose and open spots, then the weave is poor.

The loops of the pile, which absorb the moisture, should be closely packed. In a well-constructed towel, the moisture absorbed remains in the surface loops and does not reach the underweave. Therefore, a better-quality towel will absorb more moisture and dry faster after use. Another consideration with regard to the loops is that the longer the loops, the greater the absorbency of the towel. Also, loosely twisted loops are more absorbent than tightly twisted ones. However, on this point, personal choice must be a

Enlarged view showing how the loops (uncut pile) in terry cloth are formed.

Cross-section showing how terry loops are formed on both sides at the same time.

Courtesy Cannon Mills, Inc.

Fast selvage   Overedged selvage   Hemmed selvage

factor since some people prefer soft towels with loosely twisted loops, some prefer medium-soft towels, and others prefer a rough, hard towel with tightly twisted loops. Of course, in a well-constructed towel, good absorbency usually may be expected since the close weave naturally will result in a close, thick pile.

• *Hem and Selvage.* The hems of the towel should be sewn with small close stitches and finished with the edges either backstitched at the corners or turned and continued across the width of the hem.

There are three types of satisfactory selvages, if properly made. One is the fast selvage, which is the ordinary type of selvage found on any fabric. It should be closely woven. The second is an overedged selvage, and the third the hemmed selvage.

• *Length and Width.* Terry towels are divided by size into five groups: guest, small, bath, extra large, and beach. The guest towels are 11 × 18 inches. The small size, used for hands and face, are from 16 × 26 inches to 18 × 36 inches. The bath size are from 20 × 40 inches to 22 × 44 inches. The extra large size bath towel is 24 × 46 inches to 25 × 48 inches. The beach size is 35 × 70 to 36 × 72 inches.

GLOSSARY OF COTTON FABRICS[1]

airplane fabric. Plain weave. Closely woven, desized, durable medium-weight and lightweight fabric used in the manufacture of airplane wings and parts. Made of combed and mercerized yarns; usually in square weave. Many fabrics go under this name. Most important is fancy, irregular broken weave.

armure. Drapery fabric with a small woven design, usually on a rep foundation. Can be either Jacquard or dobby weave. Pattern is made by floating warp threads over the surface, giving a raised effect.

backing or back cloth. Gray goods, usually print cloth, used to take up surplus dye and to reinforce fabric on the printing machine.

[1] Specially prepared by The Cotton Textile Institute, Inc.

balloon cloth. Plain weave. Of finest Pima yarns. High thread count. The extremely fine yarns give the fabric luster. Usually mercerized. When used for balloons, given a special coating. Also used for frocks, shirts, typewriter ribbons.

batiste. Plain weave. A sheer, soft-finished fabric of the lawn family. Comes in various grades from coarse to very fine. Generally woven of combed yarns, but occasionally of carded. Often given high mercerization, bleached, dyed, or printed. Sometimes embroidered.

beach cloth. A strong, coarse fabric of plain weave, heavy yarns, and low thread count. Has the appearance of crash. There are a number of versions of this fabric.

Bedford cord. A carded yarn, wale, or cord material. Two-ply warp yarns and heavier single or ply yarns used as a backing. These heavy yarns are caught at intervals in the weaving of the fabric. Single yarns sometimes used in cheaper versions; the effect of the cord is obtained in the weaving. Wale runs in warp. Can be napped in back, bleached, dyed, or printed. Often the face of the fabric is given a suede finish.

bengaline. Rib effect in filling with a high luster. Has somewhat the appearance of grosgrain. For draperies and frocks.

bird's-eye (diaper cloth). Fabric woven on a dobby loom of carded yarns in tiny geometric designs that look like the eye of a bird, or in diamond effect. Heavier filling yarns are loosely twisted, making the fabric absorbent.

blanket cloth. Plain or twill weave, 60 × 80 inches and over. Coarse, soft filled yarns, filling heavily napped both sides. Generally bleached, yarn dyed in plaids or stripes, or with colored filling edge.

book cloth. Coarse, plain-weave print cloth or sheeting. Dyed, heavily sized, often pyroxylin coated, or embossed.

box loom. Fabrics made with right-hand and left-hand twist in filling, notably box-loom crepe. Such fabrics as ginghams and plaids are also made on box looms.

broadcloth. Plain, closely woven fabrics of either carded or combed yarns with a rib effect fillingwise. Originally a poplin or adapted from poplin construction, broadcloths are of lighter weight with a finer rib. Ribs are made by using finer warp yarn and medium filling. Many more warp threads than filling. Better broadcloths are combed ply yarns and high thread counts. Coarser fabrics often have both ply and single carded yarns.

brocade. Basic weave is satin. Elaborate lustrous design woven on a Jacquard loom. Has a raised appearance, usually on a sateen ground but often on twill or rep. The design is on the surface only. Multicolored yarns used.

brocatelle. A heavier version of brocade. Woven on a Jacquard loom with two, three, four, or more shuttles. Ordinary warp yarns but fewer twists in filling yarns. Has extra backing threads. The floating warp yarns over the backing yarns make the design stand out in relief.

bunting. Plain weave, in low or medium thread count. Open weave similar to cheesecloth or scrim. Dyed or printed.

calico. A low-count or medium-count cotton print cloth with special designs called calico designs. Many Early American designs are still in use.

cambric. Originally linen, now cotton print cloth or lightweight sheeting construction. Given special sizing and calendered finish.

canton flannel. Warp-faced twill flannel with a heavy, soft filling yarn and lighter warp than filling yarn. Has a long nap on one side only. Comes unbleached or bleached. Used for men's work gloves, infants' wear, linings.

challis. Plain or twill weave, printed or dyed. Given a soft finish and very slight nap.

chambray. Pattern is formed by the use of colored yarn warp and natural or white filling. This gives a tiny check or mottled effect. There are endless variations of this fabric, such as stripes, satin stripes, and so on. The end-to-end chambrays are woven with alternate colored and natural or white yarns in warp and all natural or white yarns in filling, or vice versa. Many novelties on the market.

cheesecloth (and tobacco cloths). Loose, open, plain light weave with low thread count. Print cloth yarns. Cheesecloths range from 25 to 55 inches in width. Tobacco cloths are 36 inches and over in width with a somewhat lower thread count than cheesecloths. When bleached, starched, or permanently finished, known also as scrim. Other names, depending on finish, are gauze, bunting.

chenille. Fluffy or fuzzy faced fabric made with a cotton warp yarn and a cotton chenille filling yarn that has a fuzzy pile protruding from all sides. Some imitations are made by tufting and use no chenille yarn at all.

cheviot. A strong twilled fabric woven with a colored stripe or check.

chiffon. A sheer voile with a dull finish; of fine, hard-twisted yarns. Often dyed or printed.

chintz. A print cloth or high-count fine sheeting with bright attractive floral or geometric designs, both large and small. Often given a permanent or semipermanent glaze; then known as glazed chintz. For draperies, slip covers, frocks.

clokay. A plain woven fabric with an embossed surface of some geometric pattern. Rather compact weave. Embossed design is permanent if the fabric is laundered only in lukewarm water with a mild soap.

corduroy. A ribbed pile fabric with a high, soft luster. Made with extra filling threads or extra warp threads. In weaving, the extra filling yarns form loops or floats over the ground threads. After weaving, the loop threads are cut on a special machine. The threads are then brushed, forming a pile.

cottonade. Generally three-harness, left-hand, warp-faced twill of coarse yarns. Comes mostly in dark stripes on a solid or medium-dark ground. Durable finish.

coutil. A strong three-harness herringbone or reverse-twist twill weave of high count. For suits, corsets, and other purposes in which a durable fabric is required.

covert. A medium-weight or medium-lightweight fabric with warp-faced left-hand twill. Usually of two-ply warp yarns and single or two-ply filling. Mixed yarns, such as natural and color in warp and matching color alone in filling. Has a mottled appearance. Often made with slack-twisted single yarns consisting of two rovings, one white and one color in warp and all color in filling.

crash. Name given to fabrics having coarse, uneven yarns in both plain and twill weaves. Usually sheeting, osnaburg, or twill-weave construction with a special finish. Used for toweling and drapery purposes. In lighter weights used for suits and dresses.

crepe. Has a pebbly or crinkled surface produced by use of special crepe yarns. Can be either crepe, granite, or plain weave. Generally, mixed-twist crepe yarns used in both warp and filling, but occasionally crepe yarns used only in the warp or the filling. Mostly woven on a box loom.

cretonne. Generally, a medium or heavy sheeting or osnaburg printed in bold, bright designs. Used for draperies and other household articles.

crinoline. Cheesecloth, tobacco cloth, or loosely woven sheetings given a stiff starched or plastic finish. Gives a firm appearance and feel.

damask. Design, woven on Jacquard loom, on both sides of the fabric. Usually given a lustrous, smooth finish when used for tablecloths and a soft or lustrous finish for draperies or upholstery.

denim. A durable fabric of the twill family. Usually of single hard-twisted yarns with colored warp and natural or white filling.

dimity. A sheer white, dyed, or printed fabric of plain weave with a spaced rib made with warp cords. This rib may be single, double, or in groups. Comes also in checks and other novelty versions. Coarser small-check dimities are known as pajama checks.

dobby. Woven on a dobby loom. All material with small figures, such as dots and geometric designs; floral patterns woven in the fabric, such as certain shirtings, huck towels, diaper cloth, certain dress goods, drapery and upholstery fabrics. Can be dyed, bleached, or yarn-dyed in many colors.

domett flannel. See also "Outing flannel." Plain or twill weave. Generally white with a longer nap than outing flannel, although the names are interchangeable. Soft filled yarns of medium or light weight.

dotted swiss. Generally a voile or lawn construction woven with either clip spots or swivel dots. The clip spot is the more popular version. The fabric is given a crisp, clear finish, which may be permanent or semipermanent. Often yarn-dyed dots are woven on a white ground, or a dark ground has white dots. Many imitations on the market, pigment dots, wool dots, and others.

drill. A durable fabric of medium weight. Usually, three-harness warp-faced twills made of carded sheeting yarns. Comes in various weights and thread counts. When dyed, known as khaki, tickings, silesia, herringbones. One thread goes over two filling yarns, then under.

druid's cloth. See "Monk's cloth."

duck. The name duck covers a wide range of fabrics. It is the most durable fabric made. A closely woven, heavy material. The most important fabrics in this group are known as number duck, army duck, and flat or ounce duck. Number and army ducks are always of plain weave with medium or heavy ply yarns; army ducks are the lighter. Ounce ducks always have single warp yarns woven in pairs and single or ply filling yarns. Other names for variations of these fabrics are sail duck, belt duck, hose duck, tire duck (such as breaker, cord, chafer), wide and narrow duck, biscuit duck, harvester duck, oil press duck, wagon duck, enameling duck, boot duck, canvas, and so on. Generally of ply yarns in warp and yarns of various sizes and weights in filling.

duvetyn. See "Suede cloth."

eponge. See "Ratiné."

express stripe. Warp-faced twill with a woven stripe. A durable fabric. An even number of unbleached and blue yarns are used in the pattern, forming a stripe.

friezette. An uncut loop or pile ribbed fabric similar to a heavy rib or rep. Of heavy yarns, usually mixed in color.

gabardine. A distinctive steep-diagonal warp-faced twill of carded or combed yarns. Twill is to the left if made with all single yarns, and to the right when ply warp and single filling are used.

gauze. See "Cheesecloth." Usually bleached; often specially treated, as when used for bandages. Better cheesecloths are also used for less expensive infants' items under trade names.

gingham. Plain-weave, medium-weight, or lightweight fabrics. Can be either combed or carded yarns. Usually woven on a box loom. Colored and white yarns or multicolored yarns form the pattern. Same number and variation of yarns in the warp as in the filling, forming squares, plaids, and similar patterns. Strange to say, a solid-color gingham is called a novelty gingham. Endless variations in color and design. Tissue ginghams are sheer ginghams made with lighter-weight yarns.

glazed chintz. Generally a print cloth or percale or a lightweight sheeting having bright, attractive floral or geometric designs. The fabric has a semipermanent or permanent glaze finish. Sometimes calendered or given a plastic finish. Fine twills are also used for this purpose.

granite. See "Mummy cloth."

grosgrain. Plain-weave fabric similar to poplin but with a heavier rib effect and coarser, lower thread count. Made with single or with ply filling.

hickory cloth. Resembles ticking somewhat, but of lighter weight and not so firm a weave.

holland. Usually a low-count print cloth or high-count cheesecloth, heavily sized and glazed. Occasionally, sheeting constructions are used.

hopsacking. Made of yarns about the same weight as osnaburg in a loose and low thread count. Sometimes made with spiral yarns. It has a soft texture and is of the homespun family of cottons. Sometimes made with fine warp and heavier filling. Many versions of this fabric.

huck. Small-figured dobby weave used for towels. Has a rough surface. Comes bleached or with yarn-dyed striped border.

Indianhead. A porous fabric of a plain weave. The yarn is somewhat thick. The fabric feels wiry, resembling butcher linen but not as stiff or as lustrous.

jaspé. A durable, narrow woven stripe made on a dobby loom with multicolored threads or with different shades of the same color. Has a shadow effect. Sometimes printed versions are shown in the market. Often small dots are woven into the fabric. Used for draperies and slip covers.

jeans. Three-harness warp-faced twills of lightweight sheeting yarns. One warp thread goes over two or more filling threads, then under, moving one pick higher for each return filling thread. Sometimes made in chevron or herringbone versions.

kasha cloth. Flannel with napped face and mottled color. Usually tan or brown. An unbleached soft filled sheeting. Mixed yarns are used with sized warp yarns that take dye and filling yarns with natural wax that do not take dye. When bale-dyed, the result is a mottled appearance.

khaki. See "Twill."

lawn. Sheer and medium-sheer plain-weave fabrics made with lightweight yarns and medium to high count. Can be bleached, dyed, or printed. When finished, it is also known by the name of such special finishes as batiste, organdy.

linene. See "Osnaburg."

longcloth. Also known as fineplain. A plain-weave, closely woven, high-count, fine-quality fabric. The weight is between a print cloth and lawn. Generally combed finer yarns, and with more threads to the square inch than percales. A few are made of print cloth yarns.

madras. Usually woven in stripes, cords, dobby, and Jacquard. Mostly all white, but in a number of cases done with a patterned warp and white filling, such as white and color warp, or color-and-color warp and white filling, or vice versa. Often a stripe is woven in solid colors. A number of variations of the above.

marquisette. Lightweight open-mesh fabric of low thread count. Can be either a gauze or leno weave. Made with ply or single yarns. Dots and figures can be woven in. Either combed or carded. Generally the ply yarns are combed. Can be bleached, dyed, or printed.

matelassé. Woven on a box loom. A real matelassé is a double warp-faced fabric, stitched together in warp and filling. Face of cloth has a fine warp and filling, the back a fine warp and heavy filling. Other matelassé crepes are made by interlacing crepe yarns with ordinary yarns in warp and filling, or in filling only. Comes in dobby or Jacquard designs. Has a slightly quilted appearance.

moiré. A fabric with a compact plain weave with a shimmering effect on the surface. The finish is permanent provided the fabric is washed with lukewarm water and a mild soap. Bleach should not be used.

moleskin. Mostly a right-hand filling-faced twill with a soft, smooth, shiny face. High thread count, usually many more fine filling threads and fewer heavier warp threads. Generally a napped back.

monk's cloth. Basket weave, a variation of the plain weave. Made with heavy rough yarns. Can be a 1×1, 2×2, 4×4, or 8×8 thread; the best known is the 4×4. These four threads in warp and filling are placed flat together and woven over and under in a plain weave; the resulting appearance is that of a basket.

mummy cloth. Sometimes called granite cloth; also momie cloth. Although this fabric has the appearance of crepe with a crinkled surface, it is not made with crepe yarns but with ordinary yarns and is woven on a dobby loom. Can be bleached, dyed, or printed.

muslin. Coarse type of cotton fabric made of carded yarns; of various thread counts up to 140. Gray print cloths and lightweight sheetings known as unbleached muslins.

nainsook. Plain weave. Mostly fine combed-yarn lawns, given a soft finish and light luster. Comes bleached and sometimes dyed.

netting. A lightweight or heavy open-weave, knotted fabric. The knots come at each corner of the square. Ranges in weight from very sheer to very heavy fabrics, from fine nets to fishing or laundry nets.

oilcloth. Sheetings or print cloths that are printed, bleached, or dyed, and given a special linseed oil and pigment preparation.

organdy. Plain weave. A sheer transparent lawn of lightweight yarns. Slightly lower construction than ordinary lawns. The filling is slightly finer than the warp yarns. Fewer filling than warp threads. Comes in many variations, such as permanent crinkles, leno effects, embroidery, plain or crinkled mixtures, clip spots. Bleached, dyed, or printed. Given a stiff finish, either starched or a permanent stiff, starchless finish.

osnaburg. A plain weave made of low-grade cotton, medium and heavy coarse yarns. Low thread count. When made of waste mixed with low-grade cotton, it is known as part-waste osnaburg; when of short-staple, low-grade white cotton, known as clean osnaburg. Woven with colored stripe and check effects, known as crash toweling. Comes in both wide and narrow widths and in innumerable variations in weight and thread count. Known also under the names of drapery crash, linene, hopsacking, suiting. Has a number of uses.

outing flannel. Can be either plain or twill weave. Lightweight or medium-weight soft filled single yarn with nap on both sides. Mostly yarn-dyed. Woven in stripes, plaids, or checks. Sometimes bleached or piece-dyed, and occasionally printed.

oxford. A plain weave of medium and heavy weights. Made with a variety of yarns. The majority of oxfords are of combed yarns, with heavier filling than warp yarns. Cheaper grades are mixed carded and combed yarns, and sometimes all carded yarns. Two warp yarns, placed flat next to each other, are woven other and under one heavier filling thread. Usually mercerized. A number of variations of this weave are on the market. For shirtings, frocks, and similar purposes.

pajama check. A lightweight or medium-weight plain-weave fabric with small-sized or medium-sized cord checks. Usually carded yarns. Of the dimity family.

percale. Plain-weave medium-weight-yarn fabric in the print cloth group. Thread count, 80 × 80 and over. Usually given a firm finish. Can be bleached, dyed, or printed. Has innumerable uses.

percaline. In the lightweight, low-count print cloth or lawn group with a bright, soft finish. Usually mercerized. Made in both fine and cheap versions. Used for the lining of furs.

picolay. A compact fabric with a plain weave. The cloth is embossed with a diamond pattern to resemble diamond piqué. With careful laundering, the design is permanent.

piqué. Has a warp or filling wale or cord, usually warp. Can be carded or combed yarns. It is woven on a dobby loom or with a dobby motion. A heavy stuffer yarn is used in back of the cloth; this heavy yarn is caught at intervals by a filling thread. Groups of fine warp yarns are woven on the surface over the back stuffer yarn, forming a rib. Many of the cheaper versions are woven without this stuffer yarn. Other versions of piqué are irregular or novelty wales, woven dots, bird's-eye, diamond squares, ladder effects.

plissé. A plain-weave crepe or crinkled fabric that has been specially treated. The plain fabric, which can be print cloth, lawn, or lightweight sheeting, is bleached, dyed, or printed, then covered with a gum in the desired pattern—stripe, check, floral, or geometric. The fabric is then passed through a caustic soda bath. The soda crinkles or crepes the fabric, leaving the gummed sections plain. When the gum is washed off, the pattern is revealed.

plush. Plain-weave fabric with occasional twill or novelty versions. A deep velvetlike pile woven on a cam loom in what is known as a velvet weave. Many plushes are made on a Jacquard loom in the form of patterns with many colored yarns. The ground yarns are generally two-ply carded. The double fabric is woven face to face and the warp yarns severed on the loom. Generally piece-dyed, and occasionally printed.

pongee. Plain weave adapted from the early silk fabric of that name. Generally combed yarns. More and heavier filling yarns than warp. Schreinerized to have a silklike finish.

poplin. Has a heavier rib effect than broadcloth. Heavier filling than warp yarns, and more threads in the warp than filling. Print cloth yarns mostly. Combed yarns in the better cloths. Many mixtures made. Poplin comes in many variations, such as slubs, nubs, and yarn-dyed checks and stripes. Mainly dyed solid colors or printed. Often given special finishes, such as water-repellent, fire-retardant, mildewproof.

print cloth. Carded cloth made with same yarns as cheesecloth, but with more warp and filling threads to the inch. Most print cloths are made in narrow widths up to 40 inches. Given a range of finishes, thus producing cambric, muslin, lawn, longcloth, and printed percales.

ratiné. A plain-weave loosely woven fabric with a rough, nubby appearance. This is obtained by the use of ratiné yarns; that is, one heavy and two fine, twisted together at different tensions, thus forming a knotty ply yarn. In less expensive versions, ordinary yarn is used in the warp with ratiné yarn in the filling. Can be bleached, dyed, or printed, and given a high luster or other finishes.

rep. Plain weave. Has a rib running across the fabric. The rib stands out more than in broadcloth or poplin. Usually given a high luster, although not always. Rib produced by heavy warp ends or extra floating filling. Also formed by using two warp beams with slack and tension warp ends. Two slacks are woven as one, and the tension is woven plain.

sateen. A satin weave. Usually woven so that the surface is smooth and the finish lustrous, resembling satin. Can be either a strong warp-faced sateen or a softer filling sateen. Often, though not always, filling sateens have a softer finish than warp sateens. Can be either carded or combed yarns.

scrim. A durable plain weave. Generally ply yarns and low thread count. Somewhat similar to voile but a much lower thread count. Cheesecloth

with a special finish is often referred to as scrim. Comes in many variations. Usually has a selvage. Generally carded, but a few combed varieties on the market.

seersucker. A plain weave. Usually a medium-weight or medium heavy-
weight fabric with a woven crinkled stripe, check, or plaid. Yarn-dyed
or bleached, occasionally overprinted. The woven crinkle is made by
alternating slack tension in warp yarns. Not to be confused with plissé.

shantung. Plain weave. Has a rib effect formed by slub yarns. Certain parts
of the yarn are not given the usual number of twists. These places
form the slub in the rib.

sheetings. Plain weave. Mostly carded but occasionally combed yarns in all
weights, light, medium, and heavy. Generally about the same number
of yarns in warp as in filling, but often warp yarns are heavier than
filling. Sheetings come in both wide and narrow widths. Yarn sizes
range from 10s to 29s.

silesia. Generally a lightweight twill lining with a calendered glaze.

suede cloth. Sheeting napped on one side to resemble leather suede. Duvetyn, which is similar to suede, has a longer nap.

tapestry. A closely woven yarn-dyed figured material with two or more sets
of warp and filling, often plied. Woven on a Jacquard loom. Comes in
both fine and coarse versions. The reverse side is smooth.

terry cloth. A fabric having uncut loops on both sides. Woven on a dobby
loom with terry arrangement. Various sizes and numbers of yarns are
used in picks and ends, forming different versions of terry cloth. Can
also be woven on a Jacquard loom to form designs. Can be yarn-dyed
in different colors to form patterns. Bleached, piece-dyed, and even
printed.

tickings. A variety of fabrics are known by this name. The main weave is a
closely woven, strong yarn twill. Spaced colored and natural or white
yarns repeated in the warp, and all natural or white in the filling, forming a stripe. Several color combinations used, such as blue and white,
brown and white, red and white. Heavy warp sateens as well as heavy
sheetings are printed and sold as tickings. Jacquard damask tickings
woven in lovely damask effects also sold for this purpose, as well as
other fabrics, such as drills.

tobacco cloth. See "Cheesecloth."

twill. Cotton fabric in twill weave. May be right-hand or left-hand twills.
Known as drills, jeans, gabardines, denims, serge, canton flannel,
cottonade, tickings, and others, depending on the finish and thread
count.

typewriter ribbon cloth. Fine fabric of plain weave. Often balloon cloth.
Made with finest regular yarns, then cut into strips, and specially
finished.

velveteen. Twill or plain weave with a short, glowing, lustrous pile. Ply or single yarns are used, which can be either combed or carded. Many more filling yarns than warp. The extra soft-twisted filling threads that float over the surface of the cloth are cut, forming the pile. Thickness of pile depends on the number of threads used. Can be dyed or printed.

venetian. A durable warp-faced eight-harness sateen of fine reverse-twist yarns.

voile. A soft yet firm sheer fabric of plain weave. Generally made of combed hard-twisted single yarns, although ply yarns are also used. About the same number of yarns in warp as in filling. Occasionally dots are woven in, and a crisp finish given the fabric; then it is sold as swiss.

whipcord. A serviceable fabric with a prominent steep twill effect. Often mercerized and preshrunk. Generally a left-hand warp twill. Many are finished with a slight nap at the back of the cloth. While some are woven in solid colors, others have mixed warp and solid matching color filling.

wigan. Usually made of print cloth or lightweight sheetings. Dyed in dark colors and starched and calendered. Used mostly for interlinings.

► TEST YOURSELF ON THIS CHAPTER

1. What are the by-products of the cotton plant? For what are they used?
2. How would you judge cotton fabrics?
3. Name the more important varieties of cotton grown in the United States, according to their quality.
4. What climate is necessary for the growth of cotton?
5. Which country produces coarse, wiry cotton?
6. Discuss the advantages of cotton fabrics.
7. How can cotton be made to simulate linen? Wool? Silk?
8. What is the difference between muslin and percale?
9. How are sheets labeled? What is the basis for labeling?
10. How may the strength of a fabric be determined? The amount of sizing?
11. Why are long fibers separated from short fibers? How may the consumer identify finished goods made from long staple?
12. Name some of the finishing processes used for cotton fabrics.
13. What is ginning? What are linters? Hulls?
14. Why is the more expensive method of vat dyeing used for such an inexpensive fiber as cotton?
15. Why are cotton lisle hose preferred to plain cotton hose by men?
16. What determines the strength of a terry towel? How can the consumer determine whether a towel is strong?

17. What determines the absorbency of a terry towel? How can the consumer determine whether a towel will be absorbent?

18. Obtain three samples of fabrics used in cotton clothing. Attach to each a record showing the name of the fabric, the kinds of yarns, the weave, the thread count, and the finish. State the uses and probable durability of each sample.

10 | LINEN

Cool and Enduring

The fiber obtained from the stem of the flax plant was probably the first textile fiber to be used by mankind. Historical records show that linen cloth was produced and used far back in antiquity, the earliest record being the use of flax for fish nets by the neolithic lake dwellers of the Stone Age some ten thousand years ago. The Bible contains references to the use of linen.

The bodies of early Egyptian kings and nobles were swathed in yards of delicate linen, indicating that the art of spinning and weaving had reached a high state of perfection in that country six thousand years ago. Such linen burial wrappings have been found to be in good condition, proving the amazing durability of the flax fiber.

Linen has always been considered the fabric of luxury. In some ancient countries, linen was used only for ceremonial purposes, as the symbol of purity. This symbolism is readily understood by recalling the fact that the descriptive phrase "pure linen" is customarily used to describe all-linen fabrics. This symbolism is apparent when it is realized that linen always looks cool, crisp, and clean, and it gives an attractive and immaculate appearance to the persons and objects it adorns.

In some countries, certain grades of linen are more readily available and are less expensive than cotton, which is generally considered the most economical fabric. But in the United States, fine-quality linens still retain the reputation of luxuriousness and expensiveness because the finest linens are imported into this country. The flax plant must be grown in countries where there is plenty of cheap labor as well as natural facilities for extracting the fiber. Even the manufacture of the fiber into fabric requires unusual care throughout each process to retain the strength and beauty of the fiber.

The seed of the flax plant is valuable as the source of linseed oil, which is used in the manufacture of paints, varnishes, linoleum, oilcloth, patent leather, and oiled silk. To obtain the seed, flax must be allowed to overripen. As overripening destroys the value of flax as a textile fiber, the method of raising the plant is influenced by the purpose for which it is required.

Flax-producing Countries. The countries that produce flax of various grades are Russia, Belgium, Ireland, Poland, Scotland, France, Germany, Czechoslovakia, Austria, The Netherlands, Australia, and New Zealand. Flax is grown in Canada and in the United States (Michigan, Minnesota, and Oregon), but chiefly for its seed.

Qualities and Grades of Flax. Courtrai flax, which comes from the Lys district in Belgium, produces the finest and strongest yarns. The water of the Lys River in Belgium and of the Scheldt River in The Netherlands is free from minerals and has proved especially desirable for decomposing the woody tissues of the plant, a necessary step in treating the linen fiber.

Belgium has a reputation for producing the best quality of linen, but Ireland is noted for the best workmanship. Irish linen is also prized for its fine white color and strength. The flax is spun while it is wet, and the cloth is grass-bleached, two processes reserved for good-quality linen.

Scotch linen is lighter in color than Irish linen. It is used extensively in making heavy-grade fabrics, such as twine and canvases for tarpaulins.

French linen ranks high. It is characterized by fine designs and the use of round yarns, as the cloth is not put through the beetling process.

Russian flax is used for medium and coarse yarns, which are dark gray in color. Russian linen sometimes cracks because the fiber is not so carefully processed as in the countries that have a reputation for fine-linen production.

German linen is generally of medium grade. Austria, Czechoslovakia, and Poland also produce medium-quality flax.

Cultivation of Flax. The flax plant requires deep, rich, well-plowed soil and a cool, damp climate. Premature warm weather affects the growth and the quality of the fiber. Level land with a plentiful supply of soft, fresh water is essential. As the soil in which flax is grown must be enriched for six years before it will yield a good harvest, only one crop in seven years can be raised on a specified portion of land. Therefore, the crops must be carefully rotated. In recent years, shorter periods of rotation have been tried with success.

The flax seeds are sown by hand in April or May. When the plants are a few inches high, the weeds must be pulled by hand with extreme care to avoid injury to the delicate sprouts. In three months, the plants become straight, slender stalks from 2 to 4 feet in height, with tapering leaves and small blue or white flowers. The plant with the blue flower yields the finer fiber. The white-flowered plant produces a coarse but strong fiber.

• *Harvesting.* By the end of August, the flax turns a brownish color, which indicates that the plant is about to mature; it is ready for harvesting. There must be no delay at this stage; otherwise, the fiber will lose its prized luster and soft texture. The plants are often pulled out of the ground by hand. However, there is a machine which can efficiently pull the flax. If the stalk is cut, the sap is lost; this loss affects the quality of the fiber. The stalk must be kept intact, and the tapered ends of the fiber must be preserved, so that a smooth yarn may be spun. The stalks are tied in bundles, called *beets,* in preparation for extraction of the fiber.

Preparation of the Fiber. The seeds and the leaves are removed from the stems of the flax plant by passing the stalks through coarse combs. This process is called *rippling.*

The bundles of plants are then steeped in water. The plants are weighted down with heavy stones to insure complete immersion. This allows the tissue or woody bark surrounding the hairlike flax fiber to decompose, thus loosening the gum that binds the fiber to the stem. This decomposing or fermentation is called *retting.*

• *Dew retting* is the method used in Russia. The flax straw is spread on the grass and is exposed to the atmosphere for three or four weeks. This method produces strong flax, dark gray in color.

• *Pool, or dam, retting* is done in Ireland. It requires less time than dew retting, from ten to fifteen days. As stagnant pools of water are used, this method sometimes causes overretting, which is responsible for brittle and weak flax fibers. Pool retting darkens the flax, giving it a bluish-gray color.

• *Stream retting* produces the best quality of flax fiber, as the process of fermentation can be retarded and easily controlled. The flax straw is placed in streams of cool, soft running water for five to fifteen days. This method produces superior strong linen of a pale yellow color.

• *Chemical retting* can shorten the retting process, but chemicals affect the strength and color of the flax fiber. The use of soda ash, oxalic soda, and caustic soda in warm water, or boiling in a dilute sulphuric acid solution, are the chemical methods used.

• *Mechanical retting* also shortens the retting process, but the subsequent fabric is susceptible to mildew and mold.

Retting only loosens the woody bark. If flax is not retted enough, the removal of the stalk without injury to the delicate fiber is difficult. If flax is overretted, the fiber is weakened. The retting operation, as well as all other processes for producing linen fabric, therefore, requires great care.

Courtesy Brown Shamrock

Spreading flax to dry after retting.

The stalk becomes partially separated from the fiber when the wet plants are laid in the fields to dry. When the decomposed woody tissue is dry, it is crushed by being passed through fluted iron rollers. This *breaking* operation reduces the stalk to small pieces of bark called *shives*.

• *Scutching.* The scutching machine removes the broken shives by means of rotating wooden paddles, thus finally releasing the flax fiber from the stalk. This operation can be done by hand as well as by machinery.

• *Hackling.* The simple combing process known as hackling straightens the flax fibers, separates the short from the long staple, and leaves the longer fibers in parallel formation. For very fine linen, hackling is usually done by hand and is repeated, a finer comb being used with each hackling treatment. Coarse linen is hackled by machine.

Classification of Flax Fibers. The short-staple flax fibers, called *tow,* are used for the spinning of irregular linen yarns. Tow is put through a carding operation, similar to the carding of cotton staple, which straightens the fibers and forms them into a sliver ready for spinning into yarn.

The long-staple fibers are used for fine linens. These are called *line,* sometimes *dressed flax.* Line fibers are from 12 to 20 inches in length. They are put through machines, called spreaders, which combine fibers of the same length, laying them parallel so that the ends overlap. The sliver thus formed passes through sets of rollers, making a rove for the final spinning process, which inserts the necessary twist.

Spinning Flax Fiber into Yarn. Although flax is one of the strongest fibers, it is inelastic and requires carefully controlled warm, moist atmosphere for the spinning operations. Two methods are used: dry spinning and wet spinning.

• *Dry spinning* does not use moisture. It produces rough, uneven yarns, which are not especially strong. These yarns are used for making coarse, heavy, and inexpensive linen fabrics.

• *Wet spinning* produces finer yarns. By passing the roving through hot water, the gummy substance on the fiber is dissolved, permitting drawing out of the roving into a fine yarn of high yarn count. Wet spinning requires a temperature of 120 degrees Fahrenheit, which is conducive to the production of soft, fine, even yarns.

Linen Yarn Count. The standard measure of flax yarn is the *cut*. If 1 pound of flax fiber is drawn out to make 300 yards, the yarn is known as No. 1s. When drawn out to make twice 300 yards, it is labeled No. 2s. The higher the yarn count, the finer the yarn. Exceptionally fine linen yarns for fine laces have been spun as high as 600s.

Weaving Linen Yarns. The inelasticity of the flax fiber presents a problem also in the weaving process because the fiber breaks easily under strain. A dressing is applied to the warp yarns by passing them over rotating brushes. This dressing helps linen yarns to withstand the strain of being lifted by the heddles during weaving. A very moist atmosphere is also required.

Linen fabrics usually have a balanced or squared construction, with the exception of double damask and certain sheer linens. The thread count therefore is always expressed as one number.

With the exception of some toweling, linen is seldom made in the pile weave. The pile weave increases absorbency, and this quality is already possessed to a large degree by any linen fabric. The twill weave is seldom used, as the fiber possesses natural strength; for the same reason, ply yarns are not necessary. The plain, satin, and Jacquard weaves are predominant. The twill weave, however, is used for linen drills in the South American market.

• *Table Linens.* Fine table linens are always woven with the Jacquard construction; there are two kinds of construction, depending on the weave.

The designs in damask result from the manner in which the warp yarns pass over the filling yarns. The background is always the same on both sides.

A five-shaft satin construction on the Jacquard loom is used for *single-damask linen*. Most single damasks have the same number of warp and filling yarns, and the thread count ranges from 100 to 200 to the square inch. Some single damasks may be overwefted about 10 to 15 per cent, but the cheaper qualities are usually underwefted; that is, some skimping is done with respect to the equalization of filling and warp.

The weave used for *double-damask linen* is an eight-shaft satin construction on the Jacquard loom. There are twice as many filling yarns as warp yarns, which gives greater distinctness to the pattern; the thread count ranges from 165 to 400 to the inch.

The construction and appearance of single damask may be compared with double damask.

Double damask is superior to single damask only if good yarns and quality construction are used.

Originally, double-damask linen was considered superior to single damask. This is no longer true. Today, the weave alone does not produce a superior product, because inferior yarns as well as high-quality yarns are used in all weaves. Double damask may range in quality from mediocre to excellent, and may be regarded as superior to single damask only if good yarns and quality construction are used.

If single and double damasks having thread counts approximately the same are compared, the single damask is preferable because shorter floats give greater serviceability. The threads hold more firmly. A double damask with a thread count less than 180 threads is not advisable for home use.

Finishing Linen. Linen is usually bleached in the piece, except yarns for dress linens. Two methods of bleaching are used. *Grass bleaching* produces the finest results. *Chemical bleaching* is chiefly used, but it may adversely affect the durability of the finished fabric.

The bleaching process produces four grades in the finished product: fully bleached, three-quarters bleached, half or silver bleached, quarter bleached. Unbleached linen makes a fifth grade.

A fully bleached linen fabric is less enduring than any other grade. Unbleached linen is the strongest because the natural strength of the fiber has not been weakened by the bleach; it is sometimes called gray linen or brown linen.

The natural characteristics of linen are enhanced by such finishing processes as:

Sizing—for added body
Mercerizing—for luster
Beetling—for softening and uniform thickness
Calendering—for luster and smoothness

Linen is never napped. The fiber does not lend itself to this process, nor would napping be desirable for long-staple yarns of hard surface. Where some crease resistance is obtained by reducing the yarn to short staple, the chief attribute of linen—strength—is sacrificed. Thus, any fuzziness in a linen fabric indicates the use of short staple or the presence of cotton.

Dyeing Linen. Linen is seldom yarn-dyed. The surface of the natural flax fiber is hard and nonporous, and is therefore impenetrable to dyes. The cells of the fiber are held together with tissue that can be broken down only in a severe bleaching process. Therefore, highly colored linens will not give lasting service because they must have been fully bleached to absorb the dye.

Judging Linen Fabrics. The term "linen" has long been used to refer to such household necessities as tablecloths, napkins, towels, pillowcases, sheets, and decorative coverings. Every consumer knows that these articles are not necessarily made of pure linen. They may be made of cotton or spun rayon, even of linen mixed with such fibers. However, it is always a woman's ideal to possess pure linens because they satisfy a desire for the beautiful and the luxurious, and may remain in families as heirlooms.

When linens are chosen wisely, their additional cost is well worth while. There is no doubt that linen is still the best fabric for table covering because of its durability as well as its exceptional beauty when thus displayed.

• *Pure Linen.* Even when a fabric is labeled "pure linen," it is necessary to know whether the yarns are line or tow. Fine linen fabrics, such as high-grade table damask and dress linens, are usually made of line, the long uniform staple. Line may be distinguished from tow by untwisting and examining the length of the fibers. The popular peasant linen is made of tow, but it is constructed with a very fine weave.

Pure linen is free from lint; therefore, the presence of lint indicates adulteration with cotton, or possibly oversizing. Cotton yarns are frequently mixed with linen to produce inexpensive fabrics. The name "Union Linen" is given to a fabric of which half or more is cotton. Linene is a trade name for an all-cotton fabric that simulates linen.

• *Strength.* Linen is especially durable. Among the natural fibers, it is second in strength to silk. It is the fourth strongest of all fibers.

• *Sizing.* As excessive sizing indicates the probability of poor construction or imperfections in weave, a sample may be tested for oversizing by holding it to the light, by rubbing, or by washing.

• *Weight.* In linen, weight may be considered a criterion of durability. Damask weighs from 4 to 7 ounces to the square yard.

• *Crease Resistance.* The inelasticity of the flax fiber causes linen to wrinkle easily, which somewhat offsets its otherwise excellent qualities as a fabric for summer apparel. But it is possible to buy dress linens that have been given one of the patented crease-resistant processes described in Chapter 6.

• *Heat Conductivity.* Linen is most suitable for summer apparel, as it allows the heat of the body to escape.

• *Absorbency.* When absorbency is the main consideration, linen is preferable to cotton. It absorbs moisture and dries more quickly than any other fabric. It is therefore excellent for handkerchiefs and towels.

• *Cleanliness and Washability.* Linen launders well and gives up stains readily; its softness is enhanced with repeated washings. Linen can be boiled and made absolutely sterile. It is desirable for surgical dressings and bandages. Bacteria do not thrive on linen because of its hard, smooth surface.

• *Shrinkage.* Linen does not shrink a great deal. In fact, linen will shrink less than cotton.

• *Fastness of Color.* When buying colored linens, look for the words "Guaranteed Fast Color" on the label, or get a guarantee of colorfastness from the store. If a label states that the fabric is vat-dyed, it has been given the fastest color possible to withstand washing.

• *Resistance to Mildew.* Like cotton, linen is vulnerable to mildew.

• *Resistance to Moths.* Also like cotton, linen is not damaged by moths.

• *Reaction to Alkalies.* Linen, like cotton, is highly resistant to alkalies. Linen may also be mercerized.

• *Reaction to Acids.* Linen is damaged by hot dilute acids and cold concentrated acids. Cold dilute acids will not harm linen.

GLOSSARY OF LINEN FABRICS[1]

art linen. Closely woven round-thread linen, used chiefly for embroidery, generally in the plain weave. Bleached, unbleached, and colors. Also used for dresses and table linens.

bisso linen. Fine, sheer linen; sometimes called altar linen. Made of wiry yarns. Has a crisp feel. Used for altar cloths.

cambric. Fine, closely woven fabric with a high thread count. Plain weave; white and colors. Used chiefly for handkerchiefs.

canvas. Many fabrics come under this heading. Two principal types: (1) Open-mesh canvas; used for embroidery; made of hard-twisted yarns; very durable. Most popularly known in this group is Java canvas. (2) Close-woven canvas; made from coarse hard-twisted yarns in the plain weave; comes in various weights. Finishes range from heavily sized to soft.

crash. A relatively coarse fabric made of uneven slack-twisted yarns. Made in various qualities; plain weave. Used for towels, suitings, dresses, depending on the weight.

damasks. In satin weave as well as the Jacquard pattern. Two types: single damask and double damask. Single damask has a five-shaft satin construction; if given a high thread count is more durable than double damask. Double damask is more lustrous because of the longer float of the eight-shaft construction; it is reversible because the design is made on both sides.

handkerchief linen. Same as linen cambric. Sometimes called linen lawn or linen batiste. Plain weave, often corded.

[1] Specially prepared by the Linen Trade Association.

huckaback. Coarse fabric, having a rough surface. Many variations in weave; may have small figures. Colors range from semibleached to white.

sheeting. Firmly constructed plain-weave cloth. Used industrially. The closer constructions used for bed linens. May be unbleached or white.

toweling. General name that covers all types of linen woven in special widths for towels. Some are terry, huckaback, crash, bird's-eye, glass.

► TEST YOURSELF ON THIS CHAPTER

1. Why is linen a desirable fiber?
2. Why is linen not used as frequently as cotton?
3. What disadvantages may there be in the use of linen fabrics?
4. Why are linens expensive?
5. What kind of climate is necessary for the growth of flax?
6. What are the methods of retting? Which method is used in Russia? In Ireland? In Belgium?
7. Which method of retting produces the finest linen?
8. From what part of the flax plant is the fiber taken? From what part of the cotton plant is the fiber taken?
9. What are line and tow?
10. Would you prefer a cotton blouse to a linen blouse? If so, why?
11. What country grows the flax plant for its seed? What is the seed used for?
12. Why should the short fibers be separated from the long fibers? What process accomplishes this?
13. What characteristic of the linen fiber makes it difficult to spin? Why would a wet fiber be more easily twisted?
14. In what weaves are linen yarns woven? Name some fabrics in each weave.
15. What finishing processes are given to linen fabrics?

Originally, wool was borne on wild species of sheep as a short, fluffy under-coat concealed by hair. When wild sheep were killed by primitive man for food, he used the pelts as covering for his body. The fluffy undercoat probably became matted by usage, thus giving early man the idea of felting it into a crude cloth. It is believed that ancient shepherds in the first century A.D. discovered that Merino sheep could be bred to improve the fleece.

At first, wool was a very coarse fiber. Its development into the soft, fleecy coat so familiar on domesticated sheep is the result of long-continued selective breeding; the quality has been greatly improved by careful crossbreeding of fine-wool and long-wool sheep.

The breeding of the animals and the production of the wool fiber into fabric are more costly processes than the cultivation of plant fiber and its manufacture. Consequently, wool fabrics are more expensive than cotton and linen. But wool provides warmth and physical comfort that no other fabric can give so completely. These qualities, combined with its soft resiliency, make wool a necessity for apparel as well as for such household uses as rugs and blankets.

Wool is not overabundant; the factor of scarcity adds to its value. Wool is also a delicate fiber. This makes intelligent buying and care more than ever a responsibility that the consumer must assume if he wishes serviceability and durability.

Wool and Hair. Wool fiber and hair fiber differ in basic structure. Wool is distinguished from hair by its overlapping scales, which give wool fiber its felting property. Hair is straight, lustrous, and comparatively inelastic; it is stronger and smoother than wool.

Strictly speaking, such animal hairs as camel's hair, mohair, cashmere, llama, alpaca, and vicuna differ enough from wool to be classified as *hair fibers*. However, as these hairs are included by the United States Government under specification standards for wool fabrics, they are described at the end

173

of this chapter. They have all the qualities of wool. In general, they are even more expensive than wool. Vicuna is the world's costliest textile product and surpasses all other textiles in fineness and beauty. These hairs are often mixed with wool, adding rather than detracting from the quality of any wool fabric in which they appear.

Wool-producing Countries.

The quality of the wool fiber is determined by the breeding, climate, food, and general care and health of the sheep. Cold weather produces a hardier and heavier fiber; excessive moisture dries out natural grease; insufficient or poor food retards growth. Certain countries are more suitable than others for large-scale sheep raising and consequently produce the greatest quantities of wool. The chief wool-producing countries are Australia, United States, Argentina, South Africa, British Isles, and India.

Classification of Sheep Bred for Wool.

There are about forty breeds of sheep. Counting the crossbreeds, there are over two hundred distinct grades of sheep. Those that produce wool may be classified into four groupings according to the quality of the wool produced.

• *Merino*. Merino sheep produce the best wool. The variety originated in Spain and was so prized for its outstanding quality that during the Middle Ages it was a capital offense to export a Merino sheep from Spain. The staple is relatively short, ranging from 1 to 5 inches, but the fiber is strong, fine, and elastic, and has good working properties. There is a maximum number of serrations, totaling as many as 3,000 to the inch. Merino is used in the best types of wool clothing. The Ohio Merino, Austrian Silesian, and French Rambouillet are all Merino sheep. Other types are now found in Australia, New Zealand, South America, South Africa, and Spain.

• *Class Two Wools*. These sheep originated in England, Scotland, Ireland, and Wales. They have helped make the British Isles famous for their fine wool fabrics. They are, however, no longer limited to that area and are now raised in many parts of the world. While not quite as good as the merino wool, this variety is nevertheless a very good quality wool. It is 2 to 8 inches in length, has a large number of serrations per inch, and has good crimp. The fibers are comparatively strong, fine, and elastic, and have good working properties. Some of the better-known sheep of this variety include Bampton, Berkshire, Blackface, Cornwall, Devonshire, Dorset, Hampshire, Hereford, Exmoor, Kent, Norfolk, Shropshire, Southdown, Sussex, Oxford, Welsh Mountain, Wiltshire, Westmoreland, Irish, and Ryeland.

• *Class Three Wools.* These sheep originated in the United Kingdom. The fibers are about 4 to 18 inches long, are coarser, and have less serrations and less crimp than merino and the class two wools. As a result, they are smoother, and therefore have more luster. These wools are less elastic and resilient. They are nevertheless of good enough quality to be used for clothing. In fact, some of these sheep, such as Leicester, Cotswold, Cheviot, Harris, Lewis, and Shetland, have given their names to wool fabrics.

• *Class Four Wools.* This class is actually a group of mongrel sheep sometimes referred to as half-breeds. The fibers are from 1 to 16 inches long, are coarse and hairlike, have relatively few serrations and little crimp, and are therefore smoother and more lustrous. This wool is less desirable, having the least elasticity and strength. It is used primarily for carpets, rugs, and inexpensive low-grade clothing.

Classification of Fleeces. Sheep are generally shorn of their fleeces in the spring; but the time of shearing naturally varies in different parts of the world. In the United States, shearing takes place in April or May; in Australia, in September; in Great Britain, in June or July. Although sheep are normally shorn only once a year, Texas and California sheep are shorn twice a year because of the warm climate.

Sheep are not washed before shearing. Sometimes, they are dipped into an antiseptic bath, but this is done only when prescribed by law. Formerly,

Courtesy U.S. Department of Agriculture

A fleece after shearing.

sheep were shorn by hand, but today the fleeces are removed in one piece by machine clippers, which shear closer as well as faster than hand clippers.

Wool shorn from young lambs differs in quality from that of older sheep. Also, fleeces differ according to whether they come from live or dead sheep. This necessitates standards for the classification of fleeces.

• *Fleece Wool, or First Clip.* The first fleece sheared from a lamb about six to eight months old is known as fleece wool, or first clip. This wool is of very fine quality; the fibers are tapered because the ends have never been clipped. Such fibers produce a softness of texture in fabrics that is characteristic only of fleece wool. However, because of its immaturity, fleece wool is not as strong as fully developed wool of the same sheep.

• *Hogget (Hogg or Teg) Wool.* This wool comes from sheep, twelve to fourteen months old, that have not been previously shorn. The fiber is fine, soft, resilient, and mature, and has tapered ends. Hogget wool is a very desirable grade of wool and, because of its strength, is used primarily for the warp yarns of fabrics.

• *Wether Wool.* Any fleece clipped after the first shearing is called wether wool. This wool is usually taken from sheep older than fourteen months. These fleeces contain much soil and dirt.

• *Pulled Wool.* When sheep are slaughtered for meat, their wool is pulled from the pelt by the use of lime, by sweating, or by a chemical depilatory. Such wool fiber, called pulled wool, is of inferior quality for two reasons: (1) because sheep that are raised for meat generally do not have a good quality of wool, (2) because the roots of the fibers are generally damaged by the chemicals and the tension exerted in pulling.

• *Dead Wool.* The grade of wool fiber known as dead wool is sometimes mistaken for pulled wool. The term is correctly used for wool that has been

One fleece produces different qualities of wool fiber. The parts are here numbered according to softness, fineness, and length of fiber, No. 1 yielding the best quality.

recovered from sheep that have died on the range or been accidentally killed. Dead wool fiber is decidedly inferior in grade; it is used in low-grade cloth.

• *Cotty Wool.* Sheep that are exposed to severe weather conditions or lack of nourishment yield a wool that is matted or felted together and is hard and brittle. This very poor grade is known as cotty wool.

• *Taglocks.* The torn, ragged, or discolored parts of a fleece are known as taglocks. These are usually sold separately as an inferior grade of wool.

Government Classification of Wool.

There has never been a sufficient supply of new wool stocks to take care of a steadily increasing demand for wool. To meet this situation, wool fibers have had to be recovered from old clothing, rags of all kinds, and waste from wool manufacturing; all are important sources.

This wool is variously called "salvaged," "reclaimed," "reworked," or "remanufactured," but it is best known in the textile industry as *shoddy*. This term is misunderstood by the average consumer, who is inclined to believe that wool fabric containing remanufactured fibers is necessarily of inferior quality. This is not so.

As wool fiber is the weakest of the natural textile fibers, the hardier though less resilient remanufactured fibers, when obtained from good original stock and combined with new wool from lamb, hogget, or wether fleeces, add durability to the soft new wool. Thus, remanufactured fibers contribute ability to withstand hard wear, although there is some sacrifice in warmth, softness of texture, and resiliency.

The use of remanufactured fibers also makes wool clothing available to consumers who cannot afford expensive wool fabrics.

To correct wrong impressions concerning the use of remanufactured wool, and also to protect consumers against unscrupulous practices, the United States Government passed the Wool Products Labeling Act. This act provides that every article of wool clothing must be labeled according to the type of wool used in its manufacture. The label must state: (1) amount of wool fiber in the fabric; (2) percentage by weight of "new or virgin wool" fibers; (3) percentages of "reprocessed" fibers or "reused" fibers; (4) percentage of each fiber other than wool, if such fibers constitute 5 per cent or more of the total; (5) aggregate of other fibers; (6) nonfibrous loading, filling, or adulterating substance.

It should be noted that the law does not require labeling as to the type of sheep or the type of fleece from which the wool has come. The law is, therefore, of only partial and limited value to the consumer.

New definitions of the type of wool fibers used in labeled garments were established by this act. The following descriptions are in accordance with Government specifications.

1. *Wool*. The simple term "wool," according to Government standards, must always mean "new wool" that has not been made up in any form of wool product. New wool comes directly from a fleece. It has never been previously woven, felted, or worn.

2. *Reprocessed Wool*. According to the Government classification, "reprocessed wool" is fiber that has been reclaimed and remanufactured from "unused" wool materials. Such materials may be combings and scraps of wool obtained during the manufacturing processes, sample swatches, or pieces of all-wool cloth from apparel manufacturing.

3. *Reused Wool*. The Government gives the special classification of "reused wool" to fiber that is salvaged from all kinds of "used" consumers' goods.

Virgin Wool. The term "virgin wool" is now used by the textile industry to designate new wool from a sheep's fleece, but the term is too all-inclusive to serve as a criterion of quality. Although the term testifies to the fact that virgin wool does not contain remanufactured wool fibers, it can be used to identify the less desirable fibers of a fleece as well as a specially fine quality of wool. Virgin wool may also include pulled or dead wool, which may be of definitely inferior stock.

The consumer should not feel that a fabric labeled "100 per cent new wool" is necessarily more serviceable than one containing any of the remanufactured wool fibers, for there are many different grades of new wool. It is important to remember that a high grade of reprocessed wool makes a more serviceable fabric than one having a low grade of new wool. This is attested to by the fact that after stringent tests the United States Army prefers overcoat material made of 65 per cent new wool and 35 per cent reprocessed or reused wool.

Garnetting. Reprocessed and reused wool fibers are obtained by separately reducing the unused and used materials to a fibrous mass by a picking and shredding process called *garnetting*. The fibers are then put through a dilute solution of sulphuric or hydrochloric acid, which destroys any vegetable fibers that may be contained in the raw stock. This process is known as *carbonizing,* and the resultant wool fibers are called *extracts*. The new staple ranges from $\frac{1}{4}$ to $1\frac{1}{2}$ inches in length.

The quality and cost of reprocessed and of reused wool fibers depend on the original stock from which they were obtained. A good grade of reprocessed wool may cost five times as much as a poor grade of virgin wool.

Preparation of Wool Fiber.

Domestic wool reaches the mill in loosely packed bags; imported wool comes in tightly compressed bales. Each fleece contains different grades or *sorts* of wool, and the raw stock must be carefully graded and segregated according to length, diameter, and quality of the fiber. The raw wool or newly sheared fleece is called *grease wool* because it contains the natural oil of the sheep. When wool in the grease is washed, it loses from 20 to 80 per cent of its original weight. The grease, known as *yolk,* is used for lanolin compounds, which are valuable because they can be absorbed by the human skin. Lanolin is widely used in the pharmaceutical and cosmetic industries.

• *Sorting.* Wool sorting is done by skilled workers who are expert in distinguishing qualities by touch and sight. As many as twenty separate grades of wool may be obtained from one fleece if the sorting is especially rigid. Each grade is determined by type, length, fineness, elasticity, and strength.

Wool from different parts of the body of the sheep differs greatly. The shoulders and sides generally yield the best quality of wool, as the fibers from those parts are longer, softer, and finer.

• *Scouring.* The next step in preparing raw wool for manufacturing is a thorough washing in an alkaline solution; this process is known as *scouring.* The scouring machines contain warm water, soap, and a mild solution of soda ash or other alkali; they are equipped with automatic rakes, which stir the wool. Rollers between the vats squeeze out the water. If the raw wool is not sufficiently clear of vegetable substance after scouring, it is put through the carbonizing bath of dilute sulphuric acid or hydrochloric acid.

For some consumers' goods, the term "naphthalated wool" is used, which means that the grease and dirt found in the fleece when originally sheared from the sheep's back have been removed by a series of naphtha baths, followed by clear water which removes the naphtha. When wool has been thus treated by a cleansing agent, dyestuff penetrates better.

• *Drying.* Wool is not allowed to become absolutely dry. Usually, about 12 to 16 per cent of moisture is left in the wool to condition it for subsequent handling.

• *Oiling.* As wool is unmanageable after washing, the fiber is dipped in, or sprayed with, a light emulsion of virgin olive oil or mineral oil to prevent it from becoming brittle and to lubricate it for the spinning operation.

Courtesy Wool Bureau, Inc.

*At the upper right of the picture, wool is dropping into
the first tank for the scouring process. The raised spikes
move slowly toward the rear of the tank, drop, and
then move forward to force the wool through the solution. This action is constantly repeated.*

Dyeing. If the wool is to be dyed in the raw stock, it is dyed at this stage.
The advantage of stock dyeing has been described in Chapter 7. Some wool
fabrics are piece-dyed.

Blending. Wool of different grades may be blended or mixed together at
this point. It is not uncommon for taglocks and inferior grades of wool to
be mixed with the better grades. The use of a mixture with a coarser grade
of fiber is a legitimate practice if the purpose is to make a hardier product
and a less expensive one, provided the label on the finished goods indicates a
true description of the raw materials used.

In the manufacture of "Union" fabrics, a small amount of cotton is
blended with raw wool. A greater amount of twist can be given to such
yarns, with a resultant increase of strength in the fabric. Because of its crimp,
Peruvian cotton is frequently mixed with raw wool stock. Such mixtures have

Courtesy Wool Bureau, Inc.

Various types of scoured wool are blended on a combination scale that indicates the amount of each type of wool to be used in the blend.

a place in certain finished goods, but the amount of cotton used must be indicated on the label.

Carding. The carding process introduces the classifications of *woolen yarns* and *worsted yarns*. Manufacturing processes from this point differ, depending on whether the wool fiber is to be made into a woolen or a worsted product.

The length of staple and its strength determine the use of the fiber. Carding machines align the wool fibers, separating the short from the long staple, by means of cylinders covered with cloth through which the ends of tough wires protrude.

The shorter fibers, from 1 to 4 inches in length, are called *carding wools,* sometimes referred to as *clothing wools.* They are generally used in the manufacture of such woolens as shetland, flannel, cheviot, and tweed.

Fibers of very short staple, which are coarse, harsh, and wiry, are called *carpet wools.* They are suitable for carpets and are also used for coarse wool blankets.

The shortest fibers, called *noils,* are removed in the carding process. These fibers are used as filler in woolen fabrics made of reprocessed wool, helping to produce a sturdier cloth.

*Carded wool in fine spider-web form is being drawn
from the cylinder at the left into wool sliver (at right).*

The long staple is reserved for worsted yarns, which require additional combing processes.

Combing. The carded wool is put through a gilling operation, which straightens and elongates the fibers and eliminates the shorter staple, called *combing noils.* Combing noils are of good quality and can be used as filler for other types of wool fabrics.

The long-staple fibers, called *combing wools,* or *tops,* are over 4 inches in length and excel in color, feel, and strength. They are used in the production of such worsted fabrics as serge, whipcord, gabardine, and covert.

Drawing. Drawing is an advanced combing operation which doubles and redoubles slivers of wool fibers. The process draws, drafts, twists, and winds the stock, making the slivers more compact and thinning them into slubbers. Drawing is done only to worsted yarns.

Roving. This is the final stage before spinning. Roving is actually a light twisting operation to hold the thin slubbers intact.

Spinning. In the spinning operation, the wool roving is drawn out and twisted into yarn. Woolen yarns are chiefly spun on the mule spinning machine. Worsted yarns are spun on any kind of spinning machine—mule, ring, cap, or flyer.

How the manufacture of woolens and worsteds differs.

There are two different systems of spinning worsted yarns.

1. In the English system (Bradford), the yarn is oiled before combing, and a tight twist is inserted. This produces smoother and finer yarns. The more tightly twisted yarn makes a stronger, more enduring fabric.
2. In the French system, no oil is used. The yarn is given no twist; it is fuzzier, and therefore suitable for soft worsted yarns.

The differences between woolen and worsted yarns are summarized as follows:

Woolen Yarn	Worsted Yarn
Short staple	Long staple
Carded only	Carded and combed
Slack twist	Tightly twisted
Weaker	Stronger
Bulky	Finer, smoother, even fibers
Soft	Hard
Uneven twisting	Even twisting

Yarn Count. The fineness or thickness of wool yarns is based on different systems for woolen and worsted. One pound of worsted yarn yielding 560 yards is identified as No. 1s. Ply yarns are numbered according to the number of the single yarn from which they are spun. Thus, 2/60s worsted means two-ply yarns of No. 60 singles, twisted together.

In woolens, the size of the yarn is based on two separate systems: the cut, and the American run. The latter is more generally used.

The *cut system,* sometimes called the Philadelphia because of its use in that area, uses a base of 300 yards to the cut. Thus, 1 pound of woolen fiber drawn out to 300 yards sets a standard for No. 1s.

In the *American run system,* sometimes called the New England, 1 pound of woolen yarn yielding 1,600 yards is identified as No. 1s.

Warping. The yarn that leaves the spinning frame is not of sufficient length to serve as warp yarn on the loom. It is first wound on bobbins or spools and placed on a large rack or frame called a creel.

As in the warping operation explained in Chapter 4, the warp yarns on the bobbins or spools are evenly wound on the warp beam. They may be immersed in a solution of starch, gum, or similar compound to make them smooth and strong for weaving.

In the production of better-quality wool fabrics, a hard-twisted two-ply yarn is frequently used for the warp yarn, as the plied construction gives greater strength.

Weaving Woolen Fabrics. Basically, the weaving process for wool resembles the process described in Chapter 5. The short, curly woolen yarns obtained in the carding process are made into woolen fabrics by using the plain weave, sometimes the twill. The weave pattern is not discernible because woolen fabrics have a napped surface.

The thread count of woolens is usually less than that of worsteds, as the construction is not so compact.

Woolen fabrics are soft, fuzzy, and thick; they are warmer than worsted, but not so durable. Napping gives woolens a soft surface, which acts as a protection against objectionable luster. But napping can conceal poor construction and the quality of the yarns used; therefore, woolens can be more easily adulterated than worsteds. The napped surface tends to catch and hold dirt, but stains can be easily removed.

If poorer yarns have been used in woolens, the fabric is less expensive than worsted. Woolens are desirable for sportswear, jackets, sweaters, skirts, blankets, and similar general use.

Long-staple fibers produce the smooth worsted yarn shown in the upper part of this drawing. Short-staple fibers produce an uneven yarn with protruding short ends, as in the lower drawing.

Weaving Worsted Fabrics. The worsted yarns, which have been specially carded and combed, are woven into fine worsted fabrics with distinctive patterns, chiefly by means of the twill weave. The plain weave is infrequently used. The thread count of worsteds is higher than that of woolens because the finer yarn is more closely constructed.

Worsted fabrics are flat, rough, and harsh when worn next the skin. They are more durable than woolens and more resistant to dirt. They wrinkle less and hold creases and shape, but they become shiny with use.

Worsted fabrics are costlier than woolens. They are appropriate for tailored and dressy purposes, for spring and summer coats and suits, and for tropical suits. They are suitable for business wear.

Fulling. After the weaving process, woolen and worsted gray goods are placed in warm soapy water and are pounded and twisted to make the wool fibers interlock. This application of heat, moisture, and pressure, followed by a cold rinse, is called *fulling* (also *felting* or *milling*). Sometimes, chemicals are used to help moisten, soften, and lubricate the minute fibers so that matting will occur.

Fulling produces a desired shrinkage and gives the fabric additional thickness and a firmer, fuller texture. The longer the fulling operation, the greater the shrinkage, with consequent increase in the strength of the fabric.

The fulling process and other finishing operations for woolens and worsteds yield *flocks,* extremely short staple ranging from ⅛ to ¾ inch in length. Flocks are felted into the poorer grades of woolens to add weight. They are also blended with other raw wool stocks.

Other waste material reclaimed from fulling is termed *mungo.* This is the lowest grade of waste; it is used for blending, and is combined with yarn for low-grade wool fabrics.

Crabbing. To set the cloth and the yarn twist permanently, wool fabric is passed over several cylinders that rotate in hot water and is then immersed quickly in cold water. The cloth is held firmly and tightly to avoid wrin-

Courtesy Wool Bureau, Inc.

Woven pieces are sewed end to end and fed into the fulling machine where, in moisture and heat, the cloth is tumbled and pounded. This shrinks the fabric in length and width to give it body and evenness.

kling. Repetition of the treatment with increased pressure results in setting the cloth and the finish.

Unfinished Worsteds. Unfinished worsteds are popular because they have the durability and tailored appearance characteristic of worsted fabrics and the comfort, greater warmth, and freedom from luster characteristic of woolens.

The name *unfinished worsted* refers to worsteds that have a softness in their texture due to additional manufacturing processes, such as fulling, brushing, or napping. Since unfinished worsteds require more processing in production, the term "unfinished" gives a wrong impression.

The napped surface in the unfinished worsted gives softness of texture, serves the functional purposes of napped fabrics, and gives the beauty found

Courtesy Wool Bureau, Inc.

The drying machine permits the cloth to be dried to a predetermined width before going into the dry finishing department.

in woolens. In addition, the fabric possesses the durability of worsteds. With continued wear, however, the nap rubs off, and these areas show an objectionable luster or shine. Such consumers' goods can be renapped by a cleaning establishment, but this is generally avoided since the renapping can weaken the cloth. One can enjoy longer serviceability by selecting an unfinished worsted in a light color; light colors, such as gray, do not show luster as readily as do the darker shades.

Additional Finishing Processes.   Wool fabrics are also given the following finishing processes:

Perching—examining cloth for defects while it is run over two rollers.
Burling—removing loose threads and knots.
Mending—darning flaws and defects, if any.
Shearing—cutting and shaving for a uniform surface.
Singeing and steaming—for the characteristic hard finish of worsted fabrics.
Pressing—improving appearance and giving final shape to the cloth.
Steaming, sponging, or shrinking—removing excess glaze, setting cloth to proper width.
Decating, or decatizing—may be done wet or dry, a shrinking operation in conjunction with cylinder shrinking. In decating, the cloth is shrunk

by winding it under tension on a perforated cylinder through which steam is then forced. The process frequently serves as a substitute for London shrinking.

Judging Wool Fabrics. The presence of reprocessed or of reused wool in a fabric does not condemn it so long as the product is properly labeled and the consumer understands the limitations as well as the advantages of such wool fabrics. A fabric made of new or virgin wool may be of inferior quality if it is made of inferior grades or of extremely short staple.

• *Strength.* As wool is the weakest of the natural textile fibers, the fabric is made more durable by the use of selected grades of reprocessed or reused wool, although the durability is gained at the expense of texture and resiliency. To determine whether strength has been given by the use of flocks, brush and whip the fabric vigorously. Then examine the surface and selvages for powdery particles, which are the signs of short staple.

Wool fabric is also strengthened by the use of ply yarns. A hard-twisted two-ply yarn may be regarded as an assurance of durability. Tightly twisted single yarns also make a strong fabric.

The structure of the fabric should be examined to determine whether it has been weakened by excessive napping.

• *Crease Resistance.* Because wool fiber has a high degree of elasticity, wool fabric wrinkles less than any other; wrinkles disappear when the garment or fabric is steamed. Good wool is very soft and resilient; poor wool is harsh. When buying a wool fabric, grasp a handful to determine its quality. If the fabric retains the wrinkles and feels inelastic, this may indicate a mixture with cotton or an inferior grade of reused wool.

• *Heat Conductivity.* As wool fibers are nonconductors of heat, they permit the body to retain a temperature close to the 98.6 degrees that is required for perfect health. Thus, wool garments are excellent for winter clothing; they are also protective on damp days throughout the year. Lightweight wool of sheer construction may be worn in the summer for its thermostatic quality.

• *Absorbency.* Wool fabric absorbs a great deal of moisture without feeling damp; it dries slowly. This makes it most suitable for bathing apparel.

• *Cleanliness and Washability.* Dirt tends to adhere to wool fabric. Unless thoroughly cleaned, wool retains odors. Consequently, wool requires frequent dry cleaning or washing, if the fabric is washable. Extreme care is required in laundering. Wool is softened by moisture and heat, and shrinking and felting occur when the fabric is washed.

• *Shrinkage.* Shrinkage is greater in woolens than in worsteds, but all

DIFFERENCES BETWEEN WOOLEN AND WORSTED FABRICS

	Woolen Fabrics	Worsted Fabrics
Fiber	Short, curly fibers	Long, straight fibers
Yarn	Carded only; slack twist; weaker yarns	Carded and combed; tightly twisted; greater tensile strength; generally yarn-dyed
Weave	Indistinct pattern; usually plain weave, sometimes twill; thread count generally less than worsteds	Distinct pattern; chiefly twill weave, infrequently plain weave; more closely woven than woolens
Finishing	Soft finish; fulling, flocking, napping, steaming; as napping can conceal quality of construction, woolens are easily adulterated	Hard finish; singed, steamed; unfinished worsteds are napped; adulteration more difficult as fillers would be easily discernible
Appearance and touch	Soft, fuzzy, thick	Flat, rough, harsh
Characteristics	Warmer than worsteds; not so durable; nap acts as a protective agent against shine; soft surface catches and holds dirt; stains easily removed	Wrinkle less than woolens; more durable; hold creases and shape; become shiny with use; feel harsh when next to skin; more resistant to dust
Uses	Generally less expensive than worsteds if poorer yarns are used; desirable for sportswear, jackets, sweaters, skirts, blankets, winter use	Costlier yarns; appropriate for tailored and dressy wear; spring and summer coats and suits, tropical suits; good for business wear
Typical fabrics	Tweed, homespun, flannel, broadcloth, shetland, cassimere	Gabardine, whipcord, serge, worsted cheviot, tropical worsted, Bedford cord

fabrics made of wool are subject to shrinkage; they will shrink less if dry-cleaned. "Chlorinated wools" have been subjected to good preshrinkage, but the strength of the fabric is diminished.

• *Fastness of Color*. Because of their high affinity for dyes, wool fabrics dye well and evenly. The use of chrome dyes assures fastness of color.

• *Resistance to Mildew*. Wool is not ordinarily susceptible to mildew; but if left in a damp condition, mildew develops.

• *Resistance to Moths*. Wool fabrics are especially vulnerable to moths. They should be protected in some manner as discussed in Chapter 6.

• *Reaction to Alkalies*. Wool is quickly damaged by strong alkalies. For that reason, it is imperative to use a mild soap or detergent when laundering wool fabrics.

• *Reaction to Acids*. Although wool is damaged by hot sulphuric acid, it is not affected by other acids, even when heated. This property permits wool to be carbonized without damage.

HAIR FIBERS: WARMTH WITHOUT WEIGHT

Hair fibers that have the qualities of wool are obtained from certain kinds of animals throughout the world. The hair of these animals has been so adapted by nature for the climate in which they live that the cloth produced from the fiber gives warmth without weight. Some of these animals are used primarily as burden carriers; others are bred for their fleeces, which produce the most expensive fibers in the textile industry.

These hair fibers are used alone or are combined with sheep's wool for construction into fabrics whose cost varies according to the amount and quality of the blend. The consumer must be careful to analyze descriptions of certain of these blends. Parts of the names of rare animals are sometimes used to convey false or nonexistent values to mixtures of cotton and wool that contain such insignificant quantities of the lowest grade of hair fibers that they could not possibly add quality to the fabrics.

Camel's Hair. Camel's hair is a fine hair that is known to the American consumer chiefly in the form of high-quality coat fabrics. This textile fiber is obtained from the two-humped Bactrian camel, which is native to all parts of Asia. The climate of the desert countries, where the camel is used as a burden carrier and as a means of transportation, is exceedingly hot during the day and extremely cold at night. This constant change has produced a

Courtesy S. Stroock & Co., Inc.

*Sources of fine hair fiber are the camel (top left), the
llama (top right), the Cashmere goat (center), the
vicuna (bottom left), and the alpaca (bottom right).*

protective hair covering that is a nonconductor of both heat and cold; it is
also naturally water-repellent.

In the spring, the year's growth of hair, which hangs from the camel in
matted strands and tufts, falls off in clumps to make room for the new
growth. Masses of hair that are shed throughout the year are also accumulated. The camel is sometimes plucked to obtain the down or underhair.

Camel's-hair fabrics are ideal for comfort, particularly when used for
overcoating, as they are especially warm but light in weight. Camel's hair

is characterized by strength, luster, and smoothness. The best quality is expensive when used alone. It is often mixed with wool, thus raising the quality of the wool fabric by adding the fine qualities of camel's hair. The price of a mixed cloth is naturally much less than that of a fabric that is 100 per cent camel's hair.

In the textile industry, camel's hair is divided into three grades. Grade 1 is the soft and silky light-tan underhair found close to the skin of the camel. This is short staple or noil of 1 to 5 inches but is the choicest quality. Until recent years, it was the only true camel's hair used in the manufacture of apparel.

In wool, noils represent the less valuable short staple; but in the hair fibers, the short fibers are the prized product and are the only ones used in high-grade hair fabrics.

Grade 2 is the intermediate growth, consisting partly of short hairs and partly of coarse outer hairs. Grade 3 consists entirely of coarse outer hairs measuring up to 15 inches in length and varying in color from brownish black to reddish brown. This grade has no value for apparel manufacture; it is suitable only for cordage and for low-quality rugs.

Mohair. Mohair is the hair of the Angora goat, which is native to the province of Angora, Turkey. This species of goat is now raised to a considerable extent in the United States, principally in Oregon, California, and Texas. Some of the domestic mohair, particularly that obtained from Texas, is of excellent quality.

Imported mohair is of long staple, 9 to 12 inches long, and represents a full year's growth. The domestic goat is shorn twice a year, yielding a shorter staple, from 8 to 10 inches. Imported mohair can be spun to a fineness of 60s in yarn count. The highest count possible for domestic fiber is 40s. The domestic fiber has a great amount of coarse, stiff hair, known as *kemp,* which does not process readily or allow thorough penetration of dye.

Mohair is a smooth, strong, and resilient fiber. It does not attract or hold dirt particles. It absorbs dye evenly and permanently, and its fine silklike luster permits unusual decorative effects. Mohair fiber is more uniform in diameter than wool fiber. Under the microscope, it shows almost no serrations; its indistinct scales do not project from the shaft as is characteristic of wool fiber. Therefore, mohair does not shrink or felt as readily as wool.

When mohair is used in pile fabrics, the naturally strong fiber combined with the strength of the pile weave makes an especially durable and serviceable fabric. Mohair fabrics are wrinkle-resistant and do not mat readily because of the natural resiliency of the fiber. The fabric can be made mothproof. Because mohair is very resilient and is stronger than wool or the other hair fibers, it is used to great advantage in such a wide range of consumer goods as quality floor coverings, better grades of upholstery and drapery materials, and summer suitings.

Cashmere. The Cashmere goat is native to the Himalaya region of China and India. The fleece of this goat has long, straight, coarse outer hair of little value; but the small quantity of underhair, or down, is made into luxuriously soft wool-like yarns with a characteristic highly napped finish. This fine cashmere fiber is not sheared from the goat but is obtained by frequent combings during the shedding season.

The microscope reveals that cashmere is a much finer fiber than mohair or any wool fiber obtained from sheep. The scales are less distinct and are farther apart; the fiber appears to be made of sections placed within each other.

Cashmere first became familiar in the beautiful soft, light cashmere shawls for which India has been famous. Today, it is used for such garments as sweaters, sports jackets, and overcoats. Cashmere is desirable because it is soft, lighter in weight than wool, and quite warm. However, because it is a soft, delicate fiber, fabrics produced from cashmere are not as durable as wool.

Llama. The llama is allied to the camel in species, having many of the characteristics of that animal, but being about one-third its size. The llama is the traditional burden carrier in the higher parts of the Andes Mountains in South America and therefore has not been bred for its fleece. Its hair fiber is generally coarse and brownish in color and is valued because it may be mixed with the hair of the alpaca, an animal of the same species that is raised for its fleece alone. Some noils are obtained from the undercoat of the llama, also.

When llama is part of a blend of fibers, it gives exquisite natural colors that can be found in few fabrics. Llama mixtures have a characteristic high insulative property with little weight and are used for high-quality coat fabrics, as they embody the essential qualities of wrinkle resistance, fastness of color, and extreme durability.

Alpaca. In the higher regions of the Andes, 14,000 feet above sea level, is found another fleece bearer, the alpaca, a domesticated animal that resembles the llama. The fiber is valued for its silky beauty as well as for its strength.

The alpaca is related to the camel and the llama but is bred only for its luxurious fleece.

The hair of the alpaca is stronger than ordinary sheep's wool. It is also water-repellent and has a high insulative quality. The staple is relatively long, ranging from 6 to 11 inches; yet it is as delicate, soft, and lustrous as the finest silk.

Alpaca consists of two varieties of fiber: soft, wool-like hair; and stiff beard, or outer hair. Of the many colors obtainable, ranging from white to brown and black, the reddish-brown variety is considered the most valuable.

A more highly selected type of alpaca is the *suri*—a superbreed just as the Merino is the highest type of sheep. The fiber of the suri is sought by manufacturers of outer apparel because the staple is longer, silkier, and finer, and has curl throughout its length. A crossbreed, with the alpaca as sire and the llama as dam, produces the *misti*. Another crossbreed, the *huarizo,* is the result of breeding a llama sire and an alpaca dam.

Vicuna. The rare animal whose fiber makes the world's most costly and most exquisite cloth, surpassing all others in fineness and beauty, is found in an almost inaccessible area of the Andes Mountains, at altitudes between 16,000 and 19,000 feet.

The vicuna, one of the wildest of animals, is less than 3 feet high and weighs 75 to 100 pounds. A single animal yields only ¼ pound of fine hair; thus, forty animals are required to provide enough hair for the average coat. Formerly, the animals were killed to obtain the hair; but to preserve the species, the vicuna is now under the protection of the Peruvian and Bolivian governments. Attempts to domesticate this animal have not been very successful but are still being made in Peru.

The fiber of the vicuna is the softest and most delicate of the known animal fibers, yet it is strong for its weight, is resilient, and has a marked degree of elasticity and surface cohesion. It is used in costly suitings and overcoat fabrics.

GLOSSARY OF WOOL FABRICS[1]

alpaca. The lower grades of alpaca were originally used as linings, and the better grades for fine dress goods. The fabrics currently being sold as alpaca merely resemble an alpaca fabric in finish; the use of the term for such fabrics is incorrect.

[1] Courtesy of Associated Wool Industries.

astrakhan. A rough fabric with a closely curled face resembling that of the Astrakhan lamb's pelt. Often made with cotton warp or cotton back.

batiste (wool). A lightweight wool fabric in a plain weave similar to plain cambric. Wool batiste should be all wool unless otherwise described.

Bedford cord. A vertically ribbed fabric of substantial construction used where severe wear is encountered. The rib is pronounced and runs in the same direction as the warp. Originally an all-wool fabric, it is now also made of other fibers. The term describes the weave rather than the material.

bengaline. A thin fabric made generally of silk and wool, usually with a relatively inconspicuous rib running at right angles to the warp. The name does not denote any particular fiber blend.

bolivia. A soft plushlike fabric of wool, usually containing some special wool fiber, such as alpaca or mohair. The term is properly applied only to an all-wool product, closely woven and of fine stock.

bouclé. A fabric woven from curled or specially twisted yarn in such a way as to produce small loops on the surface, giving a kinky appearance. The curled nap does not cover the entire surface but occurs at intervals, distinguishing it from astrakhan. This type of fabric is usually made in coating weights but is also made in lighter weights for use as dress goods.

broadcloth. A fine wool fabric openly woven and then fulled to achieve uniform texture. The surface is then napped, closely sheared, and polished. The term originally was applied only to wool fabrics, but it is also applied to a cotton fabric used principally for men's shirtings. Not only is the fiber content of these fabrics wholly dissimilar but also the construction, finish, and use, so that they cannot be confused.

camel's hair. In undyed form, camel's hair is light tan. Fabrics that merely have this distinctive color cannot be correctly called camel's hair. The best grade is very expensive, and even then camel's hair is sometimes mixed with sheep's wool or other fibers.

candlewick. A soft woolen dress fabric made in imitation of the candlewick bedspread, with tufted patterns similarly applied.

cashmere. A real cashmere fabric is woven only from the hair of the Cashmere goat. It is of fine close twill weave and extremely soft. The total amount of cashmere wool available is strictly limited.

cassimere (not to be confused with cashmere). Cassimere is a woolen fabric closely woven with a plain twill weave, and fulled. Most woolen fabrics that do not fall into some other classification are referred to as cassimeres.

challis. A lightweight sheer fabric of all wool or of silk and wool. Sometimes made with a woven pattern but more often printed with designs after weaving. The designs are commonly of the type found in silk goods. Challis is made of fine yarn; it is very thin, light in weight, and soft and pliable.

cheviot. A rough, somewhat harsh woolen fabric, but woven from finer yarns than are used in typical tweeds. Usually in either plain colors or herringbones but may be made in other fancy patterns. Woven from woolen yarns except for the more expensive cheviots made from worsted yarns, generally in high colors, and referred to as worsted cheviots.

chinchilla. A thick, heavily napped fabric with a close curled surface in imitation of chinchilla fur. The tufts are close together, covering the entire surface. Generally dyed in the piece in solid colors. Used for women's and children's coats and hats.

covert. Twilled fabric made from highly twisted woolen or worsted yarns, usually of two colors, which give it a speckled appearance. Closely woven with a fine, smooth face. Used largely for men's topcoats and women's coats or mannish tailored suits.

crepe (wool). Wool crepe is a lightweight worsted fabric with a more or less crinkly appearance, obtained by using warp yarns that are tightly twisted in alternate directions. The term is often applied to lightweight worsted fabrics for women's wear that have little or no crepe surface.

doeskin. A very close and compact wool fabric with exceptionally smooth face. The weave is similar to a satin, but the smooth finish generally obliterates any trace of the weave on the face.

flannel. A fulled and napped woven fabric, made generally of woolen yarn but sometimes with worsted yarn used in the warp or filling. Usually woven with a twill weave, which may be obscured by the nap. Distinguished for its softness. Used for bathrobes, skirts, men's suits and trousers. Cotton flannel or flannelette is not dissimilar in appearance.

fleece. A wool fabric with a deep, soft nap. This term may be properly applied to flat woven or knit woolen fabrics as well as to those woven on the pile principle. The long nap or pile, as the case may be, provides many air spaces, resulting in a fabric with high insulative properties.

gabardine. A firm, hard-finished worsted fabric in the twill weave with a fine diagonal wale.

homespun. A coarse and loosely woven woolen material made to simulate homemade cloth—in effect, a coarse, rough tweed. Yarn is usually heavy and contains coarse wool fiber unevenly spun.

hopsacking. A rough open-weave woolen fabric made of coarse yarn, usually in a basket weave. Used for novelty effects.

jersey. An elastic knitted fabric made from either woolen or worsted yarn. The rib that results from the knitting is clearly discernible on one side of the fabric.

kersey. A medium-weight woolen fabric, well fulled in the finishing, with a napped and closely sheared surface that obscures the weave. Used extensively for military and civil uniforms.

mackinaw. A heavy woolen fabric, heavily fulled or felted, sometimes napped, with the result that no weave is apparent on the surface. In general construction, the same as melton except that the latter is usually made in plain colors, whereas mackinaw cloth is commonly woven with large distinctive plaids or color effects. Usually made of the coarser wools.

melton. A well-fulled or felted overcoating fabric with smooth finish and a close-cropped nap. Generally in plain colors. The coarser meltons are similar to mackinaw cloth, but are sometimes made of fine, soft wools to produce a smooth coating fabric with a finish similar to that of broadcloth.

mohair. Yarns and fabrics of mohair are bright and lustrous. Warp yarns of cotton or worsted are generally employed in the manufacture of flat mohair fabrics. The mohair pile fabrics used in automobiles and for upholstery usually have the pile introduced as a warp, but in such a fashion that the special system of threads is not subjected to severe tension.

nun's veiling. A fine, lightweight plain-weave woolen fabric, very soft and thin, originally for veils but now used for women's and children's dresses. Plain colors.

plaid back. A type of construction used in overcoatings. The face may be finished like melton, fleece, or similar fabrics. The back is a fancy or tartan plaid.

poplin (wool). Originally a fabric having a silk warp and a filling that consisted of a wool yarn heavier than the silk, thus producing a ribbed surface something like a rep. Now made of different fibers or combinations thereof.

rabbit's hair. Rabbit's hair is used in combination with other fibers. It is soft and lustrous. In the better fabrics, enough hair may be present to justify the use of the term.

ratiné. A rough, pebbly woolen fabric the surface interest of which is obtained by the use of novelty yarns with a fancy twist.

Saxony. A term applied to certain flannels and to smooth woolen fabrics made from fine wools similar in nature to Saxony wools.

serge. A fabric with a diagonal twill and a smooth finish. The twill is visible both on the face and on the back. Dark blue is the color most commonly used, but other plain colors are made for certain purposes.

sharkskin (wool). A term descriptively applied to wool fabrics woven in a 2 and 2 right-hand twill, with a 1 and 1 color arrangement of yarns in the warp and filling. This combination of weave and color results in color lines running diagonally to the left, opposed to the direction of the twill lines, and a distinctly sleek appearance and feel that suggests the texture of the skin of the shark. Modifications of this design are often loosely designated as sharkskin.

sheers (wool). A general classification under which may be grouped all thin lightweight women's-wear fabrics. Usually woven from worsted yarns, although some woolen fabrics are sufficiently thin to be classified as sheers.

shetland. The term is now applied to fabrics made of wool with the characteristics of Shetland Islands wool. Shetlands are extremely soft. The herringbone weave is common.

snow cloth. A term for fabrics designed for outdoor winter use. It may be applied to meltons, kerseys, heavy flannels, and similar fabrics. It is often used to indicate that these fabrics have been given a water-repellent finish.

suede (wool). A fine, soft fabric with closely clipped nap made to imitate suede leather.

tropical weights. Lightweight suitings of woolen or worsted, usually the latter, used for men's and less frequently for women's summer suits. The weave should be firm but open, as the fabric is especially designed for hot-weather wear.

tweed. A term broadly applied to the sturdier types of fabrics made of the coarser grades of wool. Tweed fabrics originally derived their interest from the color effects obtained by mixing stock-dyed wools. More recently the term includes monotones, which derive their interest from weave effects. The most popular weaves for tweeds are the plain, the twill, and variations of the latter.

velour (wool). A smooth, sleek fabric with a closely cut pile face. The upright pile, which yields in any direction, gives the fabric an exceedingly smooth feel.

vicuna. Short, soft, exceedingly fine hair fiber, very valuable because of the limited supply. It is rarely used by itself, although a few vicuna coats are manufactured each year. Sometimes mixed with wool to produce special soft coating fabrics. The term and certain derived and coined names have been much misused.

whipcord. A sturdy wool fabric with a pronounced diagonal wale. It is closely woven and smooth-finished; principally used for riding habits and other garments subjected to hard wear. In the heavier weights used as upholstery.

► TEST YOURSELF ON THIS CHAPTER

1. What are the advantages of wool fabrics?
2. Name the classification of fleeces according to quality.

3. What countries supply the world with wool?
4. Explain the Government classifications of wool.
5. What qualities are found in fleece wool?
6. How are grease and dirt removed from the fleece? What by-product is obtained from the grease?
7. Name six differences between woolens and worsteds.
8. Name three woolen fabrics and three worsted fabrics.
9. What are unfinished worsteds?
10. How would you judge quality wool fabrics?
11. What finishing processes are used for woolens?
12. Which finishing processes are used for worsteds? Why?
13. How do worsteds compare with woolens as to appearance and touch?
14. Which type of wool fabric is warmer? Why? Which stronger? Why? Which higher in price? Why?
15. Discuss the qualities of the hair fibers, telling their sources and how they are used.

Soft, Strong, Luxurious

The possibility of making cloth from the filament that the silkworm spins into a cocoon was first discovered in China about 2600 B.C. The Chinese cultivated the silkworm and developed a silk industry, endeavoring to keep the source of the raw material a secret. They succeeded for many years, but eventually Chinese emigrants introduced the silkworm into Japan in A.D. 300.

Eggs of the silk moth were smuggled out of China into southeastern Europe in A.D. 550. Spain began to produce silk in the eighth century, and Italy in the twelfth. It was the sixteenth century before the industry developed in France and England.

Attempts have been made to cultivate the silkworm in the United States, but they have not succeeded commercially because of the higher labor and production costs in this country. The silk industry is an important one, however, because the United States has become the greatest importer and consumer of silk. That part of the industry that manufactures raw silk into fabrics closely touches the lives of American consumers. The possession of silk fabrics has always represented an ideal of luxury to Americans, perhaps more than to the inhabitants of other countries. Silk will probably always be prized by the consumer even though man-made and synthetic fibers now have qualities that were formerly possessed only by silk.

Silk-producing Countries. When farmers in the Asiatic countries first raised silkworms, the many diseased worms and defective cocoons resulted in poor grades of finished goods. The farmers were raising silkworms only as an additional means of support.

Japan was the first country producing silk in large quantities to use scientific methods in cultivating the silkworm on farms as well as in factories. Japan has therefore always ranked highest in the production of fine silk, although satisfactory types are made in other silk-producing countries— China, Italy, Spain, France, Austria, Iran, Turkey, Greece, Syria, Bulgaria, and Brazil.

Cocoons are being picked from nests of twigs origi-nally provided to aid the silkworms in their spinning.

The cultivation of the silkworm requires extreme care and close super-vision, and the reeling of the filament from the cocoons can be undertaken only by skilled operators whose training is the result of many generations of experience.

Cultivation of Silk Cocoons. Since the discovery, so many years ago, that the fiber, or filament, that composes the cocoon of the silkworm can be unwound and constructed into a beautiful and durable fabric, silkworms have been bred for the sole purpose of producing raw silk. The production of cocoons for their filament is called *sericulture.* The cocoon of the silkworm is the second stage of development of the life cycle of the *Bombyx mori,* a species of moth. Experiments have proved that this moth produces the finest quality of raw silk.

In sericulture, all four stages of the life cycle of this moth are important, because some of the better cocoons must be set aside to permit full develop-ment, thus supplying eggs for another hatching. Under scientific breeding, silkworms may be hatched three times a year; under natural conditions, breeding occurs only once a year. The life cycle is:

1. The egg, which develops into the larva or caterpillar; that is, the silk-worm.

2. The silkworm, which spins its cocoon for protection, to permit development into the pupa or chrysalis.
3. The chrysalis, which emerges from the cocoon as the moth.
4. The moth, of which the female lays eggs, so continuing the life cycle.

Within three days after emerging from the cocoons, the moths mate, the female lays 350 to 400 eggs, and the moths die. Each healthy egg hatches into a grub, or larva, about ⅛ inch long. The larva requires careful nurturing for approximately twenty to thirty-two days. During this period, the tiny worm has a voracious appetite. It is fed five times a day on chopped mulberry leaves. After four changes of skin, or moltings, the worm reaches full growth in the form of a smooth grayish-white caterpillar, about 3½ inches long. Of importance to the silk industry is the small opening under the jaws, called the *spinneret*.

When the silkworm reaches maturity, its interest in food ceases; it shrinks somewhat in size and acquires a pinkish hue, becoming nearly transparent. A constant restless rearing movement of the head indicates that the worm is ready to spin its cocoon. Clusters of twigs or straw are provided for this purpose.

The silkworm begins to secrete a proteinlike substance through its spinneret, and with a bending motion the filament is spun around the worm in the form of the figure eight. The silkworm is hidden from view within twenty-four hours; in three days, the cocoon is completed. It is about the size and shape of a peanut shell. The filament is in the form of a double strand of *fibroin*, which is held together by a gummy substance called *sericin*, or silk gum. The liquid substance hardens immediately on exposure to the air.

If left undisturbed, the chrysalis inside the cocoon develops into a moth within two weeks. To emerge, the moth must break through the top of the cocoon by excreting an alkaline liquid that dissolves the filament. As this cutting through damages the cocoon so that the filament cannot be unwound in one long thread, the life cycle is terminated at this point by a process known as *stoving* or *stifling*. The cocoons are heated to suffocate the chrysalis, but the delicate silk filament is not harmed.

Filature Operations.   The cocoons that are raised by silk farmers are delivered to a factory, called a *filature,* where the silk is unwound from the cocoons and the strands are collected into skeins. Some cocoons are scientifically bred in such factories.

   • *Sorting Cocoons.* The cocoons must be sorted according to color, size, shape, and texture, as all these factors affect the final quality of the silk.

Cocoons may range from white or yellow to grayish, depending on the source and the type of food consumed during the worm stage. Cocoons from China are white; Japanese cocoons are creamy white and yellow; Italian are yellow.

• *Softening the Sericin.* After the cocoons have been sorted, they are put through a series of hot and cold immersions, as the sericin must be softened to permit the unwinding of the filament in one continuous thread. Raw silk consists of about 80 per cent fibroin and 20 per cent sericin. At this time, only about 1 per cent of the sericin is removed because this silk gum is a needed protection during the further handling of the delicate filament.

• *Reeling the Filament.* The process of unwinding the filament from the cocoons is called *reeling.* The care and skill used in the reeling operation prevent defects in the raw silk. As the filament of a single cocoon is too fine for commercial use, three to ten strands are usually reeled at a time to produce the desired diameter of raw silk thread.

The cocoons float in water, bobbing up and down, as the filaments are drawn upward through porcelain eyelets and are rapidly wound on wheels or drums while the operator watches to detect flaws.

As the reeling of the filament from each cocoon nears completion, the operator attaches a new filament to the moving thread. Skilled operators have an uncanny ability to blend the filaments, always retaining the same diameter of the rapidly moving silk strand. The sericin acts as an adhesive. It aids in holding the several filaments together while they are combined to form the single thread. On old-style reeling machines, at high speed, an operator could handle five to seven threads; on the newest models, it is possible to handle twenty-five threads.

The usable length of the reeled filament is from 1,000 to 2,000 feet, approximately a quarter of a mile long. The remaining part of the filament is used as valuable raw material for the manufacture of spun silk.

The term *reeled silk* is applied to the raw silk strand that is formed by combining several filaments from separate cocoons. It is reeled into skeins, which are packed in small bundles called *books,* weighing 5 to 10 pounds. These books are put into bales, ranging in weight from 135 to 145 pounds. In this form, the raw silk is shipped to all parts of the world.

Manufacture of Silk Yarns.

From the filature, the books of reeled silk go to the throwster.

• *Silk Throwing.* Reeled silk is transformed into silk yarn—also called silk thread—by a process known as *throwing.* The term is derived from the

Anglo-Saxon word "thrawn," meaning "to twist." Persons who are engaged in this work are called *throwsters*. Silk throwing is analogous to the spinning process that manufactures cotton, linen, or wool fibers into yarn. Unlike these other fibers, the manufacture of silk yarn does not include carding, combing, and drawing out, the usual preparatory processes for producing a continuous yarn.

The raw silk skeins are sorted according to size, color, and length or quantity, then soaked in warm water with soap or oil. This softening of the sericin aids in handling the thread. After mechanical drying, the skeins are placed on light reels, from which the silk is wound on bobbins.

During this winding operation, single strands may be given any desired amount of twist. If two or more yarns are to be doubled, they are twisted again in the same direction or in a reverse direction, depending on the kind of thread to be made. To equalize the diameter, the thread is run through rollers. The thread is then inspected and packaged ready for shipment to manufacturers for construction into fabric.

• *Kinds of Thrown Silk Threads.* Several kinds of silk yarns or threads are used in the manufacture of silk goods. The type of yarn and the amount of twist depend on what the weaver desires.

• *Singles.* Usually, three to eight strands of silk filaments are twisted together in one direction to form a yarn called a single. There are loose-twist singles, having two or three twists per inch, and hard-twist singles, having a much greater number of twists per inch. Loose-twist singles are used primarily for the filling yarns in many silk fabrics; hard-twist singles are used in the sheer fabrics.

• *Tram.* Tram is used only as a filling yarn. Usually, two to four untwisted singles are combined with only a slight twist of about three to five turns per inch. The number of turns may be increased for especially heavy silk fabrics. Tram is rarely twisted more than five turns to the inch, except in such fabrics as radium and taffeta, which use a special hard-twisted tram of about thirty turns per inch.

• *Voile.* As the name implies, this yarn is used for such sheer crepes as voile. The yarn is composed of three untwisted singles, which are combined with thirty-five to forty S turns per inch.

• *Georgette or Crepe de Chine.* This yarn is composed of two untwisted singles, which are combined with a very hard twist of about seventy to seventy-five turns of either S or Z twist per inch. The result is a very fine, strong, elastic yarn that is used for warp yarns and for sheer crepe fabrics such as georgette or crepe de chine.

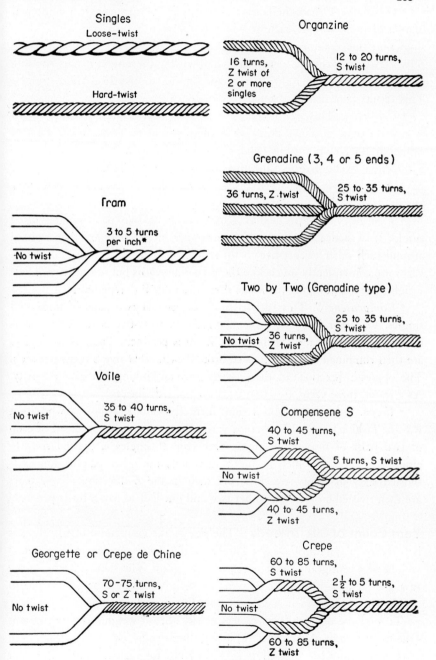

Singles
Loose–twist

Hard–twist

Organzine

16 turns,
Z twist of
2 or more
singles

12 to 20 turns,
S twist

Fram

No twist

3 to 5 turns
per inch*

Grenadine (3, 4 or 5 ends)

36 turns, Z twist

25 to 35 turns,
S twist

Two by Two (Grenadine type)

No twist

36 turns,
Z twist

25 to 35 turns,
S twist

Voile

No twist

35 to 40 turns,
S twist

Compensene S

40 to 45 turns,
S twist

No twist

5 turns, S twist

40 to 45 turns,
Z twist

Georgette or Crepe de Chine

No twist

70–75 turns,
S or Z twist

Crepe

60 to 85 turns,
S twist

No twist

$2\frac{1}{2}$ to 5 turns,
S twist

60 to 85 turns,
Z twist

Types of thrown silk yarns.

* Descriptions of all turns are per inch.

• *Organzine.* Organzine is used primarily for warp yarns. It is composed of two or more singles, each of which has sixteen Z turns per inch. These singles are then combined by twisting them around each other in the opposite S twist twelve to twenty turns per inch. Twisting the singles in this opposite direction around each other causes the singles to interlock more tightly. This results in a firmer, stronger yarn.

• *Grenadine.* This yarn is composed of three to five singles, each of which is given a twist of about thirty-six Z turns per inch. These highly twisted singles are then combined by being twisted around each other in the opposite S direction twenty-five to thirty-five turns per inch. Although these yarns have a high twist, they are nevertheless fine and are used for such sheer fabrics as organdy and grenadine.

• *Two by Two* (*Grenadine Type*). Each of two pairs of untwisted singles is twisted about thirty-six Z turns per inch. These are then twisted around each other twenty-five to thirty-five turns in the S direction. These yarns are consequently much like the grenadine yarns but are heavier. Their weight, body, and high twist make them desirable for crepe fabrics.

• *Compensene S.* This yarn is made of each of two pairs of untwisted singles. One pair is twisted together forty to forty-five S turns per inch; the other is twisted forty to forty-five Z turns per inch. These twisted pairs are then combined by being twisted around each other five S turns per inch. The opposite directions of these twists prevent kinking but give elasticity. As a result, these yarns are often used for knitted fabrics.

• *Crepe.* Some crepe fabrics (and formerly some silk hosiery when that was the fashion) are made of crepe yarns. These yarns are composed of each of two pairs of untwisted singles. One pair of singles is twisted sixty to eighty-five turns per inch in the S direction; the other pair of singles is twisted sixty to eighty-five turns per inch in the Z direction. These pairs are then twisted around each other two and one-half to five S turns per inch.

Yarn Count of Silk Threads. The size or the yarn count of silk threads is based on a system of weight known as the *denier*. A denier represents a weight of 5 centigrams; that is, .05 or 1/20 gram. The standard length of a raw silk skein is 450 meters. A 450-meter skein weighing 1/20 gram contains a 1 denier thread, which is an extremely fine thread.

To find the denier of 450 meters of silk thread weighing 70 centigrams (the usual weight of skeins from Japan), divide 70 by .05, or 1/20. The result is 14. The denier is expressed as 13/15 to allow for variation in the diameter of the thread.

In the laboratory, the denier size of a silk thread is obtained by a different method of figuring. The weight of a 450-meter skein is multiplied by 20. This figure is used because 20 denier equals 1 gram, as 1 denier equals 1/20 gram. For example, if the 450-meter skein weighs 2.16 grams, multiplying this weight by 20 gives 43.2, which is expressed as a 42/44 denier to allow for variation.

The most common size of raw silk from Japan was 13/15 denier. This is as fine as a 350s cotton yarn. In the spring crop, a 13/15 denier requires four to five cocoons to a thread, whereas the summer and autumn crops require five to six cocoons to the thread. As each cocoon comprises two filaments, a 13/15 denier may contain eight to ten or twelve to fourteen filaments, depending on the season. The greater the number of cocoons used, the coarser the thread and the higher the denier.

Degumming. Thrown silk threads still contain some sericin, which must be removed in another soap bath to bring out the natural luster and the soft feel of the silk. As much as 25 per cent of the weight of the silk is lost by the degumming process.

Degumming may take place after the silk thread is thrown in order to prepare it for yarn dyeing, or it may be done in any finishing process after the fabric is woven. For example, the tightly twisted yarns used for crepe effects still contain sericin. A small amount of sericin is sometimes left in the yarn or in the fabric to give the finished product added strength or a dull finish. Ecru and souple are examples of silk fabrics from which sericin has been partially removed.

When the gum has been removed, the silk fiber or fabric is a creamy-white color, beautifully lustrous and luxuriantly soft.

Weighting. The amount of weight that silk loses in the degumming process is an appreciable factor in manufacturing costs because the manufacturer buys silk by weight. As is customary in any business, the price of the finished product must offset this loss; therefore, silk has always been an expensive fabric. The weighting of silk fabric with metallic substances to make up for the weight lost by degumming is an accepted practice in the silk industry. This procedure lowers the cost of silk to the consumer.

Weighted silk is less compactly woven than unweighted silk, and less silk is used in the construction of the cloth. In other words, weighting rather than compact construction gives firmness and body to the fabric.

Weighting is done in the dyeing process. To weight colored silks, stannic chloride is used, followed by treatment with sodium phosphate. Black silks are weighted with metallic mordants, such as iron salt and logwood.

A small amount of metallic weighting, correctly applied to a fabric that is well woven to hold the weighting, is not considered injurious. In addition to lowering the cost, it is claimed that weighting gives silk crispness, luster, and firmer body and feel. When weighted silk is pleated, the crease is retained. Weighted silk, however, loses the natural elasticity of the silk fiber and is subject to deterioration when exposed to sunlight, perspiration, and dry cleaning. When the fabric is not properly constructed, threads shift. If the fabric is not woven sufficiently wide to allow for natural shrinkage, there is an unsatisfactory amount of shrinkage.

Taffeta is a commonly used fabric that is usually heavily weighted, because today there is little demand for pure-dye taffeta. Weighted taffeta is apt to crack and split at the places subjected to the strain of wear and when folded for a length of time. (Rayon and acetate taffeta do not contain any metallic weighting.)

Because the consumer cannot determine the percentage of weighting in a silk fabric, the Federal Trade Commission ruled in 1938 that weighted silk must be marked as such, and the percentage of weighting must be indicated on the label.

Pure-Dye Silk. As silk is weighted during the dyeing process, the term *pure-dye silk* indicates that weighting was not added at that time. According to the Federal Trade Commission rulings, pure-dye silk is defined as a fabric made exclusively of silk fibers containing *no metallic weighting whatsoever*; but the use of such water-soluble substances as starch, glue, sugar, or gelatin in the dyeing and finishing processes is allowed. Such foreign substances are limited to 10 per cent for white or colored silks and 15 per cent for black silks.

Well-constructed pure-dye silk requires a greater amount of silk thread than weighted silk because pure-dye silk is usually more compact. Thus it is generally superior, having the qualities of elasticity and durability, because the natural elasticity of the silk fiber has not been lessened, and its great natural strength has been retained.

Spun Silk. Short lengths of inferior silk filaments obtained from waste material are not used in producing reeled silk. After the short lengths have been carded and combed, they are spun together much as cotton, linen, or wool yarns are spun. Spun silk threads are soft, but they are less lustrous than reeled silk and are not as strong or elastic. Spun silk fabric tends to become fuzzy after wearing because the yarn is made of short staple.

There are several sources of staple silk: (1) pierced cocoons, the result of breeding moths that have emerged from their cocoons; (2) double cocoons, the result of two cocoons having been spun by two silkworms too close together; this is sometimes called *doupioni* silk; (3) floss, brushed from cocoons before reeling; (4) frison, the coarse and uneven silk fiber at the beginning and end of each cocoon; (5) scrap, the machine waste left from reeling, throwing, and the like.

Spun silk is less expensive than reeled silk. Although spun silk has less strength and elasticity than reeled silk because of the shorter staple used, it possesses all the general characteristics of reeled silk. Tub silk fabric, for example, is made of spun silk; yet it gives good service when the quality of the fiber is good. Spun silk is used for shantung and pile fabrics; for dress trimmings, linings, elastic webbing, and sewing silk; for summer wash silks, for velvets, and for umbrella fabrics. Spun silk is also used for insulative materials.

• *Yarn Count of Spun Silk Threads.* The method of determining the size of spun silk thread is similar to that used for cotton yarn. In cotton, the term 2/60s signifies a two-ply yarn consisting of two single strands twisted together, each having a yarn count of 60.

In spun silk, a two-ply yarn is indicated by the figures 60s/2. Although this term appears to be only the reverse of the cotton term, it does not mean the same. In spun silk, 60s/2 means that two yarns with a separate yarn count of 120 have been doubled, producing a ply yarn with a new count of 60.

Wild or Tussah Silk.

Wild species of silkworm live on oak leaves instead of the mulberry leaves that form the food of the cultivated species. This coarser food produces an irregular and coarse filament, which is hard to bleach and hard to dye. The tannin in the oak leaves gives wild silk its tan color, and the silk is commonly woven with the naturally colored thread; it is rarely dyed except in solid shades.

Wild silk is less lustrous than cultivated silk as only a low percentage (about 11 per cent) of sericin is removed in the degumming process. Wild silk fabrics are durable and have a coarse irregular surface. They are washable. Typical fabrics made from wild silk are rajah, shantung, tussah, and pongee.

The standard wild silk thread differs from the standard reeled silk thread in size, as it is made from eighteen cocoons. It averages 32/34 denier. Generally, fabrics made from wild silk are less expensive than pure-dye silk fabrics.

Finishing Processes. The usual finishing processes that enhance the appearance of fabrics and add to their serviceability are given to silk fabrics. Various special finishes may be used to make the fabric water-repellent. The most essential finishes for silk are:

Singeing—for smoothness.
Bleaching—very little required when silk is completely degummed.
Stiffening—for cheaper grades.
Embossing—if such patterns as moiré are desired.
Calendering—for enhancing luster.
Steaming—for pile weaves.
Wringing and stretching—softening the fiber and increasing the luster.
Pressing—removing wrinkles from finished fabric by passing it through heated rollers. The fabric is soaked in dilute acid to develop luster.

Judging Silk Fabrics. In spite of its high cost, silk has been one of the most popular fabrics because of its unique properties. Soft, supple, strong, and lighter in weight than any other natural fiber, silk is prized for its lightness with warmth, sheerness with strength, and delicacy with resiliency.

• *Strength.* Silk is very durable when the fabric is well constructed. Its use for parachutes is the highest recommendation that can be given for the strength of its filament. The great length of the filament, a factor in strength, imparts smoothness to the constructed cloth. There are fewer fiber ends in silk fabrics than in any fabric made of other natural fibers.

• *Crease Resistance.* Silk fabrics retain their shape, resist wrinkling, and recover easily from creasing because of the natural elasticity of the fiber. This is particularly true of the fabrics made from pure-dye silk and from wild silk. Those that contain a large percentage of weighting or those made from the short-staple spun silk do not have this degree of elasticity.

• *Heat Conductivity.* Like wool, which is also a nonconductor of heat, silk is desirable for winter apparel. Even silk fabrics of sheer construction are comfortably warm when used for lingerie and linings. Silk is worn in the summer because of its smoothness and crease resistance, which help to retain a fresh appearance. The warmth-giving quality is materially lessened by weighting, as the metallic content causes the fabric to become a conductor of heat.

• *Cleanliness and Washability.* Silk is a hygienic material because its smooth surface does not attract dirt, and any that gathers is given up readily when silk is washed or dry-cleaned. All silks are easily spotted by water, but subsequent washing or dry cleaning restores the appearance of the fabric. Weighted silks preferably should be dry-cleaned, but wild silk and spun silk fabrics may be washed. As perspiration deteriorates silk, undergarments should be washed immediately after each wearing.

• *Shrinkage.* Because of the straightness of the filament, smooth-surfaced silk fabrics have only a normal shrinkage, which is easily restored by ironing. Crepe effects shrink considerably in washing, but careful ironing with a moderately hot iron will restore the fabric to its original size.

• *Fastness of Color.* Dyed silk is colorfast under most conditions, but its resistance to light is unsatisfactory. The resistance of weighted silk is particularly poor. Therefore, silk is not recommended for window curtains. Pure-dye silks may be redyed by the consumer, provided a suitable commercial dye is used and the directions on the container are carefully followed.

• *Resistance to Mildew.* Silk will not mildew unless left for some time in a damp state, or under the extreme conditions of dampness found in tropical countries.

• *Resistance to Moths.* Silk is not attacked by moths.

• *Reaction to Alkalies.* Silk is not as sensitive to alkalies as is wool. However, silk can be damaged by alkalies if the concentration and temperature are high enough. It is therefore advisable to use mild soaps and lukewarm water when laundering silk.

• *Reaction to Acids.* Concentrated mineral acids will dissolve silk faster than wool. Organic acids do not harm silk.

• *Reaction to Perspiration.* Silk fabrics are damaged by perspiration. The silk itself deteriorates, and the color is affected, causing staining.

GLOSSARY OF SILK FABRICS

bengaline. A ribbed fabric having cotton or wool yarns for the filling and silk for the warp. Similar to poplin but having a heavier corded effect. Used for coats, suits, dresses.

broadcloth. A fine, smooth, closely woven fabric in plain colors or in woven stripes; also known as silk shirting. It has a plain weave. Used for shirts and dresses.

brocade. Most figured silk fabrics in a Jacquard weave are known as brocades. The pattern is raised above the general surface of the fabric. Used mainly for elaborate evening wear.

canton crepe. Characterized by a heavy filling and a finer warp. Heavier than crepe de chine, having pronounced crinkle and greater durability. Used chiefly for dresses.

chiffon. A transparent sheer fabric in a plain weave. Extremely light in weight but very strong. It usually has a soft finish. Used for evening dresses, lingerie, blouses, and handkerchiefs.

China silk. A very soft, extremely lightweight silk made in a plain weave, used chiefly for linings. Irregularities of threads, caused by the extreme lightness and softness of China silk, are characteristic of the fabric.

crepe. Fabrics with a crinkled effect, produced either by the use of tightly twisted yarns or by the method of weaving.

crepe-back satin or satin crepe. Satin weave with a crepe-twist filling. As the fabric is reversible, interesting effects can be obtained by contrasting the surfaces. Used for dresses, blouses, linings.

crepe de chine. Soft but strong; lighter in weight than canton crepe. Has a fine crinkled effect produced by alternately twisted filling yarns. Popular for dresses, lingerie, blouses, and scarves.

crepe meteor. Similar to georgette in construction on the reverse side. Satin construction on its face, thus showing more luster than any of the flat crepes. Light in weight, drapes well, has a soft feel and finish.

damask. Reversible figured silk fabrics woven on the Jacquard loom. Pattern flatter than in brocade. Used for upholstery and draperies; the lighter weights, for dresses and lingerie.

ecru silk. Thrown silk from which a small amount of sericin has been removed.

faille. A silk fabric of the grosgrain type. In plain weave with flat ribs in the filling. Has good body and wears well if not too loosely constructed. Usually slightly lustrous finish. Used for dresses, coats, and handbags.

faille crepe. Lighter weight than faille with creped filling. Used for dresses.

faille taffeta. Stiff and crisp with a fine cross-ribbed appearance. Used for dresses and coats.

flat crepe. Similar to crepe de chine but with a flatter surface.

foulard. A lightweight silk fabric with a soft finish. Made with a twill weave. Usually printed with small figures on dark and light backgrounds. Suitable for dresses, robes, and scarves.

georgette. Highly creped sheer silk fabric. Used chiefly for dresses and blouses.

grosgrain. A fine cross-ribbed fabric of close texture having a heavy filling, which is sometimes made of cotton yarns. Ribs are rounder than in faille, heavier than in poplin. Used chiefly for ribbons and trimmings.

habutai. Similar to China silk but heavier. A closely woven, pure-dye fabric. Used for lamp shades, dresses, blouses, lingerie, curtains.

lamé. Silk in which metal threads form the pattern or the background. Used for evening wear.

marquisette. Very sheer silk fabric in the gauze weave. Sometimes called silk gauze. Used for evening dresses and trimmings.

matelassé. A fabric having a raised figured pattern in a blistered quilted effect. Woven on a Jacquard loom. Used for dresses and blouses.

merveilleux. An all-silk or silk-and-cotton mixture in twill weave. Used as lining in men's outer apparel.

moiré. Watermark designs embossed on plain-weave fabrics that have crosswise ribs.

mousseline de soie. Sheer transparent silk in a plain weave. Similar to chiffon but with a more open texture and a stiffer finish produced by the use of sizing. Used chiefly for evening dresses.

ottoman. Heavy plain-weave fabric with wide, flat crosswise ribs that are larger and rounder than in faille. Filling may be cotton, silk, or wool. Used for dress coats, suits, trimmings.

pongee. Also called tussah silk. Made from wild silk. Has a rough, uneven texture. Generally in its natural colors of cream to light brown, but may be dyed. Used for dress goods and household decoration.

radium. A lustrous, supple fabric having the drapability of crepe and the crispness of taffeta. Plain weave. Used for women's dresses, slips, negligees, blouses, linings, draperies.

satin. Silk fabric with a highly lustrous surface and usually a dull back. Made in different weights according to its uses, which vary from lingerie and dress goods to drapery and upholstery fabrics. May be made with a cotton back. Sometimes double-faced for use as ribbon.

shantung. Low in luster, heavier and rougher than pongee. A plain weave in which large, irregular filling yarns are used. Sometimes used to describe a heavy grade of pongee made in China.

souple silk. Silk dyed in the skein, only part of the sericin being removed.

surah. A soft, strong silk with a twill weave. Used for dresses and scarves.

taffeta. A smooth, closely woven fabric in a plain weave. Often weighted to produce its characteristic crispness. Sometimes has a moiré pattern. Used for dresses, suits, coats, and lingerie.

velvet. Silk velvet has a silk pile and a silk back. Some velvets are made with a silk pile and a rayon or cotton back. *Transparent velvet* is a sheer velvet having a rayon pile and a silk back. *Panne velvet* has a special luster that is produced by pressing the pile in one direction.

► TEST YOURSELF ON THIS CHAPTER

1. Name the silk-producing countries. What is the cultivation of silk called?
2. Describe the life cycle of the silkworm.
3. What process in the production of silk is analogous to the spinning process for other fibers?
4. What is the difference between weighted silk and pure-dye silk?

5. Describe the degumming process and its effects on various types of silk fabrics.
6. For what purpose would you select silk rather than other fabrics? Why?
7. What finishing processes are given to silk fabrics?
8. What is spun silk? How does it differ from cultivated silk?
9. Why is silk weighted? What are the advantages of weighting? The disadvantages?
10. How does wild silk differ from cultivated silk? How does the difference affect the consumer?
11. Why are most wild silk fabrics tan in color?
12. Name some fabrics usually made from wild silk.
13. For what purposes is pongee most desirable?
14. Why is silk not recommended for window curtains?
15. List the essential qualities of silk, and show the effect of each quality on finished goods.

13 | RAYON AND ACETATE

Cellulosic Man-made Fibers

The production of a fiber such as rayon, the first of the man-made fibers, had been prophesied as long ago as 1664 by Robert Hooke, the English naturalist. He believed that it was possible to make an "artificial glutinous composition, much resembling, if not full as good, nay better, than that excrement, or whatever other substance it be out of which the silkworm wire-draws his clew." In 1710, René A. de Réaumur, the French scientist, suggested the possibility of making silk filaments out of gums and resins— for example, threads of varnish. One hundred and thirty years later, in 1840, Louis Schwab invented an apparatus that drew synthetic filaments through small holes.

In 1855, Georges Audemars, a Swiss chemist, discovered how to make cellulose nitrate. This was the first step toward the nitrocellulose process of making rayon. Almost thirty years later, in 1884, Count Hilaire de Chardonnet produced the first synthetic textile fibers from nitrocellulose. He became known as the "father of rayon." Chardonnet obtained the original French patent and won the financial support that built the world's first rayon factory.

These and other chemists of their day, as well as those who are constantly experimenting today on new fibers, have been guided by a desire to produce beautiful, smooth, light, supple fabrics with just the right amount of luster— the characteristics for which silk has long been noted—at a price within the income of every consumer.

Man-made textile filaments were officially recognized in 1925, when the Federal Trade Commission permitted the use of the name *rayon* for yarns obtained from cellulose or its derivatives. As the production and types of man-made fibers had increased and been given various trade names, the Federal Trade Commission ruled again in 1937 that any fiber or yarn produced chemically from cellulose must be designated as rayon.

Over the period of the next fifteen years, however, confusion developed among garment manufacturers, and particularly among consumers, because

Courtesy American Viscose Corp.

Wood pulp and cotton, the sources from which rayon and acetate are made.

there were as many as four different types of "rayon" with some similar and some different properties. Some rayons would fade faster than others; some would dry more quickly than others; some would stick to the iron and melt, while others would iron nicely. The cause of this lay in the fact that there were basically two groups of rayons: one consisting of regenerated pure cellulose, the other of a cellulose compound. These different compositions gave different properties.

Therefore, the Federal Trade Commission ruled that, as of February 9, 1952, there would be two categories of cellulosic fibers: rayon and acetate. All fabrics and garments containing rayon and/or acetate must be labeled as such and the per cent of content of each fiber must be indicated.

The rules also incorporated the first official designation of rayon and acetate products as "man-made" rather than "synthetic." In the chemist's terminology, rayon and acetate are not synthetic because natural materials—cotton linters and wood pulp—are used in their manufacture, rather than chemical elements. This differentiation has been used in this text, but the reader should remember that in many other publications the two terms are used interchangeably.

RAYON

Basic Method of Producing Rayon Filament. The natural process by which the silkworm transforms the cellulose of mulberry leaves into two fine filaments is simulated in the process of making rayon.

A liquid substance of cellulose is forced through a metal cap or nozzle about the size of a thimble. This nozzle is called a spinneret because it performs the same function as the silkworm's spinneret. The cap is usually made of platinum because that metal is not affected by acids or alkalies; it is perforated with small holes that are almost invisible to the naked eye. Through each of the tiny holes, a filament is extruded, which is solidified by a liquid bath as it comes from the spinneret. This is similar to the hardening by air of the raw-silk substance spun by the silkworm.

The number of holes in the spinneret may be varied, thus producing at one time any number of filaments of the same size. In a subsequent operation, these filaments are doubled and twisted to make any required size of rayon yarn.

Methods of Producing Rayon. There are three principal methods of making rayon. The fibers differ in important characteristics because the methods differ in: (1) the raw material from which the cellulose substance is obtained; (2) the chemicals that change the cellulose into fluid form for spinning; (3) specific features of manufacture.

These rayons, *viscose, cuprammonium,* and *nitrocellulose,* have been classified as regenerated rayons because the original raw material, the cellulose, is changed chemically into another form, which is then changed— that is, regenerated—into cellulose again. This second change produces the final product—purified cellulose.

Nitrocellulose Rayon. Although Chardonnet produced the first man-made textile fibers from nitrocellulose, seventy years ago, the nitrocellulose

The spinneret that forms the spinning solution into filaments.

Courtesy American Viscose Corp.

Courtesy American Viscose Corp.

Production of viscose rayon yarn.

process is no longer a significant factor in the world production of rayon.

In the nitrocellulose process, cotton linters are treated with a mixture of nitric and sulphuric acids. The linters are dissolved in a mixture of alcohol and ether, which forms a spinning solution called collodion. As this solution is forced through the spinneret, the alcohol evaporates, and the filament hardens. Its nitrate element is removed by a sodium hydrosulphide treatment, yielding a filament of purified cellulose.

Viscose Rayon. Viscose rayon is made from cotton fiber or wood pulp usually obtained from spruce, hemlock, and pine trees. The chemical process of dissolving wood pulp was first discovered in 1840 by F. G. Keller, a noted Saxon weaver. The viscose method of using wood pulp to manufacture rayon was developed in 1892, more than fifty years later, by C. F. Cross and E. J. Bevan, two English scientists. The first viscose manufacturing plant in the United States was established in 1910.

In the viscose process, the wood pulp or cotton fiber is soaked in caustic soda to produce alkali cellulose. This substance is broken up into fluffy white flakes or grains called cellulose crumbs, which are aged for two or three days under controlled temperature and humidity. Liquid carbon disulphide is then added; this turns the cellulose crumbs into xanthate, a light-orange substance, still in crumb form.

The xanthate crumbs are dissolved in a weak solution of caustic soda and transformed into a thick viscous solution, called viscose, resembling honey in color and consistency. If the rayon is to be delustered, titanium dioxide is added at this point. The viscose is aged, filtered, and vacuum-treated to remove air bubbles, as they would cause the filament to break. The viscose is then forced through the holes of the spinneret into sulphuric acid, which hardens the newly formed rayon filaments.

Courtesy E. I. du Pont de Nemours & Co.

*Liquid viscose, after being forced through the many
fine holes of the spinneret, in a short space becomes
separate rayon filaments, which, farther on, form the
rayon thread clearly shown in the gloved hand.*

Twist is inserted in the hardened filament, which is finally washed, bleached, dried, and wound into skeins or on cones or spools ready for manufacture into fabric.

Cuprammonium Rayon.

Cuprammonium Rayon.   The cuprammonium process of manufacturing rayon was first developed by L. H. Despaisses in France in 1890. This kind of rayon is made from cotton linters, which are boiled with caustic soda and soda ash, bleached with chlorine, and then washed and dried. The pulp is dissolved in copper oxide and ammonia, forming a solution ready for spinning. The name cuprammonium is derived from these two substances.

The spinning solution is forced through large holes in a spinneret, which are intentionally larger than the diameter of the filament will be, because the filament is to be stretched and twisted to a finer diameter by a process called *stretch spinning,* which subjects the filament to tension while it is being hardened. This stretch-spinning feature was developed and patented by E. Elsaesser of Germany.

As the spinning solution is pumped through the large-sized holes of the spinneret, it passes into a glass funnel, through which flows soft deaerated water at a constant temperature. On its way through the funnel, the filament

Courtesy American Viscose Corp.

Production of cuprammonium yarn.

is stretched and twisted. As it leaves the funnel, the filament enters a bath of mild sulphuric acid, which removes the copper and ammonia, leaving a solidified filament of pure cellulose, which is ready to be wound in skeins or on cones for the finishing and weaving processes. Final washing and bleaching are not required because these are initial steps in the processing of the cotton linters.

The stretch-spinning feature of the cuprammonium process produces fine yarn that can be given a great amount of twist. For its weight, it has greater elasticity than viscose filaments. The fine threads can be woven into the sheerest of fabrics. The high twist contributes to drapability.

Rayon Yarn Count. The count of rayon yarn is expressed in denier, the unit of weight explained in Chapter 12. The denier of rayon yarn is controlled by the size and the number of holes in the spinneret. The number of denier required to weigh one skein of yarn, 450 meters long (the standard length), is the denier that indicates the size of the yarn in that skein.

Because the sizes of yarns differ according to the purposes for which the yarns are intended, the weights of the skeins differ, even though the skeins are of the standard length. The finer the yarn, the less the skein weighs, and the lower the figure that expresses its weight in denier.

Single rayon yarns may be composed of from 13 to 270 filaments, which may vary from 2.5 to 4 denier each. Thus, when 40 or more filaments are combined, the yarns will vary from 100 to 150 denier; these are the yarns generally used for rayon dress fabrics. Coarser dress-fabric yarns may run as high as 10 denier for a filament; the resultant denier of such yarns would naturally be higher than 150.

• *Monofilament Yarns.* Monofilament yarns are composed of a single filament. The viscous solution is extruded through a spinneret with only one hole. Spinnerets, each with a different-sized hole, are used, depending on the denier of yarn desired. Monofilament yarn is used for a variety of products including hosiery. The term *monofil* is applied to a type of mono-filament yarn used in the millinery industry as a substitute for horsehair, which has limited use because of its short length.

• *Multifilament Yarns*. Multifilament yarns are composed of more than one filament, usually a great many twisted together. These filaments are extremely fine, sometimes less than 3 denier. Multifilament yarns are supple, pliable, and stronger than monofilament yarns of the same denier. They are used for a wide variety of fabrics including sheers.

Delustering. When rayon was first developed, the yarn had an objection-able luster. In the early days, a dulling effect was obtained by using tight twist in the manufacture of the yarn or by a calcimine coating as a final finish on the fabric. Today, rayon is easily delustered while the filament is being made by including colorless pigments in the spinning solution; of these, the most important is titanium dioxide. Rayon can be manufactured to retain a permanently high luster or a semidull or a dull appearance.

Rayon thus treated is referred to as delustered rayon. It is preferable to rayon delustered in the finishing processes by emulsions of oil, wax, or paraffin.

Spun Rayon. The long, continuous rayon filaments produce rayon fabrics having smooth surfaces or crepe surfaces. The filament can be adapted for

Staple fibers from which spun rayon is made.

Courtesy American Viscose Corp.

other effects by cutting it into short uniform lengths, usually 1 to 6 inches. These lengths are spun into yarns similarly to the spinning of cotton or wool. Such spun rayon yarns have an entirely different character from the ordinary rayon yarns.

According to the amount of twist inserted in the spinning process, spun rayon yarn can be made stronger, less lustrous, and adaptable to napping and other finishes, so producing fabrics that resemble wool, linen, or cotton. Such short-staple rayon can also be combined with any of the other fibers to make effective and useful fabric. This blending would not be possible with the long rayon filament.

Thus, spun rayon provides new finishes and a variety of low-priced fabrics that formerly were made only from natural fibers, with a consequently higher production cost.

Trade Names of Rayon Yarns.   The many companies that manufacture rayon yarns use one of two methods of making the rayon: viscose or cuprammonium. To identify their products, the manufacturers have given trade names to their rayon yarns, which the consumer often finds on labels or tags attached to garments and fabrics. Some of the better-known trade names are classified here according to the type of filament.

A cake of long-filament rayon yarn.

Courtesy American Viscose Corp.

VISCOSE

Bright Filament	*Semidull Filament*	*High Tenacity*
Briglo	Dulesco	Cordura
Crown	Newlow	Rayflex
Delray	Perlglo	Super Narco
DuPont		Tenasco
Enka	*Dull Filament*	Tyron
Narco	Chalkelle	
Newbray	Chardonize	*Spun*
North America	Dul-Tone	Avisco
Premier	Englo	Fibro
Spun-lo	Newdull	Tufton
	Tubize	
	Veri-Dul	

CUPRAMMONIUM

(*All bright filament*)

Aristocrat	Bemberg	Imperial	Matesa

ACETATE

The Process. The cellulose acetate process was developed in England in 1918 by Henri and Camille Dreyfus. In the United States, their product is known as Celanese. Acetates were developed much later by manufacturers in this country.

Acetate is not a pure cellulose product like viscose and cuprammonium.

Courtesy American Viscose Corp.

Production of acetate yarn.

Although it is made principally from the cellulose derived from cotton linters, the pulp is treated differently and becomes a chemical compound of cellulose. The pulp is steeped in acetic acid and allowed to age for a period under controlled temperature. After aging, it is mixed with acetic anhydride, which transforms it into a thick, clear liquid—cellulose acetate.

After further aging, the cellulose acetate solution is precipitated as pure white flakes by running through water. The flakes are dried and then dissolved in acetone, and filtered several times to remove impurities. The result is a clear, white spinning solution of the consistency of sirup. If delustered yarn is required, titanium dioxide is added at this stage.

The spinning solution is then forced through a spinneret. Instead of passing through a liquid bath, the solution passes through warm air, which evaporates the acetone and solidifies the filament. The filament is then ready for winding on spools, cones, or bobbins. No washing or bleaching is required as the solution was cleaned and filtered before it passed through the spinneret.

The filament produced by the acetate process differs from the rayons not only in the chemicals used to digest the cellulose raw material but in the chemical nature of the final product. It manifests different characteristics and requires different dyes. Acetate filament is thermoplastic; that is, it may be softened or plasticized by application of heat. For example, embossed effects, such as moiré patterns, are permanent on acetate.

• *Further Operations.* As with rayon, acetate may be spun into yarns of similar count. Multifilament and monofilament yarns may be obtained. The fibers may also be delustered by the addition of a substance such as titanium dioxide to obtain bright, semidull, and dull yarns. Acetate may also be cut into staple, generally from 1 to 6 inches in length, and spun into fuzzy yarns to be blended with or used in place of other short-staple fibers.

• *Trade Names of Acetate Yarns.* About 30 per cent of the cellulosic yarns are acetate, which is manufactured by different companies. Some of the better-known acetate yarns are:

Acele	Seraceta	Fortisan (high tenacity)
Celanese	Tubize Dull	Teca (crimped staple)
Koda		

Judging Cellulosic Fabrics. In studying each of the natural fibers, cotton was rated highly for its economy and versatility. It was shown that linen excelled cotton in certain qualities, such as strength, luster, absorbency, cleanliness, and crispness. With respect to warmth and resiliency, wool and silk take first place.

The development of a man-made fiber possessing many of the above-mentioned prized qualities of the natural fibers is a tribute to the ingenuity of man. If the supply of natural fibers were insufficient or even nonexistent, man-made fibers could fully meet the situation.

• *Strength.* Viscose and cuprammonium rayons are about half as strong as silk; acetate is a little weaker than the rayons. Yet all produce a durable, economical, and serviceable fabric whose smoothness of surface withstands the friction of wear. Rayon and acetate suffer only slight deterioration with age. Acetate is more resistant to perspiration than rayon and is unaffected by salt air.

Strength combined with sheerness of construction is possible in rayon fabrics by means of multifilament yarns. High-tenacity yarns afford a lightness with strength that is unsurpassed even by silk.

Smooth-surfaced rayon fabrics are unusually slippery. Therefore, the seams of rayon garments will slip unless the French seam or the flat felled seam is used. Also, when cut on the bias, loosely constructed rayon fabrics may slip.

• *Crease Resistance.* Because rayon lacks the resilience natural to wool and silk, it creases readily; but it should be remembered that the resistance of a fabric to creasing depends on the kind of yarn, weave, and finishing process. For example, the extremely fine filaments used in multifilament rayons have a greater resistance to creasing. Any of the crepe surfaces produced by tightly twisted yarns also resist creasing. Fabrics treated with one of the better patented crease-resistant finishing processes are highly resistant to creasing. Also, a soft surface produced by napping, typical of spun rayon, has some degree of crease resistance because of the softness and flexibility of the short staple, which recovers easily from wrinkles. This also applies to acetate, except that acetate is a little more elastic than rayon. Since acetate is thermoplastic, it holds pleats and creases better than rayon. This advantage permits the blending of acetate and such other thermoplastic textiles as nylon in garments where permanent pleating is desired.

• *Drapability.* Rayon possesses a marked quality of drapability because it is a naturally heavy pure-dye fabric. The filament can be made as coarse as desired, depending on the holes in the spinneret, and the yarn can be made heavy without the use of metallic filling, thus producing body substance in the fabric. Cuprammonium rayon is especially suitable for drapery fabrics because the numerous very fine filaments make the material extremely pliable.

Acetate has a high degree of drapability because of its greater weight.

• *Heat Conductivity*. Viscose and cuprammonium rayons are good conductors of heat and are therefore appropriate for summer clothing. In heat conductivity, acetate more nearly resembles silk, which is a nonconductor of heat; therefore, acetate may be used for warmer clothing. Spun rayon and spun acetate are adaptable for winter apparel because the napped finish is insulative.

• *Absorbency*. Viscose and cuprammonium rayons are suitable for summer underwear because, like silk, these rayons absorb moisture readily. Acetate absorbs only half as much moisture as viscose and cuprammonium; it absorbs slowly and dries quickly. This quality makes it highly resistant to perspiration and to odors, which explains its widespread use for linings. Low moisture absorbency, combined with an insulative quality, makes acetate an excellent fabric for bathing suits.

• *Cleanliness and Washability*. The smoothness of rayon and acetate fibers helps to produce hygienic fabrics that shed dirt and wash easily. Cellulosic man-made fibers will not become yellow when washed or dry-cleaned; white rayon and acetate remain white. Since rayon and acetate temporarily lose strength when wet, they must be handled with care when washed. When laundered, a mild soap and warm water should be used, and the garments should not be wrung but should be squeezed to remove the water. Rayon and acetate dry-clean equally well.

• *Shrinkage*. In viscose and cuprammonium rayon, the percentage of shrinkage is similar to that of cotton. Acetate shrinks less than rayon; in the flat weaves, acetate does not shrink at all. Crepe weaves or knitted fabrics always shrink to a certain extent because of the nature of the construction.

When combined with wool in sufficient quantity, rayon and acetate help to overcome the great amount of shrinkage that is characteristic of wool. All spun rayons and acetates can be Sanforset, which makes them suitable for apparel that must be frequently washed.

• *Fastness of Color*. Rayon fabrics absorb dyes evenly. Colored rayons have a high resistance to sunlight; they withstand strong light better than silk. This property makes rayon especially adaptable for window curtains.

Pigmented rayon, in which the dyestuff is put into the spinning solution, thus becoming an integral part of the yarn, is absolutely fast to washing. However, pigmented rayons are not produced in large quantities and are not widely used, as there is not a large sustained demand for specific shades.

Acetate fabrics do not absorb dyes as well as the rayons. Special dyes must be used. Sometimes the fabric does not dye evenly. Some colors, particularly gray and blue, gas-fade badly and change color to red and purple. To overcome this, the acetate solution may be pigmented before the fiber is extruded through the spinneret. Chromspun and Celaperm are such processes. They are colorfast to light, atmospheric fumes, perspiration, crocking, washing, and dry cleaning.

• *Decorative Effects*. Both rayon and acetate are often combined with other textile fibers with resulting novel and decorative effects. Moiréing is always permanent when embossed on an acetate fabric.

• *Resistance to Mildew*. Like cotton, the viscose and cuprammonium rayons have a tendency to mildew. Acetate does not mildew, and is therefore an ideal fabric for shower curtains.

• *Resistance to Moths*. Moths are not attracted to rayon or acetate fabrics. Mothproofing treatments are not necessary.

• *Reaction to Alkalies*. Concentrated solutions of alkalies disintegrate rayon and acetate. Therefore, a mild soap and lukewarm water is recommended when laundering these fabrics.

• *Reaction to Acids*. Viscose and cuprammonium rayons react to acids in a manner similar to cotton. Being pure cellulose, they are disintegrated by hot dilute and cold concentrated acids. Acetate is decomposed by concentrated solutions of strong acids.

• *Resistance to Perspiration*. Both rayon and acetate fabrics are fairly resistant to deterioration by perspiration, but the color usually is affected.

GLOSSARY OF RAYON AND ACETATE FABRICS AND BLENDS[1]

The fabrics named in this glossary were formerly made only in the natural fibers, cotton, silk, linen, wool, or in blends. When rayon and acetate were developed, these man-made fibers were used alone, in combination, or in blends with the natural fibers. Now the synthetic fibers described in following chapters are being combined with rayon and acetate in new combinations and blends. The labels, required by the Government, will identify the fibers used in any of these fabrics.

alpaca. A fabric originally containing hair of the alpaca. Now made in rayon-and-wool blends. Plain weave. Used for women's spring coats, suits, sportswear.

[1] Courtesy of American Viscose Corporation, adapted from *Rayon Fabrics*.

alpaca crepe. Two-ply. Gives somewhat the appearance of wool. Term used for a soft, dull combination crepe.

bark crepe. A fabric that produces the effect of rough bark on trees. A crepe with extreme surface interest.

batiste. Soft, thin lightweight fabric. Made of various fibers, including spun rayon. White, colors, or printed. Plain weave. Used for lingerie, dresses, blouses.

Bedford cord. A corded material that can be made with various fibers, particularly adaptable to rayon. Has tailored appearance. Cords run lengthwise. Novelty weave, a type of raised plain weave. Used for riding habits, coats, sportswear, suits.

bengaline. A ribbed fabric. Ribs run crosswise. A substantial, somewhat dressy fabric resembling poplin, but with a heavier rib. Plain weave. Used for women's formal coats, suits.

bird's-eye. A distinctive weave; small diamond twill pattern featuring a small dot in the center that resembles a bird's eye. Seen in bird's-eye piqué and diapers.

broadcloth. A fine, closely woven fabric originally made in cotton for shirtings and dress goods, and in wool for dress goods, suitings, and coatings. Now also made in rayon in shirting and dress weights. Also in wool blends in suitings, coatings, and wool-like dress weights. Plain weave. In all-rayon, used for sportswear, shirts, pajamas.

brocade. Originally, heavy silk with elaborate pattern. Now made with various fibers. Brocade has slightly raised designs or an embossed appearance as contrasted with damask, which has a very flat pattern. A contrast of surfaces in the weave may produce design, or different colors may be used. Novelty weave, Jacquard. Example: satin or twill figures on plain, twill, or satin grounds. Used for draperies and upholstery; in lighter weights, for formal evening wear.

brocatelle. A fabric similar to brocade but having designs in high relief. Weave is usually a filling satin or a twill figure on plain or satin ground. Used for draperies, upholstery.

canton crepe. A crepe with modified rippled texture. Heavier than crepe de chine.

casement cloth. A term covering many curtain fabrics of various fibers. Variety of weaves are used.

cavalry twill. A sturdy, substantial fabric with a pronounced diagonal raised cord. Twill weave. Used for sportswear, uniforms, riding habits, ski wear.

challis. Originally a silk-and-worsted fabric. A light, soft, pliable fabric. Usually printed in small floral designs, but may also be plain color. Plain weave. Used for dresses, negligees, ties, shirts, pajamas.

chambray. A plain-weave fabric generally characterized by a colored warp and a white filling, giving a mixture effect. Used for sportswear, women's and children's summer wear, men's shirts, pajamas.

chenille. A tufted fluffy yarn that looks like a caterpillar. Also a fabric made from such a yarn. Used for rugs, mats, spreads, knitting yarn, robes.

chiffon. (1) Descriptive term indicating light weight, as chiffon velvet, chiffon taffeta. (2) Thin gauzelike fabric with soft or sometimes stiff finish. Plain weave. Used for evening dresses, formal blouses, trimmings.

corduroy. A fabric having ridges or cords in the pile. Formerly made in cotton only, now in combinations. Variation of plain weave. Used for men's and women's sportswear, children's wear, infants' wraps, slip covers, draperies.

covert. Originally a medium-weight suiting of woolen or worsted yarns. Now developed in spun rayon or blends with wool. In dress as well as suiting weights. It has a speckled effect in color. Twill weave, sometimes satin. Used for sportswear, riding habits, suits, coats, raincoats.

crash. Term applied to fabrics having coarse uneven yarns and rough texture. Plain or twill weave, or twill variations. Used for sportswear, men's, women's, and children's summer suits and coats, draperies.

crepe. A fabric made of highly twisted yarn extremely versatile in texture, ranging from a fine, flat crepe to pebbly and mossy effects and, in extreme cases, to barklike, roughish textures. Rayon and acetate are used extensively in crepes. Fabrics of this family have a wide range of suitability in women's wear. Usually plain weave.

crepe de chine. A crepy fabric that, in texture interest, falls between a canton and a flat crepe. At present used mainly for lingerie; formerly for dresses.

crepe georgette. A lightweight semisheer crepe.

crepe marocain. Heavier dress-weight crepe. An exaggerated canton crepe in texture.

crepon. Originally wool crepe. Has a wavy texture with waves running lengthwise. Mostly used for prints.

damask. Flatter than brocade, and reversible. Jacquard weave. Satin or twill filling figures woven on a plain, twill, or satin ground formed by warp. Used for upholstery and hangings. In lighter weights, for formal evening wear and wraps; also tablecloths, napkins, bedspreads, face towels.

doeskin. Twilled fabric napped on one side. Twill or satin weave. Used for sportswear, coats, suits.

duvetyn. Originally a soft woolen fabric with fine downy back. Twill or satin weave. Used for coats, suits, dresses.

eponge. Soft, loose, spongy fabric similar to terry cloth. Novelty weave. Used for sportswear, summer suits, coats.

etched-out fabrics. (Also called burnt-out.) A fabric containing two different yarns in which pattern effects have been produced by acid. The acid is used to treat one of the yarns so as to remove certain portions of it, creating a patterned effect. Any of the three basic weaves or their variations. Used for dresses, curtains.

faille. A flat-ribbed fabric having body and drape. Ribs are wider and flatter than in grosgrain. Tailors well and wears well if not too loose in weave. Variation of plain weave. Used for women's spring coats, suits, dresses.

felt. An unwoven fabric that can now be made by using wool and a percentage of rayon or other fibers.

flannel. Soft lightweight fabric with slightly napped surface. Originally made in wool; now made extensively in spun rayon or in wool blends. Plain or twill weave. Used in medium weight for dresses and sportswear; in light weight for shirts and sports blouses, children's wear; in heavier weight for suitings and coatings.

flat crepe. Smoothest of crepe family. Inaccurately called French crepe.

foulard. Soft, light fabric, originally silk or wool; may now be made in rayon or acetate. Usually printed. Twill weave. Used for dresses, neckties.

frieze. Originally a heavy woolen overcoating with nap on the face. Can be made in spun rayon and wool in similar texture. Double-cloth weave with twill construction. Used for overcoats.

frise. Pile fabric of uncut loops. Variation of plain weave. Used for upholstery.

fur fabrics. Large class of pile fabrics of various fibers, imitating furs by dyeing and special finishing. Fabric can be either woven or knitted. Any variation of basic weaves. Used for popular-priced winter coats and trimmings.

gabardine. A firm, durable fabric with a diagonal rib. Modern gabardines are made in spun rayon, wool, cotton, or blends in both dress and suiting weights. Twill weave. Used for men's, women's, and children's wear, sportswear, suits, uniforms, riding habits, fabric shoes, raincoats.

gauze. A light, sheer fabric having an open, lacy effect. Leno weave.

gros de Londres. Cross-ribbed dress fabric with heavy and fine ribs alternating, or ribs of different colors. Plain weave or plain variations. Used for dresses, evening wear.

grosgrain. Firm, stiff, closely woven ribbed fabric. Much grosgrain ribbon is made of rayon. Cords heavier and closer than in poplin, more round than in faille. Plain weave or plain variation. Used for neckties, ribbons, trimmings, millinery.

hopsacking. A rough-textured fabric with open weave. Resembles sacking, as name implies. Plain weave. Used for men's slacks and shirts, women's sportswear, draperies.

jersey. Plain knitted or ribbed. Originally wool, now featured extensively in rayon and acetate in plain and novelty effects. May also be had in wool blends. Used for women's dress fabrics, sportswear, underwear.

lamé. Any fabric using metal threads in warp or filling or for decoration. Any weave. Used for formal evening wear.

linen-textured rayon. A large and important category of rayon fabrics having the distinctive textures of linens. These range from sheer hand-kerchief-linen texture to heavier, rougher butcher-linen texture. Usually plain weave. Used in lighter weight for handkerchiefs, women's and children's dresses, tablecloths, towels, sheets, pillowcases; heavier weights for summer coats, suits, sportswear.

madras. Soft fabric for shirts. May be white or yarn-dyed. Variation of plain or twill weave. Many fancy effects in weaving with corded stripes or small figures. True madras has woven figures. Used for shirts, sportswear.

marquisette. Loose, open, sheer fabric of leno construction in which warp yarns are in pairs, whipping around one another between picks of filling yarns. Each thread is locked. Novelty leno weave. Used for curtains, evening wear.

matelassé. Cloth having a raised pattern as if quilted or wadded. Rayon matelassé crepe looks somewhat blistered. A novelty double weave showing a quilted effect: plain, twill, or satin. Used for women's dresses, evening wear.

milanese. A type of warp-knit fabric, originally silk, used in gloves and women's underwear. Milanese has a distinctive diagonal cross effect.

mock romaine crepe. Similar to romaine crepe in texture and appearance. Different filling construction.

mogador. Originally a tie silk. Resembles fine faille. Plain weave. Used for ties, sportswear.

moiré. A watered or waved effect, usually on taffeta or faille, produced by a special finish. Steaming or wetting will destroy the pattern except on acetate. Plain weave. Used for women's dressy coats, suits, dresses, evening wear, bathrobes, dressing gowns, draperies, bedspreads.

mossy crepe. Sometimes called "sand crepe." Fabric with texture giving fine moss effect.

mousseline. Taken from "mousseline de soie," meaning "silk muslin." Firmer than chiffon, stiffer than voile. A sheer, crisp, formal fabric. Plain weave. Used for evening wear, collars, cuffs, trimmings.

net. Originally all nets and laces were made with a needle or with bobbins. In modern nets, the same effect is produced by machinery. There are a variety of meshes. Used for curtains, trimmings, evening gowns, veiling; heavier nets for tablecloths, bedspreads, curtains.

ninon. A sheer, crisp fabric, heavier than chiffon. Plain weave. Used for evening wear and curtains.

organza. Thin, transparent, stiff, wiry fabric. Crushes or musses, but is easily pressed. Plain weave. Used for evening dresses, trimmings, neckwear.

ottoman. Heavy cross-corded fabric having larger and rounder ribs than faille and bengaline. The heavy ribs may alternate with thinner ribs. Variation of plain weave. Used for evening wraps, formal coats, suits.

oxford shirting or suiting. Basket-weave fabrics, which may be made in plaid or two-color effects. Heavy qualities suitable for summer suits, skirts, jackets; lighter weight for sportswear, shirts.

pin check. Fine check made with different-colored yarns. Usually woven. Smaller than shepherd's check.

piqué. Originally a cotton fabric with raised stripes or welts running lengthwise or on diagonal. Knit construction may give similar effect, not so crisp. Variation of plain weave. Used for sportswear, children's wear, summer evening wear.

plush. Cut-pile fabric with a pile of greater depth than velvet. Variation of plain weave. Used for coats, trimmings, upholstery.

poplin. Originally made in silk. A cross-ribbed fabric between taffeta and bengaline in weight and appearance. The effect is created by a coarser yarn in the filling than in the warp. Plain weave. Used for women's wear, shirts, pajamas.

ratiné. A fabric made of nubby or knotty yarns. Frequently rough and spongy in texture. Plain weave or variation of basic weaves. Used for sportswear, dresses, draperies.

rep. A fabric with narrow ribs running lengthwise. Variation of plain weave. Used for women's wear, neckties, draperies, upholstery.

romaine crepe. A heavy sheer combination crepe similar to alpaca crepe but slightly flatter.

satin. A fabric with a lustrous surface in satin weave. *Crepe satin* is soft and lustrous; used for women's dresses, formal wear, negligees, draperies, and bedspreads. *Panne satin* is a stiff slipper satin; used for formal evening or bridal wear. Panne or crepe satin is used for *lining satin,* usually lighter in weight than dress satin. Panne or crepe satin can be finished as *wash satin* for blouses and lingerie. *Upholstery satin* is heavy, usually with cotton back.

seersucker. A lightweight fabric with crinkled stripes. Does not require ironing after laundering. Originally made in cotton. May be plain, printed, or cross-dyed. Plain weave. Used for women's wear, children's wear, sportswear, and, in heavier weights, for men's summer suits.

serge. A twill fabric with a smooth finish. The twill is very fine and close. Made of spun rayon, wool, cotton, or blends. Twill weave. Used for women's dresses, suits, coats, children's wear, men's suits.

shantung. Originally a silk fabric typified by uneven yarns in the filling, resulting in an interesting slubbed or nubbed texture. Now made in rayon extensively. Plain weave. Used for sportswear, women's summer suits, pajamas, robes.

sharkskin. Originally a two-color worsted suiting in various weaves, with basket-weave effects most common. Plain, twill, and basic weave variations. (1) Sharkskin suiting is now also made in spun rayon and wool blends, for men's and women's suits. (2) Term also used to describe a well-known acetate sports fabric typified by heavy, semicrisp texture. Used for men's and women's sportswear, summer suits.

shepherd's check. Fabrics having small, even checks. Usually twill weave. Used for sportswear, women's suits, dresses.

surah. Soft, flexible, lightweight, lustrous twill-weave fabric. Used for sports dresses, tailored dresses, blouses, mufflers, ties.

taffeta. A plain, closely woven, smooth crisp fabric, now in rayon and acetate. The warp and the filling are of the same or nearly the same yarn size. Plain weave. Used for dresses, children's wear, trimmings, linings, millinery, hangings, draperies, bedspreads, comfortables, lamp shades. *Faille taffeta* has alternating thick and thin crosswise ribs. *Pigment taffeta* is made of dull or pigmented yarns. *Tissue taffeta* is of very light weight.

tartan. Originally, Scotch plaids in woolens or worsteds in the distinctive designs and colors of Highland clans. Used for children's wear in particular; also women's sportswear.

tricot. Correct name for jersey cloth. Most important of warp-knit fabrics. On the right side, it appears like rib knitting; on the wrong side, the ribs run crosswise. Used for underwear, dress fabrics, sportswear, bathing suits, gloves.

tricotine. Originally, worsted dress goods resembling gabardine but woven with a double twill. Twill weave. Used for women's suits, coats.

triple sheer. Term in common usage describing a tightly woven sheer fabric with a fine, flat surface. Almost opaque.

tweed. Originally an all-wool homespun made in Scotland. Now developed in blends. A roughish fabric with wiry, somewhat hairy texture, casual or sportslike in appearance. In mixtures, nubbed, and slubbed effects. Plain, twill, herringbone twill, or novelty weaves. Used for coats, suits, dresses.

velour. A woven fabric napped on one side. Originally made in wool. Now also made in blends. Plain or satin weave. Used for women's coats, draperies, upholstery.

velvet. Broad and inclusive term covering almost all warp-pile fabrics except plush, chenille, terry, velveteen, and corduroy. Velvets are woven double, face to face, and cut apart while still on the loom. *Chiffon velvet* is of light weight. *Lyons velvet* is the name given stiff velvets. *Panne velvet* refers to the finish on lightweight velvet; the pile is laid flat in one direction. *Transparent velvet* is a very lightweight velvet.

Variation of plain weave. Used for evening wear, formal daytime fashions, negligees, draperies.

velveteen. A fabric with short pile resembling velvet but woven single. Variation of plain weave. Used for women's wear, children's wear, draperies, bedspreads.

voile. A light, transparent fabric similar to mousseline but softer and more clinging. Plain weave. Used for dresses, curtains.

whipcord. A twill fabric with pronounced diagonals. Twill weave. Used for riding habits, uniforms, sportswear.

▶ TEST YOURSELF ON THIS CHAPTER

1. How do the qualities of rayon and acetate compare with those of natural fibers? Give examples.
2. Discuss the early history of rayon.
3. How does the rayon process imitate the work of the silkworm?
4. What are multifilament yarns?
5. What is the source of rayon? How is the material made into a fiber?
6. What is the difference between rayon and acetate?
7. Why are rayon and acetate called man-made fibers?
8. How many methods are known for making rayons?
9. What is the essential difference in the ingredients of each type of rayon and of acetate?
10. What is spun rayon? Why does spun rayon resemble wool fabrics?
11. How do viscose, cuprammonium, and acetate compare as to absorbency? Warmth?
12. Discuss crease resistance in the rayons and acetate and compare with other fibers.
13. Discuss delustering as it pertains to rayon and acetate.

14 | NYLON

The Synthetic Polyamide Fiber

The word "nylon" is a generic term that designates a group of related chemical compounds. Nylon is not a trade name or a trade-mark. We refer to it here as a separate and distinct textile, such as cotton, linen, wool, silk, rayon, and acetate.

History of Nylon. Responsibility for the discovery or invention of nylon belongs to E. I. du Pont de Nemours & Company. More specifically, the credit belongs to Dr. Wallace H. Carothers and his staff of organic chemists of that company's chemical department.

Realizing that there was a need for a more active program of research to provide new developments that would insure the future growth of the company, the Du Pont Company began a long-range program of chemical exploration in 1928. Deviating from the applied research previously conducted, this "fundamental" research was primarily designed to develop basic knowledge of chemical materials and processes. No thought was given as to whether the information developed would be of immediate practical value.

Dr. Carothers was interested in obtaining a better understanding of polymerization: he wanted to know how and why certain molecules join to form "giant" molecules, such as those that occur in cotton, silk, and rubber. After many months of research, one of Dr. Carothers' assistants discovered that one polymer, which looked like clear, heavy molasses when molten, could be drawn out into a long fiber. When it cooled, the fiber could be drawn out farther to several times its original length. This strand was strong, lustrous, and silky. The question naturally arose as to whether this would make a good textile fiber.

At this point, the experiments became "practical." The Carothers group was working with a type of compound called polyesters. A great many were synthesized. However, each was deficient in one or more vital textile properties. Attempting to find a better fiber, they mixed polyesters and polyamides, which are related to polyesters. They were not successful and therefore decided to discontinue the mixtures and concentrate on the polyamides.

While working with the polyamides, one of the chemists filled a container, fitted with the tip of a hypodermic needle, with a hot viscous polyamide solution. He squirted a stream of it into the air, and the stream cooled into a fine filament. After the lustrous fiber was drawn and tested, it was found to be strong and pliable. In fact, this particular fiber had such promise that a large group of chemists and engineers were employed to make this fiber a commercial success.

During the next several years, research with a series of polyamides continued. In February, 1935, one of these was made from hexamethylene diamine and adipic acid. This polymer was called "66" because both of its component chemical compounds contain six carbon atoms per molecule. This "66" polymer proved to be best and is still the choice among hundreds of other polyamides that have been produced.

The name *nylon* was given to this material. (The name has no meaning.

Courtesy E. I. du Pont de Nemours & Co., Inc.

In these autoclaves in Du Pont nylon plants, the chemical process known as polymerization takes place. In other words, small molecules join together to make large ones, and nylon polymer is created.

It was chosen because it was "short, catchy, and hard to mispronounce.")
The discovery was made public in 1938. Since nylon is proteinlike in composition, the fiber was said to be similar in certain of its properties to silk, wool,
and hair. Furthermore, this new fiber had additional wonderful properties
of its own. On May 15, 1940, nylon hosiery went on sale throughout the
country. After that, nylon began to be used for a wide variety of garments.

Today, nylon is manufactured by the Du Pont Company and by The
Chemstrand Corporation, which was licensed by Du Pont to produce nylon
at its own plant.

Method of Manufacture of Nylon Fiber.

Nylon is actually a group of
related chemical compounds. It is composed of hydrogen, nitrogen, oxygen,
and carbon in controlled proportions and structural arrangements. Variations
can result in types of nylon plastics, such as combs, brushes, and gears. We
are here concerned with the production of nylon yarn.

• *The Nylon Process.* The process of making nylon is very complex, but
is explained here in the simplest possible terms.

By a series of chemical steps, two chemicals called hexamethylene diamine
and adipic acid are made. These are combined to form nylon salt. Then,
since the nylon salt is to be shipped to the spinning mill, it is dissolved in
water for easy handling.

Courtesy E. I. du Pont de Nemours & Co., Inc.

*Nylon polymer, pressed out on this huge casting wheel,
is sprayed with water and solidifies into a strip resembling ivory.*

At the spinning mill, it is heated in large evaporators until a concentrated solution is obtained. The concentrated nylon salt solution is then transferred to an autoclave, which is like a huge pressure cooker. The heat combines the molecules of the two chemicals into giant chainlike ones, called linear superpolymers. This process gives nylon a molecular structure somewhat like wool and silk and is also the source of nylon's strength and elasticity.

The linear superpolymer is then allowed to flow out of a slot in the autoclave onto a slowly revolving casting wheel. As the ribbons of molten nylon resin are deposited on the wheel, they are sprayed with cold water, which hardens them to milky white, opaque ribbons. The ribbons are removed from the casting wheel to a chipper, which transforms them into flakes.

• *Spinning the Yarn.* Nylon yarn can be made in several ways. The most important of these methods is the *melt process.*

Nylon flakes from several autoclaves are blended and poured into the hopper of the spinning machine to insure uniformity in the final nylon yarn. Through a valve in the bottom of the hopper, the nylon flakes fall onto a hot grid, which melts them. The molten nylon is pumped through a sand filter to the spinneret, a disk about the size of a silver dollar.

Chart showing the process of making nylon.

Courtesy E. I. du Pont de Nemours & Co., Inc.

From tiny holes in this spinneret, fine filaments of nylon are pressed out and later wound together to form nylon yarn.

Courtesy E. I. du Pont de Nemours & Co., Inc.

The spinneret has one or more holes, depending on the purpose for which the yarn is to be made. As the filaments come out of the spinneret and hit the air, they solidify. After they cool, the filaments converge, pass through a conditioner where they are moistened sufficiently to make them adhere together, and are given a few turns per inch to form a single thread and facilitate further handling.

• *Drawing the Fiber.* Up to this point, the chemical structure of the filaments is about the same as the flakes from which they were made. The filaments are opaque, have poor pliability, and are not very strong because of the random arrangement of the linear superpolymer molecules. However, this can be changed by stretching, or cold-drawing, the filaments from two to seven times their original length. The amount of stretching is dependent on the denier, elasticity, and strength desired. As the filaments are stretched, they become more and more transparent. The polyamide molecules straighten out, become parallelized, and are brought very close together. Up to a point, the nylon becomes stronger, more elastic, more flexible and pliable.

This elongation by cold-drawing, which is permanent, is accomplished by unwinding the yarn from one spool and winding it onto another spool that is rotating much faster. The speed of the second spool determines the amount of cold-drawing. That is, if the nylon filament is to be stretched four times its original length, it is unwound from one spool and wound on another at a speed that will subject it to a four-fold stretch during the operation.

Types of Nylon Yarn.

The diameter of the individual nylon filaments is determined by the rate of delivery from the pump to the spinneret, by the number of holes in the spinneret, and by the rate at which the yarn is drawn away from the spinneret. The size or denier of the yarn before drawing is determined by the diameter and number of filaments in the yarn. The denier of the yarn after drawing is determined by its original denier and the amount of cold-drawing. If it is drawn three times its original length, the stretched yarn will be one-third of its iginal denier. The individual filaments produced range from 0.1 to 15 denier.

• *Monofilament Yarns.* A 1 denier single-filament yarn is being manufactured. The monofilament yarns are being used by the hosiery industry and for industrial filters. These yarns are very fine and have little or no twist. Consequently, they are relatively weak nylon yarns.

• *Multifilament Yarns.* Multifilament yarns are made in both standard and high-tenacity forms. The number of filaments in each yarn varies according to the purpose of the yarn. The yarns range in denier from 20 to 210. Multifilament yarns are stronger than monofilament yarns because of the numerous filaments. The strength can be further increased by the amount of twist per inch given to the yarns.

• *Spun Yarns.* Nylon filaments may be cut about 1 to 5 inches in staple length. The individual filaments range in denier from 1.5 to 15. The staple is usually crimped and spun on a cotton system. These yarns are fuzzy and soft. They have a lower tensile strength but a greater abrasion resistance. They are not as elastic as the filament yarns and take longer to dry.

Delustering Nylon Yarns. Nylon yarns may be delustered by a process similar to delustering rayon and acetate. The delusterants are titanium oxide, barium sulphate, zinc oxide, or zinc sulphate. When any of these chemical compounds are mixed with the polyamide solution, they will cause the nylon to be delustered to some extent. As a result, it is possible to obtain either a bright lustrous nylon that can be used for satin, a semidull nylon, or a dull nylon that can be used for curtains.

Finishing Nylon Fabrics. Nylon fabrics can be given various finishes. The more common finishes are:

Heat setting—for permanent shape
Embossing—for pattern or design
Moiréing—for effect
Nylonizing—for increased absorbency
Water repellency—for protection against water

An outstanding feature of nylon is that a nylon fabric or garment can be subjected to a high degree of heat while being held in a particular shape.

After being heat-set, the fabric or garment will always retain its shape, creases, or pleats. Washing or dry cleaning or wear will not cause loss of shape. Properly done, heat setting will prevent nylon fabrics from shrinking or stretching out of shape. Such garments often require little or no ironing.

Since nylon is thermoplastic, the application of a hot embossing roller will cause the nylon to melt in conformity with the embossing pattern. This results in a permanent finish that cannot be removed by wearing, washing, or dry cleaning.

The same principle applies to nylon moiré. As with thermoplastic acetate, nylon moiré is permanent.

Nylon is not very absorbent. For shirts and lingerie, this is a disadvantage. To overcome this, nylon fabrics may be nylonized, a process that appreciably increases the absorbency of nylon.

Nylon fabrics may be treated with a water-repellent finish, which makes them ideal for rainwear and for shower curtains.

Judging Nylon Fabrics.   The intrinsic properties of nylon fabrics depend on the type of yarn from which the fabric is made. Furthermore, not only is it important to know whether the fabric is made of multifilament or spun yarn, but also how the fabric is woven or knitted and whether it has a close or an open construction.

   • *Strength.* An outstanding property of nylon is its strength. Next to Fiberglas, it is the strongest of all textile fibers, although it is one of the lightest. The strength of nylon will not deteriorate with age. These advantages make nylon particularly desirable for sheer hosiery, curtains, blouses, and dress fabrics.

Nylon not only has great tensile strength with light weight, but it is also tough and pliable. Nylon has the highest resistance to abrasion of any fiber; it can take a tremendous amount of rubbing, scraping, bending, and twisting without breaking down. It is a peculiar fact that spun nylon yarn has even a higher abrasion resistance than filament nylon. This property makes spun nylon very desirable for socks and upholstery.

   • *Elasticity.* Nylon is one of the most elastic fibers that exist today. It has a natural tendency to return to its original shape. Nylon has excellent resilience. Creases from knotting and crushing hang out. Pile fabrics, such as velvets, keep a neat uncrushed appearance.

It should be noted that nylon, like any other textile, has its own limit of elasticity. If it is stretched too much, it will not completely recover its shape.

Garments made of open-weave fabrics give a "window screen" effect. That is, they are cool because heat and perspiration are able to escape easily.

In spun fabrics, short crimped nylon fibers are twisted together into fuzzy yarns. The millions of insulating air spaces trap water, so drying is slower.

In addition, the type of yarn and the construction of the fabric may contribute to the behavior of the garment. For example, spun nylon is not as elastic as filament nylon. Furthermore, knitted spun nylon fabrics, such as those used in sweaters, will sag more easily than knitted filament nylon fabrics, such as those used in tricot.

• *Heat Conductivity*. Nylon fabrics may or may not conduct heat well. The warmth or coolness of a nylon garment depends on the weave of the fabric and on the type of yarn used.

The smoothness, roundness, and fineness of nylon filaments permit the manufacture of very smooth low-denier yarns. The yarns can be packed very closely when weaving a fabric. If a nylon fabric is woven compactly, it will not be porous. The tight construction will not permit air to circulate through the fabric, and the heat and moisture of the body will not readily pass through it. Rather, the heat from the body will build up between the fabric and the body, and the wearer will feel very warm. Such fabrics are good for

Water droplets slide off smooth nylon multifilaments easily. This, plus the fact that nylon itself absorbs little water, means that fabrics dry quickly.

A tightly woven material is warm, since heat and moisture are pent up. You would not want such a fabric for summer clothing.

Courtesy Du Pont Magazine

winter apparel, such as windbreakers, but are not suitable for summer garments.

On the other hand, these fine nylon filament yarns may be woven into extremely thin, lightweight, sheer fabrics. These materials are very porous and permit the circulation of air. Consequently, they are cool and can be used for summer blouses and curtains.

Spun nylon yarn will produce warm fabrics. These yarns are composed of thousands of short crimped fibers twisted together, which provide millions of tiny dead-air spaces that act as insulators. This insulation makes spun nylon fabrics warm and therefore useful for sweaters and winter socks.

• *Absorbency.* Nylon does not absorb much moisture. Fabrics made of nylon filament yarns will not readily get wet through the material. Most of the water remains on the surface and runs off the smooth fabric, which therefore dries quickly. Such fabrics are useful for raincoats and shower curtains.

Spun nylon fabrics, however, will not dry quickly. Although nylon is not very absorbent, its surface has a good affinity for water. Therefore, droplets of water tend to cling to the sides of the thousands of staple fibers, clogging up the air spaces and relatively increasing the drying time for spun nylon fabrics.

Nylon's low absorbency has a disadvantage in that the fabric feels clammy and uncomfortable in warm, humid weather.

• *Cleanliness and Washability.* Dirt particles do not cling to nylon because of its smooth surface. It can be easily washed with warm soapy water. Spots often come clean merely by using a damp cloth. However, nylon should not be bleached because it will deteriorate. Nylon also may be readily dry-cleaned. Spun nylon has a tendency to pill, or form balls, on the surface of the fabric.

Nylon filament fabrics dry very quickly. Usually, they need little or no ironing because the garments are usually heat-set to retain their shape, pleats, or creases. If a nylon fabric is to be ironed, take the same precautions as for acetate. Like acetate, nylon will melt if the iron is too hot.

• *Effect of Light.* Bright nylon is more resistant to the effects of sunlight than most other fibers. Dull nylon will deteriorate a little more quickly than bright nylon. However, even dull nylon has good resistance to light.

• *Resistance to Mildew.* Mildew has absolutely no effect on nylon. Mildew may form on nylon, but it will not weaken the fabric.

• *Resistance to Moths.* Moths and other insects will not attack nylon because it has no attraction for them.

• *Reaction to Alkalies.* Nylon is substantially inert to alkalies.

• *Reaction to Acids.* Nylon is decomposed by cold concentrated solutions of such mineral acids as hydrochloric, sulphuric, and nitric acids. A boiling dilute 5 per cent solution of hydrochloric acid will destroy nylon.

• *Affinity for Dyes.* Nylon has good affinity for most of the dyes used for silk, wool, and acetate. The colors have good resistance to fading.

• *Resistance to Perspiration.* Nylon fabrics are resistant to perspiration. The color, however, may be affected.

Nylon Fiber Blends.

The consumer uses many textile products that do not possess all the properties he would like them to have. He would, for example, like overcoats with sufficient warmth but less weight; cool, light summer clothes that would not lose their fresh, clean appearance on hot sticky days; fabrics that would wash readily, dry quickly, and not lose their shape.

Textile designers and engineers are producing new materials to meet such needs. These materials are often a combination or blend of two, or even more, fibers to give the fabrics all the properties that are desired.

• *Nylon and Cotton.* When properly combined with cotton, nylon adds strength, which allows the development of unusually fine textures that are not possible to obtain from cotton alone. Nylon provides smoothness, silkiness, and dirt rejection. It also reduces the weight of the fabric and increases its wrinkle resistance. The cotton gives softness and moisture absorption. This combination permits the weaving of fabrics that are soft, supple, and extremely serviceable.

If the combination is not properly balanced, the cotton may shrink, causing the fabric to pucker; also, the nylon fibers may cut the cotton fibers.

• *Nylon and Wool.* The proper combination of nylon and wool will produce a lighter weight fabric with greater durability. Such a fabric will retain the hand, drape, and warmth of wool as well as the elasticity, resilience, and shape retention of nylon.

Such fabrics are always labeled as to the percentages of nylon and wool that they contain. The properties of the fabric will be in direct proportion to the amount used of each of the two fibers.

• *Nylon and Silk.* In this combination, the silk improves the hand and provides moisture absorption. The nylon improves the stability or shape retention, and the elasticity and strength.

• *Nylon and Rayon.* In a blend of nylon and rayon, the nylon gives wrinkle resistance and strength. The rayon gives suppleness, drape, and moisture absorption. Such a combination makes possible a fine-quality fabric of extremely light weight.

As with cotton, if the combination is not properly balanced, the rayon may shrink, causing the fabric to pucker. Also, an improper blend of nylon and rayon may result in the nylon fibers cutting the rayon fibers.

• *Nylon and Acetate.* The acetate in such a blend provides a luxurious hand. The nylon gives light weight and strength.

This combination, however, may have, first, the disadvantages of possible improper balance mentioned for cotton and rayon. Second, neither nylon nor acetate absorbs much moisture. Such fabrics therefore may feel clammy and uncomfortable in warm and humid atmospheres.

All-Nylon Fabrics.

An ever-increasing number of nylon fabrics are being produced, similar to cotton batiste and plissé, to the texture of linen, to jersey for sweaters, and to silk, rayon, or acetate shantung and velvet. The properties of these fabrics in nylon are, of course, dependent on the inherent properties of nylon.

▶ TEST YOURSELF ON THIS CHAPTER

1. Who was responsible for discovering nylon?
2. What is nylon? May any company manufacture it?
3. What types of yarns can be made of nylon? Describe them.
4. Why are some nylon fabrics warm while others are cold?
5. Why do some nylon fabrics dry faster than others?
6. What advantage does heat setting give to nylon garments?
7. Is nylon damaged by mildew? By moths?
8. What is the reaction of nylon to alkalies and to acids? To perspiration?
9. What are the outstanding properties of a nylon-cotton fabric? What are the disadvantages?
10. What are the outstanding properties of a nylon-wool fabric?

15 | ORLON, ACRILAN, DYNEL, X-51

The Acrylic Synthetic Fibers

In recent years, several companies have been experimenting with acrylics. Basically, acrylic is a type of plastic. The acrylic fibers are composed of large polymerized molecules. In textile fiber form, these fibers look and feel very much like other fibers. They have, however, additional and valuable properties of their own.

While the fibers discussed in this chapter are not all necessarily wholly acrylic, they are sufficiently related chemically to be classified together. Some of their properties are similar, others are different. These similarities and differences are due to their related chemical compositions and their methods of production.

History of Acrylics. Dr. Carothers' discovery of the fiber-forming properties of linear superpolymers spurred research men everywhere to investigate the fiber-forming possibilities of a host of polymers. The first acrylic fiber, Orlon, became a reality when, in 1944, a "semiworks" was built under the auspices of the Research Section of Du Pont's Acetate Division. Until August, 1945, the development of Orlon acrylic fiber was concerned primarily with its possible aid in the war effort. But Orlon development was not brought to fruition when World War II ended. By early 1946, Orlon looked promising enough for commercialization. Process development continued, and in October, 1948, the Du Pont Company built a plant near Camden, South Carolina, capable of producing 6½ million pounds of yarn a year. Production of Orlon started in May, 1950.

Following the lead of the Du Pont Company, The Chemstrand Corporation developed another acrylic fiber, which they named Acrilan. A plant was built in Decatur, Alabama, and operations, with a capacity of 30 million pounds annually, were started late in 1952.

The Carbide and Carbon Chemicals Company started experimenting with superpolymers in 1934. The company contributed much to the present knowledge of these substances, but it was not until 1949 that Dynel, a partly acrylic staple fiber, was developed. The first commercial plant started production of 5 million pounds annually in July, 1950.

The newest acrylic fiber is X–51, a temporary name given by the American Cyanamid Company to its acrylic fiber. The company also has registered with the United States Patent Office the trade names of Creslan and Cyana for possible future use in identifying this fiber. In 1953, it was being produced in a limited quantity at the company's pilot plant in Stamford, Connecticut.

ORLON

Method of Manufacture of Orlon Fiber. The manufacture of Orlon resin is the result of a complicated chemical synthesis. Briefly, acrylonitrile may be made from acetylene or from ethylene. When the ethylene is treated with hypochlorous acid, a chlorohydrin is formed. The chlorohydrin is re-

Courtesy E. I. du Pont de Nemours & Co., Inc.

Hundreds of individual ends of continuous-filament yarn feed from the creel in processing Orlon acrylic fiber.

acted with sodium hydroxide to form ethylene oxide. Hydrocyanic acid is added to the ethylene oxide, producing cyanoalcohol, which is dehydrated to yield acrylonitrile.

Acrylonitrile is then polymerized into polyacrylonitrile resin, a long-chain linear polymer. The polyacrylonitrile is then dissolved in a suitable solvent, such as dimethylformamide, and extruded through a spinneret. After coagulation, the filaments are oriented and stabilized by stretching.

Types of Orlon Yarn.

After orientation and stabilization, the Orlon filament yarns are made into either multifilament or staple yarns.

• *Multifilament Yarns*. As with other filament yarns, Orlon multifilament yarns are made by twisting a number of continuous filaments around each other. These filaments are of 2.5 denier each. They are generally combined into yarns of 75, 100, 200, and 400 denier. Other deniers can be made as industry requires.

• *Spun Yarns*. Orlon spun yarns are made of 1.5 to 6 denier filaments, which are cut into staple of 1.5 to 4 inches in length. The staple is crimped and spun on a cotton or wool system into soft, fuzzy yarns. While spun Orlon yarn has a more resilient handle, or feel, and is more readily dyeable than the multifilament yarns, it is weaker and has less resistance to degradation by sunlight. Spun Orlon yarns will also stretch more easily than the multifilament yarns.

Delustering of Orlon Yarns.

Like nylon, Orlon can be made in varying degrees of luster by the addition of delusterants. These agents appear to have no effect on the inherent properties of the yarn.

Finishing Orlon Fabrics.

Several finishes can be given to Orlon fabrics to increase their usefulness. Among the most important are:

Heat setting—for permanent shape
Embossing—for pattern or design
Water repellency—for protection against water

An outstanding feature of Orlon is that a fabric or garment made of Orlon can be given a permanent shape by being subjected to a high degree of heat. After being heat-set, the fabric will retain its shape, creases, or pleats. Washing, dry cleaning, or wear will not cause loss of shape.

This thermoplastic property of Orlon also permits permanent embossing. The heat of the embossing roller melts the fabric slightly at the points of contact. On removal, the Orlon hardens, and a pattern remains that cannot be removed by washing, dry cleaning, or wear.

Orlon is not a particularly absorbent textile. To make it even less absorbent, it may be treated with Zelan. This process makes the fabric water-repellent and is therefore desirable for rainwear and children's playclothes.

Judging Orlon Fabrics. The properties of Orlon fabrics depend on the type of yarn that is used as well as how the material is woven or knitted.

• *Strength*. Orlon filament fiber is the strongest of the acrylics. Among the synthetic fibers, it is surpassed in strength only by Fiberglas and nylon. Among the natural fibers, it is surpassed by linen and silk. As compared with the filament fiber, the Orlon staple is somewhat weaker. While the abrasion resistance of Orlon is good, it cannot compete with nylon.

• *Elasticity*. Among the acrylics, Orlon is less elastic than Dynel, about equally as elastic as Acrilan, and more elastic than X-51. Compared with other fibers, Orlon is not particularly elastic. It has very good resilience, however, and therefore will not wrinkle easily. Orlon staple fabrics are not as lively in springing out from a creased position as Dacron and wool, but they are nevertheless good in this respect. The low elasticity makes Orlon useful for knitted wear, since it is not likely to stretch unduly. The high resilience makes Orlon desirable for men's slacks and suits as well as women's dresses.

• *Heat Conductivity*. Like all acrylics, Orlon does not conduct heat rapidly; therefore, Orlon fabrics can be warm. This is particularly true when staple fibers are used. Orlon is dog-bone in shape, which provides overlapping and bulk (with little weight). As a result, staple Orlon fabrics have approximately 20 per cent greater insulating power per ounce of fiber than wool fabrics. Since an ounce of Orlon fabric is thicker than an ounce of wool fabric, it is possible to obtain an Orlon fabric that, while being as thick and as warm as wool, is about 20 per cent lighter in weight.

Orlon continuous-filament fabrics are less warm than silk fabrics but are warmer than acetate, nylon, or Dacron.

• *Absorbency*. Orlon has a low water absorbency, being less absorbent than nylon. As a result, Orlon filament fabrics dry rapidly after washing because the water tends to run off rather than soak into the cloth. Fabrics made of the staple will dry more slowly because the water droplets get into the air spaces between the staple fibers and evaporate slowly. The low absorbency of Orlon has the disadvantage of making the fabric feel clammy and uncomfortable in warm, humid weather.

On the other hand, this low absorbency gives Orlon the advantage of resisting stains. Many substances that are ordinarily absorbed by other fibers merely remain on the surface of Orlon fabrics, and can be easily removed by wiping, washing, or dry cleaning.

• *Cleanliness and Washability.* Orlon fabrics do not soil or stain easily. Washing or dry cleaning quickly renews their freshness. However, a mild soap should be used in laundering since strong soaps will damage Orlon. If desired, any ordinary cleaning fluid and household bleaches may be safely used.

Orlon is essentially free from the problem of pilling, or the forming of balls of fiber on the fabric surface. In fact, it actually decreases the tendency of wool to pill when used in blends with that fiber.

Orlon fabrics should be ironed with a moderately warm iron; in fact, they may be ironed while dry. Old creases may be removed, and new ones added. Since fabrics of Orlon may be heat-set, it is often unnecessary to press them, but some ironing to smooth the cloth may be desired.

• *Effect of Light.* Orlon has outstanding resistance to the effect of light. Its extreme resistance to such degradation makes it especially useful for such outdoor purposes as awnings, curtains, draperies, and uniforms.

• *Resistance to Mildew.* Mildew may form on the surface, but it will have no effect on Orlon fabric. It may be easily wiped off.

• *Resistance to Moths.* Orlon is unaffected by moths or their larvae, or by carpet beetles.

• *Reaction to Alkalies.* Orlon has fair-to-good resistance to weak alkalies.

• *Reaction to Acids.* Orlon is exceedingly resistant to strong mineral acids as well as organic acids.

• *Affinity for Dyes.* Orlon does not have a good affinity for most dyes. The pastel and medium shades are more easily obtained. The colors have excellent washfastness but poor lightfastness.

• *Resistance to Perspiration.* All indications are that Orlon fabrics are not readily deteriorated by perspiration, but the color may be affected.

Orlon Fiber Blends.

Orlon has many desirable properties that may be imparted to fabrics containing fibers other than Orlon, depending on the relative amount of each fiber used.

• *Orlon and Cotton.* In combination with cotton, Orlon adds strength with light weight. The fabric is wrinkle-resistant and generally provides ease of care. The cotton contributes absorbency.

• *Orlon and Wool.* One of the outstanding characteristics of Orlon is its bulk, so that when the staple is blended with wool, the resulting fabric is lightweight and yet warm. It also has a soft hand. Fabrics of this combination have very good crease retention and wrinkle recovery. These blends are washable. Where there is a good proportion of Orlon, the fabrics seldom need pressing. However, too much Orlon in such a fabric makes the cloth too bulky. Such a blend will also be stronger than an all-wool fabric.

• *Orlon and Silk.* Orlon and silk together provide interesting cross-dye and texture effects. Such blends have outstanding hand and excellent stability. In addition to the good appearance, the combination gives long wear. The Orlon contributes easy-care qualities and shape retention. The silk contributes absorbency. The fabric is very resilient and may be warm, depending on its weight.

• *Orlon and Rayon.* To the versatility of rayon, Orlon adds wrinkle resistance and stability. New and unusual surface and dye effects, including cross-dyes, are possible. Orlon provides a dry, warm, soft hand as well as greater strength.

• *Orlon and Acetate.* A combination of Orlon and acetate in a fabric provides a soft, luxurious feel and excellent drapability. It also has excellent shape retention and good resilience. The fabric launders easily (with a mild soap and warm water), dries rapidly, and is easy to iron. The Orlon also provides greater strength and resistance to sunlight. However, neither Orlon nor acetate is particularly absorbent, which presents a disadvantage in warm, humid weather. Such blends will be warm and clammy.

• *Orlon and Nylon.* The strength and abrasion resistance of nylon combined with the luxurious hand and covering power of Orlon produce attractive, warm, strong fabrics. Similar qualities of Orlon and nylon, such as wrinkle resistance, crease retention, and ease of care, are increased when these fibers are combined. But such fabrics will not be very absorbent.

ACRILAN

Method of Manufacture of Acrilan Fiber. The processing of Acrilan is similar to that of Orlon. In simplified terms, natural gas and air are combined to form ammonia. Ammonia and natural gas are combined to produce hydrocyanic acid. Natural gas, at elevated temperatures, produces acetylene which, when combined with hydrocyanic acid, produces acrylonitrile. Then the acrylonitrile is polymerized. This polyacrylonitrile in powder form is then dissolved by a suitable solvent and passed through spinnerets into a coagulating bath to produce continuous filaments. These fibers are then washed, stretched, and crimped. Finally, the crimped filaments are cut into staple, dried, opened, and baled. The fiber is a light cream color and is semidull.

Types of Acrilan Yarn. Acrilan fiber is made in 3 and 5 denier diameters. Since all the fibers are cut into staple, the only form of Acrilan yarn is the spun yarn. Using a method similar to that used for rayon staple, Acrilan fiber may be spun into yarn on the cotton, woolen, or worsted system depending on the desired purpose.

Finishing Acrilan Fabrics. Acrilan may be finished similarly to Orlon. The outstanding feature is heat setting, which will permit semipermanent creases. However, care must be taken in the process because dry heat in excess of 300 degrees Fahrenheit for more than a few minutes will cause a yellowing of the fiber. With proper precautions, Acrilan fabrics will be bulky and silky.

Judging Acrilan Fabrics. Acrilan fabrics are made only of spun yarn. The properties of the fabrics are partially dependent on the manner in which the yarn is spun as well as on the construction of the cloth.

• *Strength.* Acrilan is about equal in strength to Dynel. It is weaker than both Orlon and X–51. Compared to those natural fibers with which it is

Courtesy The Chemstrand Corporation

Diagrammatic flow chart of Acrilan production.

sometimes blended, Acrilan is weaker than cotton but stronger than wool. It is also stronger than the rayons and acetate.

• *Elasticity.* Acrilan is not very elastic. Compared to the other acrylic fibers, it has an elasticity equal to that of Orlon, is less elastic than Dynel, but slightly more elastic than X-51. The low elasticity of Acrilan makes it particularly suitable for knitted wear and where retention of shape is desired.

Acrilan has very good resilience. It will not wrinkle easily and therefore is good for dresses, suits, and slacks.

• *Heat Conductivity.* Acrilan is a bulky, soft, warm fiber similar in insulating value to the other acrylic fibers. It is almost as warm as wool but lighter in weight. Thus Acrilan provides warmth with light weight. (Acrilan is the lightest fiber available for consumer use.) This combination makes Acrilan particularly suitable for blankets as well as for winter wear.

• *Absorbency.* Acrilan is not only the most absorbent of the acrylic fibers, but is the most absorbent of all the man-made and synthetic fibers, with the exception of the rayons and Vicara. It is, however, not as absorbent as any of the natural fibers. It does not dry as rapidly as many other fibers.

• *Cleanliness and Washability.* It is relatively easy to keep Acrilan fabrics clean. They may be readily dry-cleaned. Laundering is also no problem, although it is preferable to use a mild soap or detergent.

Acrilan fabrics should be ironed with a moderately warm iron. Too hot an iron or heat for too long a period will cause yellowing. However, since Acrilan fabrics may be heat-set, it is often unnecessary to iron them, although some pressing to smooth the cloth may be desired.

• *Effect of Light.* Acrilan has good resistance to the effect of sunlight although it is not as resistant as Orlon. Compared to other fibers, it is one of the most light-resistant textiles, and this property indicates its value for outdoor uses.

• *Resistance to Mildew.* Like the other acrylic fibers, Acrilan is wholly resistant to mildew. Any mildew that forms on the surface can be easily removed, and there will be no damage to the fabric.

• *Resistance to Moths.* Acrilan is unaffected by moths. Together with its warmth, this provides a particularly good advantage over wool.

• *Reaction to Alkalies.* Acrilan has good resistance to weak alkalies. Its resistance decreases as the strength of the alkali, the temperature, and the length of immersion increases.

• *Reaction to Acids.* Acrilan has good resistance to strong mineral acids as well as to organic acids.

• *Affinity for Dyes.* While Acrilan may be readily dyed with acetate dyes, the lightfastness is poor. Wool dyes provide greater fastness and a wide range of colors.

• *Resistance to Perspiration.* Acrilan, being chemically similar to Orlon, is also resistant to perspiration.

Acrilan Fiber Blends. Acrilan is readily adaptable to blending with other fibers. The chief blends are with cotton, wool, and rayons.

• *Acrilan and Cotton.* In combination with cotton, Acrilan will add warmth, light weight, and wrinkle resistance. The cotton will provide strength. The fabric will be easy to care for since it can be laundered and pressed easily.

• *Acrilan and Wool.* The primary value of blending Acrilan and wool is to provide the same warmth as an all-wool fabric but with less weight. The combination also provides a resilient, wrinkle-resistant fabric that nevertheless tends to retain creases and pleats. Acrilan will also add strength but too much will make the fabric too bulky.

• *Acrilan and Rayon.* Various surface and color effects are possible by blending Acrilan and rayon. The Acrilan provides greater resilience and shape retention. Such a fabric will also be warmer than an all-rayon fabric.

• *Acrilan and Acetate.* A combination of Acrilan and acetate would produce a soft, warm fabric with good draping qualities. Good shape reten-

Courtesy The Chemstrand Corporation

*Acrilan acrylic fiber being measured for blending with
other fibers, such as cotton, wool, or rayon.*

tion and resilience is possible. The fabric can be easily laundered or dry-cleaned.

• *Acrilan and Nylon*. The strength of nylon and the warmth of Acrilan together can produce a blend that would also be resilient and stable.

DYNEL

Method of Manufacture of Dynel Fiber.

The production of Dynel is only partially similar to that of such acrylic fibers as Orlon and Acrilan. This is because Dynel is actually only 40 per cent acrylic while the other 60 per cent is vinyl chloride. The question might be raised as to whether Dynel should not be classified more rightly as a vinyl chloride than as an acrylic. The answer is that the properties and end uses of Dynel compete more nearly with those of the wholly acrylic fibers.

Dynel is the result of copolymerization of acrylonitrile (used to produce Orlon, Acrilan, and X–51) and vinyl chloride (used to make Vinyon N). The copolymer is dissolved in acetone, producing a viscous solution similar in appearance to that of acetate. It is then passed through spinnerets into an

Courtesy Carbide & Carbon Chemicals Co.

Dynel emerges from each spinning bath as groups of endless fibers called tow.

Courtesy Carbide & Carbon Chemicals Co.

*Dynel tow is cut to length, then crimped and sent by
conveyor to the balers.*

aqueous bath from which it emerges as a tow or group of continuous filaments. The tow is dried, stretched, annealed, and cut into desired staple
lengths. The fiber is then crimped and baled for shipment to the spinner
where it is twisted and spun into yarn.

Types of Dynel Yarn.   Dynel fiber is semidull. It is made in 2, 3, 6, 12,
and 24 denier diameters. Since all the fibers are cut into staple, the only form
of Dynel yarn is the spun yarns. Using a method similar to that used for
Acrilan staple, Dynel fiber may be spun into yarn on the cotton, woolen, or
worsted system depending on the desired purpose.

Finishing Dynel Fabrics.   Dynel may be finished somewhat like the other
acrylic fibers. The outstanding feature is heat setting, which molds a fabric
or garment into permanent shape, and also permits permanent creases and
pleats. These shapes are resistant to change due to wetting and are relatively
permanent until the shaping temperature is again equaled or excelled.

Judging Dynel Fabrics.   Dynel fabrics are made only of spun yarn. The
manner in which the yarn is spun and the construction of the cloth contribute greatly to the particular properties of the fabric being considered. In
addition, the intrinsic properties of the Dynel fiber are very important in
judging the fabric.

   • *Strength.* Dynel is about equal in strength to Acrilan. It is weaker than

both Orlon and X-51. Compared to those natural fibers with which it is sometimes blended, Dynel is weaker than cotton but stronger than wool. It is also
stronger than the rayons and acetate.

• *Elasticity.* Although Dynel is not a particularly elastic fiber, it is the
most elastic of the acrylics. It is also slightly more elastic than the rayons,
acetate, and Dacron. It is definitely less elastic than nylon, wool, or silk.

However, like the other acrylic fibers, Dynel is highly resilient, thus
assuring lasting loft and softness. Dynel fabrics "bounce back" into shape.
This resilience and loft make possible fabrics with an extremely pleasant,
permanent nap (that will not pill), such as flannels and blankets.

• *Heat Conductivity.* Dynel is a soft, bulky, warm fiber similar in insulating value to the other acrylic fibers. It is about as warm as wool and as
heavy.

• *Absorbency.* Dynel is about the least absorbent of the acrylic fibers. In
fact, it is one of the least absorbent of all textile fibers. The only fibers less
absorbent are Dacron, Vinyon N, saran, and Fiberglas.

While this low absorbency has certain disadvantages, such as making a
garment uncomfortable in warm, humid weather, there are some definite
advantages. The low absorbency of Dynel accounts for its resistance to staining. Such stains as might be caused by catsup, coffee, mustard, or ink come
out in washing, leaving no trace.

• *Cleanliness and Washability.* Dynel can be washed or dry-cleaned easily.
It loses very little strength while wet and is not damaged by soaps, detergents,
or bleaches. Dynel fabrics resist shrinking and retain their shape in washing
and dry cleaning.

Dynel is one of the fastest drying fibers. Even heavily napped and
knitted fabrics dry relatively quickly.

Dynel fabrics need little ironing. When ironing is desired, the iron should
be warm or set at the "rayon setting."

• *Effect of Light.* Dynel is highly resistant to the effect of sunlight. It is
not as resistant as Orlon, but is more resistant than the other acrylic fibers.
It is one of the most resistant of textile fibers to the effect of sunlight, which
indicates its value for outdoor use and for draperies.

• *Resistance to Mildew.* Like the other acrylic fibers, Dynel is wholly resistant to mildew.

• *Resistance to Moths.* Dynel is not damaged by moths. Together with its
warmth, this provides a particularly good advantage over wool.

• *Reaction to Alkalies.* Dynel retains its full strength even after long
exposure to weak or moderately strong solutions of inorganic alkalies. Com-

mon household-cleaning alkalies, such as soap, ammonia, and detergents, have no effect on Dynel.

• *Reaction to Acids*. Acids have no weakening effect on Dynel. However, there may be some discoloration after very long exposure.

• *Affinity for Dyes*. Dynel can be dyed in a full range of colors from lights through darks with excellent fastness to fumes, crocking, washing, and good fastness to light. Almost the entire range of acetate dyestuffs, many of the direct dyes, and certain vat dyes can be used. As a result, dyestuffs can be selected to match nearly any color and withstand nearly every type of service required of the finished fabric.

• *Resistance to Perspiration*. The general inertness of Dynel indicates a good resistance to perspiration.

Dynel Fiber Blends.   Dynel has been found to be an excellent blending fiber. It works well with other staple fibers and contributes worth-while properties to fabrics.

• *Dynel and Cotton*. In such a blend, Dynel contributes softness, warmth, and a resistance to shrinkage. Cotton contributes strength. Together, the blend provides a durable, comfortable, launderable fabric.

• *Dynel and Wool*. A combination of Dynel and wool provides a warm, resilient, wrinkle-resistant fabric. The Dynel contributes shape retention and greater strength. The bulking power of Dynel also means that more warmth is possible with less weight.

• *Dynel and Rayon*. To a rayon blend, Dynel contributes warmth, light weight, resilience, and shape retention. Rayon provides the needed absorbency for greater comfort.

• *Dynel and Acetate*. In combination, Dynel and acetate produce fabrics that are richly textured, warm, and resilient. They retain their shape and creases, and they drape well. Such a fabric, however, will have a low absorbency.

• *Dynel and Nylon*. In this combination, Dynel provides warmth and nylon provides strength, abrasion resistance, and elasticity. Such a blend would produce a resilient, wrinkle-resistant, shape-retentive fabric that would launder easily and dry relatively fast.

X-51

Method of Manufacture of X-51 Fiber. The American Cyanamid Company, which owns the patents on the production of X-51 acrylic fiber (also registered under the trade names of Creslan and Cyana), has not made public, in 1953, its method of manufacture. It can be stated that, like the other acrylic fibers, the basic ingredient of X–51 is acrylonitrile. X–51 acrylic fiber is chiefly the result of polymerized acrylonitrile dissolved in a suitable solvent and extruded through a spinneret.

Both continuous filament and permanently crimped staple, 1½ to 7 inches in length, may be produced. The filament is almost white with a yellowish cast, and the staple is almost white with a bluish cast. Both can be easily bleached to white. Both are semidull with the staple slightly duller than the filament. There are also differences in strength, elasticity, and dyeing properties.

Types of X-51 Yarn. X–51 may be made into either multifilament or spun staple yarns.

• *Multifilament Yarns.* Three types of multifilament yarns are being produced.

75 denier, of 45 filaments
100 denier, of 60 filaments
150 denier, of 90 filaments

The fine filament used in these yarns gives a pleasant feel to both woven and knitted fabrics.

• *Spun Yarns.* Spun yarns are made of staple fibers of 1½ and 3 denier. Several different types of spun yarns may be produced. For example, cotton mills may spin yarns using 1½-to-2-inch staple in a manner similar to that for spinning cotton. Woolen mills may spin yarns using about 2½-inch staple, and worsted mills may spin yarns using 4-to-7-inch staple. This indicates a wide versatility for X–51 acrylic yarns.

Finishing X-51 Fabrics. Much experimentation on the finishing of X–51 fabrics was being made in 1953. The most important development is that, like the other acrylic textiles, fabrics and garments of X–51 can be permanently heat-set. They can be given pleats, creases, or any shape, heated under carefully controlled conditions, and thereafter retain the desired shape through repeated wearing, washing, and dry cleaning.

Judging X-51 Fabrics. There are some differences between the properties of X–51 continuous-filament fiber and of the staple fiber. The properties of X–51 fabrics therefore will depend not only on the construction but also on the type of fiber used in the yarns.

• *Strength.* X–51 staple fiber is about two-thirds as strong as the continuous-filament fiber. Therefore, each type of fiber is compared separately here.

Comparing X–51 continuous-filament fiber with the other acrylic fibers, it is not as strong as Orlon, but it is stronger than Acrilan or Dynel. Comparing it with other man-made or synthetic fibers, it is stronger than all except Fiberglas, nylon, or Dacron. Comparing it with the natural fibers, it is stronger than wool, but weaker than the others.

Comparing X–51 staple fiber with the other acrylic fibers, it is not only weaker than Orlon but, on the average, is slightly weaker than Acrilan and Dynel. It is nevertheless stronger than most man-made or synthetic fibers with the exception of Fiberglas, nylon, Dacron, and Vinyon N. Comparing it with the natural fibers, it is stronger than wool, but weaker than the others.

• *Elasticity.* While X–51 staple fiber will stretch a little more easily—that is, with less strain—than the continuous-filament fiber, the filament recovers from stretching slightly faster and slightly more completely.

X–51 acrylic fiber is slightly less elastic than the other acrylic fibers. In fact, it is, on the average, less elastic than all other fibers with the exception of cotton, linen, and Fiberglas. X–51 is more elastic than these latter fibers.

However, X–51, like the other acrylic fibers, has excellent resilience. It does not wrinkle easily and tends to retain its original shape after repeated use.

• *Heat Conductivity.* Like the other acrylics, X–51 does not conduct heat rapidly. Like Orlon, X–51 has much bulking power, which means that X–51 fabrics can have much body with less weight. When fabrics are made of X–51 staple, the greater bulk results in greater insulating power than would be expected from the fiber itself. Thus, X–51 staple can provide satisfactory warmth for such outerwear as jackets and coats.

Fabrics made of X–51 continuous-filament fiber are less warm than silk fabrics but are warmer than rayon, acetate, nylon, or Dacron. However, since very fine denier filaments can be made, it is possible to produce sheer fabrics of the continuous-filament yarns which would be quite cool.

• *Absorbency.* X–51 appears to have a low water absorbency. Its degree of absorbency falls between that of Orlon and of Dynel. This low absorbency gives X–51 the property of resisting stains. Since X–51 does not absorb well, many substances ordinarily absorbed by other fibers merely remain on the surface of X–51 fabrics. They may be easily removed by washing or dry cleaning.

Fabrics made of X–51 continuous-filament yarn will dry rapidly because most of the moisture tends to lie on the surface rather than be absorbed. But this also means that garments made of this fiber may not be too comfortable if worn next to the skin. They may become moist and clammy on the surface instead of absorbing the perspiration of the body or the humidity from the air.

Fabrics made of X-51 spun yarn will tend to "take on" more moisture because of the greater amount of surface area and spaces between the staple fibers. Such fabrics will also tend to dry more slowly.

• *Cleanliness and Washability.* X-51 fiber is round and smooth. Yarns, particularly those made of the continuous filament, are therefore smooth and do not tend to pick up much dirt; rather, dirt slides off. Of course, the spun yarns soil more easily.

Fabrics made of X-51 can be easily laundered with any mild soap in warm water. Strong soaps containing much alkali will cause yellowing, particularly if the water is very hot. Household bleaches may be safely used.

X-51 fabrics may be safely dry-cleaned. They have good dimensional stability. If properly constructed and finished, they will not shrink and will retain pleats and shape after washing or dry cleaning.

If ironing is desired, X-51 fabrics may be pressed while damp with a warm iron as used for nylon.

• *Effect of Light.* X-51 has fairly good resistance to degradation by sunlight. In general, it is more resistant than the natural fibers to the weakening effect of sunlight.

• *Resistance to Mildew.* X-51 is absolutely resistant to deterioration by mildew.

• *Resistance to Moths.* X-51 is unaffected by moths and their larvae, or carpet beetles.

• *Reaction to Alkalies.* X-51 has fair resistance to alkalies. Exposure to alkalies at high temperatures will cause yellowing. Higher concentrations and higher temperatures will cause more severe damage.

• *Reaction to Acids.* In general, X-51 has very good resistance to acids. There is a tendency to bleach when the acid concentration is high.

• *Affinity for Dyes.* According to laboratory tests, X-51 takes acetate, acid, direct, basic, vat, and soluble vat dyes rather well. There is some difference in results depending on whether the fiber is filament or staple.

The X-51 staple takes dyes more readily and with a greater depth of color than the filament. Colorfastness to light, washing, crocking, and perspiration is generally good for both the staple and filament.

• *Resistance to Perspiration.* All indications are that fabrics of X–51 are not readily deteriorated by perspiration.

X-51 Fiber Blends.

In 1953, fabrics had been made only from 100 per cent X–51 fiber. The manufacturer expects that one of the greatest uses of the fiber will be in blends with such other fibers as cotton, wool, rayon, and acetate. In 1953, it was too early to state with certainty the possible results of such blends, but it is likely that they will be similar to the blending of the other acrylic fibers with all other fibers.

▶ TEST YOURSELF ON THIS CHAPTER

1. What is an acrylic fiber? How does it differ in composition from other synthetic fibers?
2. Give the trade names of the four acrylic fibers. Which companies produce each one?
3. Compare the strength of acrylic fibers with each other and with other fibers.
4. Compare the elasticity of the acrylic fibers with each other and with other fibers.
5. Discuss the washability and general care of fabrics made of acrylic fibers.
6. What general types of yarns can be made from each of the acrylic fibers?
7. Discuss the reactions of each of the acrylic fibers to acids, alkalies, and perspiration.
8. Discuss the affinity for dyes and the colorfastness of each of the acrylic fibers.
9. What are the general properties of acrylic fibers that tend to improve blends?
10. What effect has mildew on each of the acrylic fibers? Moths? Other insects?

The name Dacron is a trade-mark owned by E. I. du Pont de Nemours & Company for a particular synthetic polyester fiber. Just as the Du Pont Company has the trade-mark Orlon for its acrylic fiber, so it has the trade-mark Dacron for its polyester fiber.

History of Dacron. The groundwork for the development of Dacron polyester fiber was laid by Dr. W. H. Carothers, the famous Du Pont research chemist, in his experiments with giant molecular structures. Dr. Carothers chose to devote the major portion of his research to polyamides (which resulted in the development of nylon) rather than to investigate all the possibilities of polyesters. After studying the published works of Dr. Carothers, British research chemists decided to examine further the possibilities of polyesters.

During the period of 1939–1941, investigations were conducted in the laboratories of the Calico Printers Association, Ltd., by J. R. Whinfield, J. T. Dickson, W. K. Birtwhistle, and C. G. Ritchie. Their work resulted in the development of a polyester fiber known in England as Terylene.

In 1946, the Du Pont Company purchased the exclusive rights to produce this polyester fiber in the United States. Under the temporary name of Fiber V, and in essentially the same chemical form, Du Pont conducted intensive development work. By 1951, the company was producing this polyester fiber, which it finally called Dacron, for commercial production.

Method of Manufacture of Dacron Fiber. The process of manufacture of Dacron polyester fiber is similar to that of nylon, but the chemicals used are different. The polymer is produced by the catalyzed ester interchange between the glycol and dimethyl terephthalate.

A hard porcelainlike substance is produced that melts at a temperature slightly above 480 degrees Fahrenheit. This viscous melt is extruded through a spinneret and subsequently drawn into filaments of Dacron polyester fiber

264

Types and Forms of Dacron Yarn. Dacron polyester fibers are made in three different types: 5100, 5600, and 5400. The major difference between fiber types is their strength-stretch relationship. Type 5100 is the strongest with the most stretch resistance—that is, the least stretchability. Type 5600 is second strongest with less stretch resistance (more stretchability). Type 5400 is the least strong with the least stretch resistance (most stretchability). These types of Dacron are being produced in the following forms.

   • *Continuous-Filament Yarns.* Dacron continuous-filament yarns are made in two forms: monofilament and multifilament. The multifilament yarns are:

> 40 denier, 34 filament semidull apparel yarn—Type 5600
> 70 denier, 34 filament semidull apparel yarn—Type 5600
> 70 denier, 34 filament bright industrial yarn—Type 5100
> 210 denier, 34 filament bright industrial yarn—Type 5100

Continuous-filament yarns are used for such sheer lightweight fabrics as glass curtains, tulle, voile, and organdie, which are crisp, highly wrinkle-resistant, and shape-retentive.

   • *Spun Yarn.* Spun Dacron yarns of various sizes are made of 3 denier semidull Type 5400 staple, 1½ and 2½ inches in length. This staple is spun into yarn on the cotton or wool systems depending on the ultimate yarn desired. The spun yarns are used for summer suitings, which require unusual resiliency and dimensional stability to prevent puckering and change in shape in humid weather. It is also used for heavier weight fabrics for outerwear. Dacron spun yarn is also used for knitted fabrics because of its excellent shape retention and resistance to stretch.

   • *Tow.* Semidull Type 5400 Dacron tow is produced in 3 denier and 6 denier filament forms.

Finishing Dacron Fabrics. Several finishes can be given to Dacron fabrics to increase their usefulness. Among the most important are:

   Heat setting—for permanent shape
   Preshrinking—for dimensional stability
   Antistatic finish—for reduction of static electricity

Fabrics made of continuous-filament Dacron yarn can be heat-set in substantially the same manner as nylon. Setting at temperatures ranging from 350 to 425 degrees Fahrenheit on a hot roller produces fabrics that are dimensionally stable to repeated washing and ironing. Generally speaking, fabrics made of Dacron spun yarn are effectively stabilized in normal dyeing and finishing operations.

Stabilized fabrics made of either Dacron continuous-filament yarn or spun yarn have excellent wrinkle resistance and recovery from wrinkling. Essentially permanent creases can be pressed into them at the ordinary ironing temperature for rayon (about 275 degrees Fahrenheit) and remain sharp even after the fabric is washed. Such creases, however, can be ironed out if desired. This means that such garments as suits made of Dacron staple will hold their shape and press in abnormally damp weather and even when wet.

Continuous-filament Dacron yarn is capable of 15 to 20 per cent shrinkage in finishing. This means that such fabrics will not shrink to any significant extent thereafter. It is also possible to produce fabrics with very little porosity by this preshrinking procedure.

Fabrics made of Dacron yarn are subject to the accumulation of static electricity. Where this would prove objectionable, Dacron fabrics can be treated with antistatic agents.

Judging Dacron Fabrics. In this discussion of Dacron fabrics, we are concerned with Type 5600 and to a less extent with Type 5400, both of which are used for apparel purposes. In addition to the type of Dacron, consideration also must be given to the kind of yarn and construction of the fabric.

• *Strength.* Dacron continuous-filament fiber is almost as strong as Orlon and significantly stronger than the other acrylic fibers. Compared to the natural fibers, Dacron filament fiber is a little stronger than cotton; however, Dacron staple is about as strong as the average quality of cotton.

• *Elasticity.* Dacron is often characterized as having a high degree of stretch resistance, which means that Dacron fabrics are not likely to stretch out of shape too easily. This property makes Dacron particularly suited for knitted garments; the sagging and stretching that would ordinarily occur are reduced.

Dacron has a very high degree of resilience. Not only does a Dacron fabric resist wrinkling when dry, but it also resists wrinkling when wet. For example, a suit of Dacron will keep its pressed appearance after many wearings even in rain or moist, humid weather. The original creases stay in, the unwanted wrinkles stay out.

• *Heat Conductivity.* Dacron polyester fiber is not as good a conductor of heat as the acrylic fibers. While a Dacron fabric would not be as cool as a comparable one of linen, cotton, rayon, acetate, or nylon, it would not be as warm as the acrylics, or as silk, wool, or Vicara.

• *Absorbency.* Dacron is one of the least absorbent fibers. Only Vinyon N, saran, and Fiberglas are less absorbent. This low absorbency has two important advantages. Dacron fabrics will dry very rapidly, since almost all the moisture will lie on the surface rather than penetrate the yarns. Furthermore, this low absorbency means that Dacron fabrics will not stain easily. Most substances that would stain other fabrics merely lie on the surface and can be wiped or washed off easily.

Fabrics of low absorbency have the disadvantage of being clammy and uncomfortable in humid weather. In warm weather, they will not absorb perspiration or atmospheric moisture. As a result, the wearer feels most uncomfortable. This clamminess, however, is experienced only when the fabric is worn next to the skin.

• *Cleanliness and Washability.* Since Dacron fabrics have a very low absorbency, stains lie on the surface and can easily be washed or dry-cleaned away. Strong soaps and bleaches are not needed. Fabrics of Dacron filament yarn dry very quickly. Those of spun yarn dry comparatively rapidly if wrung out well.

There is essentially no water shrinkage of Dacron fabrics. Therefore, shirts, blouses, and even slacks made entirely of Dacron (including the sewing thread) may be safely laundered.

When ironing Dacron fabrics, it is best to use a moderately hot iron as for rayon. Excessive heat will cause Dacron to melt. (Burning tobacco will quickly melt holes in such fabrics. Certain resins are being used to coat the material, thus minimizing this danger.) Actually, little ironing is needed even after long wear or after being completely wet, because garments made of Dacron hold their shape and creases after being heat-set. Furthermore, the wrinkle resistance of Dacron is extremely good.

• *Effect of Light.* Dacron has good resistance to degradation by light. Over a prolonged period of time, however, Dacron definitely does deteriorate.

• *Resistance to Mildew.* Dacron fabrics are absolutely resistant to mildew. They will not be stained or weakened.

• *Resistance to Moths.* Dacron is unaffected by moths and their larvae, or by carpet beetles.

• *Reaction to Alkalies.* At room temperature, Dacron has good resistance to weak alkalies and fair resistance to strong alkalies. At higher temperatures (boiling), Dacron has poor resistance to weak alkalies and dissolves in strong alkalies.

• *Reaction to Acids.* Dacron has excellent-to-good resistance to most acids. Such strong acids as sulphuric acid will cause decomposition if the temperature is high enough.

• *Affinity for Dyes.* Dacron can be dyed with specialized techniques to a complete range of shades. The results have good-to-excellent washfastness and fair-to-good lightfastness.

• *Resistance to Perspiration*. Dacron is not easily affected by perspiration.

Dacron Fiber Blends.

Dacron polyester fiber has been successfully blended with cotton, wool, rayon, nylon, and Orlon. There is indication that Dacron can also be blended with other textile fibers to produce satisfactory results.

• *Dacron and Cotton*. In such a blend, Dacron provides wrinkle resistance and shape retention. Cotton provides absorbency. However, unless properly constructed and properly cared for, a fabric of such a blend may pucker and lose its shape if the cotton should shrink.

• *Dacron and Wool*. In combination with wool, Dacron provides outstanding wrinkle resistance and crease retention, so that wet or dry the shape retention is improved according to the proportions used. The greater abrasion resistance of Dacron also provides longer wear. The wool contributes good draping quality and elasticity. The wool also reduces the hazard of melted holes due to burning tobacco. A blend of 60 per cent Dacron and 40 per cent wool produces a cloth sufficiently warm to use for year-round suits.

• *Dacron and Rayon*. In such a blend, Dacron gives greater resiliency, shape retention, and durability. The rayon provides absorbency and variety of color and texture.

• *Dacron and Nylon*. Nylon contributes strength and abrasion resistance. Dacron contributes outstanding wrinkle resistance. Such a combination offers stability, easy laundering, quick drying, and resistance to damage from mildew and insects. It will be clammy to the skin, however, in warm, humid weather.

• *Dacron and Orlon*. Orlon improves the hand, or feel, of a fabric when combined with Dacron, giving better body comfort and wearability. Dacron contributes even greater wrinkle resistance, especially under humid conditions.

▶ TEST YOURSELF ON THIS CHAPTER

1. What is Dacron? May any company produce it? May any company imitate it? Explain your answers.
2. Who discovered Dacron? Who produces it?
3. What types of yarns are made of Dacron? Explain the differences.

4. Discuss the washability and general care of fabrics made of Dacron.
5. How does the strength of Dacron compare to that of other fibers?
6. What is the effect of mildew on Dacron? What is the effect of moths on Dacron?
7. What reaction has Dacron to alkalies, acids, and perspiration?
8. Discuss the possible value of Dacron fabrics and blends for summer wear.
9. What are the outstanding properties of a Dacron-wool fabric?
10. What is the effect of washing and of sunlight on dyed Dacron?

A Protein Fiber

There are three man-made protein fibers: soybean fiber, from soybean protein; Sarelon, from peanut protein; and Vicara, made from corn protein. Research is being conducted on the first two mentioned. Vicara is beyond that stage and is in commercial production for consumer use.

History of Vicara. In 1935, L. C. Smallen of the Corn Products Refining Company was granted a patent for the manufacture of man-made protein fiber from the vegetable protein *zein,* which is contained in corn gluten. Subsequent research was conducted in the public interest by the Northern Regional Laboratory of the United States Department of Agriculture and the Harris Research Laboratories in Washington, D. C., to prove that a commercial textile fiber could be produced from zein. Industrial research and development were carried on over a period of years by the Virginia Carolina Chemical Corporation. This finally resulted, in 1948, in the commercial production by this company of a zein fiber, which it named Vicara, at the former Aralac plant in Taftville, Connecticut. The displacing of Aralac, a protein fiber made of the casein of skim milk, made Vicara the only man-made protein fiber being manufactured in the United States in 1949.

Method of Manufacture of Vicara Fiber. In preparing a spinning solution, the basic ingredient is the corn protein, zein. The dry powdered zein is wetted with water to produce a smooth suspension. It is then chemically treated, and a thick viscous solution results.

When the highly viscous spinning solution is properly aged, it is forced under pressure through a large spinneret, which may have as many as 270,000 holes, thus producing a large mass of filaments called tow. To coagulate the protein from the mildly alkaline spinning solution, a dilute acid precipitating bath is used. The streams of protein spinning solution enter this bath, coagulation takes place, and the filaments are gathered to make the tow, which is then wound on a large wheel while it is thoroughly washed with water to free it from acids and salts.

Courtesy Virginia Carolina Chemical Corp.

Equipment for testing Vicara tow.

At this stage, the tow is still unsatisfactory for textile uses and must be given aftertreatments to produce the best possible fiber for a particular use. The first of these is a precuring treatment with a mild solution of formaldehyde to regulate the softness or stiffness, flexibility, and strength. For example, a low cure results in greatly elongated filaments of small diameter that will be soft, flexible, and susceptible to a large amount of shrinkage in water. A high cure results in filaments that cannot be stretched much and will be heavier in diameter, coarser, stiffer, but stronger.

After precuring, the tow is usually stretched from 200 to 250 per cent in length, held under tension, and postcured. The tow is then cut into staple lengths of 0.5 to 6 inches, packed in 300- and 500-pound bales, and shipped to the spinning mills.

Types of Vicara Yarn. Vicara fiber is made in 2, 3, 4, 5, and 7 denier diameters. Since all the fibers are cut into staple, the only form of Vicara yarn is the spun yarn. Using methods similar to those used for other staple, Vicara may be spun into yarn on the cotton, woolen, or worsted system.

Vicara is often used with other fibers to produce blended yarns as well as for 100 per cent Vicara yarns.

Finishing of Vicara Fabrics. Since Vicara is often used for blending and takes a variety of finishes well, fabrics containing Vicara are generally finished according to the needs of the particular blend or of the dominant fiber. Fabrics containing Vicara are being finished by standard methods. Resin finishes are applied with excellent results, but fabrics containing Vicara usually require less resin to obtain the desired result.

Judging Vicara in Fabrics. An indicated in the manufacture of Vicara, there are slight variations in the properties of the fiber, depending on the desired results. However, the following general statements may be made.

• *Strength.* Vicara is approximately as strong as wool. While this means that Vicara is not a particularly strong fiber, its resilience and elasticity gives it good abrasion resistance so that satisfactory wear can be obtained from Vicara fabrics.

Also like wool, Vicara loses much strength while wet. In fact, Vicara will lose up to 50 per cent of its strength while wet. Therefore, care must be taken not to put undue strain, such as pulling or wringing, on wet fabrics containing Vicara.

• *Elasticity.* One of the outstanding properties of Vicara is its elasticity. Vicara will stretch 30 to 35 per cent when wet and 30 to 40 per cent when dry without breaking. Its elastic recovery is very good. After being stretched up to 5 per cent of its length, its recovery is practically 100 per cent. This elasticity rivals that of nylon. Although the elastic recovery of nylon is 100 per cent after being stretched 8 per cent, its elongation does not quite equal that of Vicara.

Vicara also has very good resilience. It resists wrinkling to a marked degree.

These properties result in making Vicara a soft and flexible fiber. Yet, fabrics of Vicara will have good dimensional stability. As a result, Vicara is very suitable for knitted goods because they will tend to retain their original shape.

• *Heat Conductivity.* The heat conductivity of Vicara is low. In other words, Vicara is a warm fiber. Laboratory tests have indicated that its insulating value is similar to that of animal fibers in fabrics of like construction.

• *Absorbency.* Vicara is inherently water-repellent. This water repellency is permanent, but at temperatures above 110 degrees Fahrenheit, it is temporarily lost. This means that, while Vicara is not absorbent at less than room temperatures, it is absorbent above room temperatures. In fact, at the higher temperatures, the absorbency of Vicara approaches that of wool.

This combination of water repellency and absorbency gives Vicara some outstanding advantages. It is suitable for outdoor wear during inclement weather. At the same time, it is comfortable to wear, since it will absorb perspiration and will not feel clammy in humid weather.

• *Cleanliness and Washability.* The water repellency of Vicara does not interfere with its washing or cleaning since the repellency is not apparent at temperatures above 110 degrees Fahrenheit. Vicara is not damaged by dry cleaning. In fact, it dry-cleans similar to wool.

If a bleach is desired, it may be safely used when washing Vicara. This is particularly advantageous when the fabric is a blend of Vicara and some such fiber as cotton.

Washing will not cause Vicara to shrink, even though the water is boiling. Nor will Vicara felt or pill. However, since Vicara weakens considerably and can elongate or stretch greatly when wet, Vicara fabrics should not be wrung or twisted to remove water. They should be squeezed and allowed to dry while lying flat. Unlike other protein fibers, such as wool, Vicara does not have a disagreeable odor when wet. It has a faint, pleasant odor that disappears completely when the fabric is dry.

Vicara may be pressed or ironed at a temperature similar to that of wool. It loses some strength at temperatures above 350 degrees Fahrenheit and will decompose at 470 to 475 degrees Fahrenheit.

• *Effect of Light.* Vicara is subject to slow deterioration by sunlight in a manner similar to animal fibers. The natural golden color of the fiber is not permanent to light. It will not deteriorate merely because of age, however.

• *Resistance to Mildew.* Vicara has good resistance to mildew.

• *Resistance to Moths.* Moth larvae and carpet beetles will not eat Vicara.

• *Reaction to Alkalies.* Unlike animal and other protein fibers, Vicara is not drastically affected by alkalies. In fact, when blended with cotton, Vicara may be safely mercerized. Certain ordinary household cleaning substances containing alkali will not harm Vicara.

• *Reaction to Acids.* Vicara also has good resistance to acids. This means that carbonizing will not damage Vicara.

• *Affinity for Dyes.* The resistance of Vicara to acids and alkalies permits it to be safely dyed by either acid or alkali dyes. Vicara may be dyed by a variety of dyes and methods used on other fibers. Where pastel shades are desired, the natural golden color must first be removed by a bleach.

• *Resistance to Perspiration.* Vicara has good resistance to perspiration. The color may be affected, but the perspiration will not weaken the fabric.

Vicara Fiber Blends.

Vicara is "the fiber that improves the blend." While Vicara may be used by itself in the manufacture of fabrics, it is recommended as a blend with other fibers. This permits the complementary blending of the properties of Vicara and of other fibers. The care of the blended fabric is dictated by the properties of the fiber with which Vicara is blended.

• *Vicara and Cotton.* To a blend with cotton, Vicara brings drape, elasticity, resilience, softness, and warmth. Cotton provides the strength. Such a blend gives a fabric absorbency and a comfortable feel.

• *Vicara and Wool.* Vicara looks and feels more like wool than any other man-made fiber. Its elasticity, resilience, absorbency, and warmth are also similar to wool. The chief advantages of blending Vicara with wool are that such a fabric will be less expensive, will not pill, felt, or shrink as much, and will feel softer.

• *Vicara and Rayon.* Vicara contributes elasticity and resilience to a blend with rayon. The fabric will drape well and feel soft. It will be warmer and more mildew-resistant than an all-rayon fabric. A greater variety of dye effects is also possible. Of course, such a fabric is not particularly strong, since neither Vicara nor rayon is very strong compared to other man-made and synthetic fibers. However, the resilience and elasticity of Vicara reduce such a fabric's tendency to fray and thereby increase the durability of the blend.

• *Vicara and Nylon.* In such a blend, Vicara provides absorbency, softness, and drape. The nylon provides strength, abrasion resistance, and shape retention.

▶ TEST YOURSELF ON THIS CHAPTER

1. What is Vicara? May any company produce or imitate it? Explain your answers.
2. What natural fiber is Vicara like? In what ways are they similar?
3. What kind of yarn is made of Vicara?
4. Discuss the washability and general care of fabrics made of Vicara.
5. How do the elasticity and resilience of Vicara compare to other fibers?
6. Compare the strength of Vicara to that of other fibers.
7. What effect do alkalies and acids have on Vicara?
8. What effect has Vicara in a blend with wool?
9. What are the properties of a Vicara-nylon blend in a fabric?
10. How well does Vicara absorb dyes? Does perspiration affect these dyes?

The Synthetic
Vinyl Resin Fiber

A vinyl resin fiber is a synthetic textile fiber. There are several varieties of these fibers. All are either polymers or copolymers containing carbon, hydrogen, and such other elements as are required to produce a particular type of vinyl resin. Actually, Dynel is a variation of a vinyl resin, but, because of its relatively high acrylonitrile content, it has been treated in this text as an acrylic. Vinyon N is treated separately here as a particular type of vinyl resin fiber.

History of Vinyon N. In 1927, the Carbide and Carbon Chemicals Corporation started general research in the field of vinylite resins. By 1933, its work became concentrated on the uses of vinylite resins in the field of textiles. These experiments resulted in the synthesis of Vinyon resin, a white powder produced by the copolymerization of vinyl chloride and vinyl acetate. In 1939, the American Viscose Corporation was licensed to produce filaments and yarns from this resin. As a result, Vinyon was the first synthetic plastic filament to be produced on a commercial scale (that is, outside a laboratory) in this country.

While Vinyon had several desirable properties, it also had some undesirable ones. Vinyon had sufficiently good strength, was highly water-repellent, was not damaged by concentrated acids, strong alkalies, or oxidizing agents, and was not affected by moths or mildew. However, Vinyon shrank and became sticky at high temperatures, could not be dyed by conventional methods, and was not particularly elastic.

Both companies continued research with Vinyon and produced several new forms of it. The Carbide and Carbon Chemicals Corporation finally produced filaments superior to Vinyon in resistance to shrinkage and heat. In 1947, the company was granted a patent for the manufacture of a new resin, which it called Vinyon N.

Method of Manufacture of Vinyon N Fiber. Vinyon N resin is produced by gradual copolymerization of 92 parts vinyl chloride and 8 parts acrylonitrile with the aid of a catalyst and an emulsifying agent in an autoclave. The resin is precipitated out of the solution, filtered, washed, and dried. At this stage, it is a fine powder varying in color from cream to amber.

The Vinyon N resin is dissolved in hot acetone and mixed in a nitrogen atmosphere. The viscous solution is then filtered, deaerated, and forced through a spinneret into long vertical cells where hot air evaporates the acetone.

The filaments thus produced are then oriented by stretching to increase their strength and stabilized with heat to reduce subsequent shrinkage. The most suitable amounts of stretch are 900 and 1,300 per cent. The degree of heat used varies from 110 to 150 degrees centigrade.

Types of Vinyon N Yarns. Stretching of the Vinyon N filaments can produce as fine a denier as 0.35. This means that the yarns may be composed of a great many very fine filaments. If such yarns are given sufficient twist, they can be rather strong. Vinyon N yarns are being produced in:

100 denier, of 60 filaments	250 denier, of 240 filaments
140 denier, of 120 filaments	270 denier, of 240 filaments
200 denier, of 200 filaments	500 denier, of 200 filaments

Judging Vinyon N Fabrics. In 1953, fabrics made from Vinyon N yarns were not yet in general use for consumers, but the following facts may be kept in mind.

• *Strength*. The strength of the fiber will vary depending on the amount of stretch given. Considering this fact, the average strength of Vinyon N is good.

Among the man-made and synthetic fibers, it is slightly stronger than Acrilan and Dynel; it is also stronger than saran, rayon, and acetate. It is, however, weaker than any of the natural fibers except wool.

• *Elasticity*. The finished Vinyon N fiber can be stretched up to 25 per cent of its length without breaking. Furthermore, it has good elastic recovery. In addition, Vinyon N has very good resilience. Therefore, it may be considered to be one of the more elastic and resilient fibers.

• *Heat Conductivity*. Vinyon N is not a good conductor of heat. One of the disadvantages of Vinyon N is its general reaction to heat. At a relatively low temperature, Vinyon N will soften. It will melt at 170 degrees Fahrenheit. This indicates that its use as a fabric for garments is very limited, since it cannot be readily laundered or ironed. Cigarette sparks would also be dangerous.

• *Absorbency.* Vinyon N has very low absorbency. (For this reason, it is practically as strong when wet as when dry.) This low absorbency makes it useful for tent and umbrella fabrics, awnings, and outdoor furniture. It also means that the fabric will not stain easily, but on the other hand, it will not take dyes too easily.

• *Cleanliness and Washability.* Vinyon N fiber produces a smooth fabric to which dirt will not readily cling. When the fabric is to be cleaned, any common dry-cleaning solvent or any soap may be safely used. But since Vinyon N has a very low melting point, it is important always to use a low temperature.

Depending on the method of manufacture of the fiber itself, the ultimate shrinkage properties of Vinyon N can be regulated. Generally, Vinyon N is so made as to have little shrinkage. In fact, since Vinyon N is thermoplastic, fabrics made of that fiber may be heat-set so as to retain their shape even after washing or dry cleaning.

• *Effect of Light.* Vinyon N loses some strength after prolonged exposure to sunlight. It is not as resistant to the effect of light as is nylon or Orlon.

• *Resistance to Mildew.* Fabrics made of Vinyon N are wholly resistant to deterioration from mildew.

• *Resistance to Moths.* Fabrics of Vinyon N are unaffected by moths.

• *Reaction to Alkalies.* Vinyon N is exceptionally resistant to even the strongest alkalies.

• *Reaction to Acids.* A chief advantage of Vinyon N is its equal resistance to acids as well as to alkalies. Even concentrated mineral acids do not harm it.

• *Affinity for Dyes.* Vinyon N can be dyed but with some difficulty. It takes acetate dyes best. These dyes are fast to laundering, have excellent crock resistance, and are not subject to gas fading. However, they are subject to fading by sunlight.

▶ TEST YOURSELF ON THIS CHAPTER

1. What is Vinyon N? What company makes it? Are there any other Vinyon fibers?
2. What are the chief advantages of the properties of Vinyon N?
3. What are the chief disadvantages of Vinyon N properties?
4. What are the best uses for Vinyon N?
5. Discuss the general care of fabrics made of Vinyon N with regard to washing, dry cleaning, and ironing.

The Synthetic Vinylidene Chloride Fiber

The word "saran" is a generic term that refers to a particular type of plastic fiber. This fiber is a linear copolymer of vinylidene chloride and vinyl chloride. It is somewhat similar to Vinyon N.

History of Saran. The chemical compound, vinylidene chloride, was discovered in 1840. It is a clear, colorless liquid that boils at 32 degrees centigrade. Although chemists since 1920 had observed that it could easily polymerize, it was not until 1936 that further research was conducted. At that time, the Dow Chemical Company began a research program, probably spurred by the successful results of other companies' research with polymers, which ultimately resulted in 1940 in the commercialization of saran.

Method of Manufacture of Saran Fiber. The raw materials used to produce vinylidene chloride are ethylene, which is derived by cracking natural petroleum, and chlorine, which is electrolyzed from sea water. Ethylene is treated with chlorine to produce trichlorethane, which in turn is treated with lime to produce unpolymerized vinylidene chloride. The vinylidene chloride is then copolymerized with a small quantity of vinyl chloride to produce a powdered resin.

The resin is melted and extruded through a spinneret into a water-cooling bath. While still being cooled, it is drawn out or stretched 400 per cent to increase its strength, similar to the way in which nylon is processed.

Types of Saran Yarns. Saran is made in monofilament, multifilament, and staple form.

• *Monofilament Yarns.* These yarns are made in a wide variety of diameters. Some companies express the thickness of the yarns in denier, others in terms of a decimal part of the inch. In denier, monofilament saran yarn is produced in 70 and 124 denier. In inches, monofilament saran yarn is produced in a range of .005 to .05 inch in diameter. It is used for a wide variety of purposes, such as window screens, handbags, millinery fabrics, and trimmings.

In addition to the usual round monofilament yarns, saran is also produced in rattanlike monofilament strips. This form is readily adapted to use for fabrics as seat covers in automobiles, buses, and railroad cars, as well as for the fabrics used on outdoor furniture.

• *Multifilament Yarns.* The production of saran multifilament yarns is more limited.

> 750 denier, of 50 filaments
> 1200 denier, of 100 filaments
> 3000 denier, of 300 filaments

The amount of twist given to each of these yarns varies depending on the desired ultimate result. This form of yarn is used for brocades and other decorative fabrics.

• *Staple.* Saran staple fiber comes in lengths of 2 to 40 inches in three forms: straight, crimped, and curled. The straight staple fiber is made in 10, 22, 30, 45, 60, and 70 denier and is used for a wide variety of purposes, including outerwear, linings, and filter cloths. The crimped staple fiber comes in 10 denier diameter. The curled staple comes in 22, 45, and 70 denier and is used primarily for blending with wool in the manufacture of carpets.

Delustering of Saran Yarn.

The natural color of saran is pale gold or straw. It may be delustered to a translucent or to an opaque appearance by the addition of a delusterant such as titanium dioxide.

Trade Names of Saran Yarns.

Several companies produce saran yarns. The basic quality of the yarns is the same, since they are all made of the same substances in the same way. The important differences among the yarns are dependent on whether they are of monofilament, multifilament, or staple, on the denier of the fibers, and on the amount of twist in the yarns.

Although saran is a generic term, it is also used as a trade name.

Lus-Trus Saran, produced by Lus-Trus Extruded Plastics, Inc.
National Saran, produced by The National Plastic Products Company
Saran, produced by the Saran Yarns Company

Velon, produced by Firestone Plastics Company, Inc., is another trade name for saran. Velon is also made in plastic sheet form for plastic tablecloths and similar protective coverings.

Except for the plastic sheets, these companies only produce the yarns. The ultimate fabrics are woven by other companies. The quality of the saran fabric will therefore depend further on the construction as well as on the type of yarn used.

Judging Saran Fabrics. Saran has some valuable properties as a textile. It also has some definite limitations.

• *Strength.* The strength of saran fiber varies with its diameter. Generally, the finer filaments are stronger than the coarser ones.

Saran is a little weaker than Vinyon N. It is considerably weaker than Orlon, which is also recommended as an outdoor fabric. Saran is stronger than wool, rayon, or acetate.

• *Elasticity.* The elasticity of saran approximates that of Vinyon N. Saran also is almost as resilient as Vinyon N. This is an important advantage that contributes to its use for seat covers and as upholstery for outdoor furniture.

• *Heat Conductivity.* Saran fabrics are not good conductors of heat. They are, in fact, rather easily affected by heat. Saran shrinks and loses strength at about 168 degrees Fahrenheit and melts between 240 and 280 degrees Fahrenheit. This places a serious limitation on saran fabrics. They cannot be easily ironed. Furthermore, cigarette sparks are dangerous, since they will melt holes in the saran fabric.

• *Absorbency.* Saran is one of the least absorbent of all textiles. In fact, it has virtually no absorbency at all. This means that saran cannot be used for such garments as underwear, shirts, blouses, and dresses, since they would not absorb perspiration or atmospheric moisture and therefore would be uncomfortable. On the other hand, saran fabrics, being virtually waterproof, would be very suitable for outerwear, such as raincoats and outdoor furniture. Tablecloths are another use for saran.

• *Cleanliness and Washability.* Saran fabrics may be easily cleaned by merely wiping them with a damp cloth. If desired, laundering or dry cleaning is safe. It must be remembered that saran fabrics should be kept away from heat because of the tendency to melt.

• *Effect of Light.* Subjection to sunlight over a long period of time will tend to darken saran fabrics slightly, but there is no appreciable loss of strength. Again, this shows saran's value as an outdoor fabric.

• *Resistance to Mildew.* Saran fabrics are wholly resistant to deterioration from mildew.

• *Resistance to Moths.* Saran fabrics are unaffected by moths or other insects.

• *Reaction to Alkalies.* Saran has good resistance to alkalies. However, it is weakened by a solution of ammonium hydroxide.

• *Reaction to Acids.* Saran also has good-to-excellent resistance to acids. This resistance to acids as well as alkalies makes saran very suitable for industrial filter cloths.

• *Affinity for Dyes.* Saran cannot be dyed by the usual methods because it is nonabsorbent. However, by adding the desired color to the solution before the saran filaments are spun through the spinnerets, it is possible to obtain an extensive variety of colors. These colors, being inside the fibers, are very fast. They will not wash or fade out because they become part of the fibers themselves.

▶ TEST YOURSELF ON THIS CHAPTER

1. What is saran?
2. What are the leading trade names for saran yarn?
3. What kind of yarns can be made of saran? What are the advantages of each of these yarns?
4. For what purposes is saran most suited? Why?
5. What are the chief advantages and limitations of saran?

The Glass Fiber

Fiberglas is the trade name for a textile fiber made of glass. But, although ordinary glass is hard, unbendable, and transparent, this textile glass fiber is transparent, fine, and pliable. The fine Fiberglas textile fibers look and feel like silk.

History of Glass Fiber.   The idea of making yarns and fabrics from glass is hundreds of years old. During the Renaissance, artisans were drawing out a "spun glass" of fine glass strands or rods for decorative purposes on goblets and vases. In 1893, Edward Drummond Libbey exhibited a glass dress, lamp shades, and other articles of woven glass at the World's Columbian Exposition in Chicago. The fabric was made of bundles of glass fibers woven together with silk threads. The experiment was spectacular, but the results were of no practical value, since the fabric was too stiff to be creased, folded, or draped.

Some progress was made during the early 1900's when several patents were issued in Germany and in England on various processes for drawing glass fibers. These fibers were relatively coarse, and the cost was high. During World War I, however, Germany suffered a shortage of asbestos and developed a somewhat primitive method of producing filaments of glass fibers from heat-softened glass rods. These fibers were used for insulating purposes.

It was not until 1931 that experiments were started in the United States to produce glass fibers that were finer, more pliable, and lower in cost. At that time, the Owens-Illinois Glass Company and the Corning Glass Works started to develop a method of drawing out glass from the molten state through fine orifices into pliable filament form. For several years, work progressed in the development of filament and staple yarns of glass fibers. By 1938, sufficient progress was made to indicate a promising future for glass fiber for practical textile purposes. The two companies merged to form the Owens-Corning Fiberglas Corporation. Their textile product is known as Fiberglas.

Method of Manufacture of Fiberglas Fiber.

There are two methods of producing Fiberglas yarns. Both begin with accurate batch formulation of selected silica sand, limestone, soda ash, and borax (or other ingredients depending on the ultimate purpose of the fiber) in an electric furnace. From the precisely controlled furnace, the molten glass at a temperature of about 2,500 degrees Fahrenheit flows to marble-forming machines that turn out small glass marbles about five-eighths of an inch in diameter.

An important reason for forming these marbles is to permit visual inspection of the glass for the purpose of eliminating impurities that would interfere with subsequent operations or lower the desired uniform quality of the fibers. The marbles are then remelted in small electric furnaces. (Later improvements indicate that textile fibers also may be drawn from the original melt, eliminating this marble operation.) From this point on, the two textile operations differ.

• *Continuous-Filament Process.* The continuous-filament process produces continuous filaments of indefinite length having an exceptional brilliance. Molten glass flows downward through temperature-resistant metal-alloy

Courtesy Owens-Corning Fiberglas Corp.

A step in the forming of the filament in the continuous-filament process of making Fiberglas is shown in the photograph on another page.

Glass marbles are remelted in electrical furnaces and drawn down through more than one hundred tiny holes, or orifices. Individual glass filaments solidify and are gathered into a single thread on a high-speed winding mechanism, revolving at the rate of more than a mile a minute. Shown here is a group of Fiberglas continuous filaments being pulled down from the melting tank by a winder from a floor below.

Courtesy Owens-Corning Fiberglas Corp.

bushings (spinnerets) having more than two hundred small openings. The strand of multiple filaments is carried to a high-speed winder. Since the winder revolves at a much faster rate than the stream flow from the melting chamber, the tension attenuates the glass while it is still molten, and thus draws out the fibers in parallel filaments to a fraction of the diameter of the openings. The winder draws out the continuous filaments at rates above two miles a minute.

After winding, the filaments are twisted and plied to form yarns by methods similar to those used for making other continuous-filament yarns. These yarns are used for the manufacture of fabrics for such purposes as curtains and draperies.

• *Staple-Fiber Process.* The staple-fiber process produces fibers that have long-staple characteristics. As the molten glass flows through small holes in the temperature-resistant bushing, jets of compressed air literally jerk the thin stream of molten glass into fine fibers varying in length from 8 to 15 inches. The fibers fall through a spray of lubricant and a drying flame onto a revolving drum on which they form a thin web.

This web of staple fibers is gathered from the drum into a sliver. The sliver is then made into yarn by methods similar to those used to make cotton or wool yarn. The yarn thus produced is used for the manufacture of tapes and fabrics primarily for industrial purposes where insulation is needed.

Types of Fiberglas Yarns. Fiberglas yarns are made in two types: continuous-filament and staple yarns. The continuous-filament yarns are produced in a wide variety of diameters with a wide variety of strands, depending on the ultimate use of the yarn. The spun yarn also may vary in diameter depending on its ultimate use.

Finishing Fiberglas Fabrics. A basic finishing operation for all Fiberglas fabrics is to subject the cloth to high temperatures. This releases the stresses that may be present in the yarns as a result of twisting and weaving. These treatments provide the fabrics with such desirable qualities as wrinkle resistance, greater durability, and good hand or feel.

After the fabrics have been subjected to the high temperatures, they may then be treated in a number of ways. Color may be applied with the aid of a binder to hold the dye to the surface of the cloth. The fabric may be coated with a protective agent to improve its abrasion resistance. For marquisettes, the finish is regulated to produce a crisp yet flexible fabric.

A patented process called Coronizing is also available. This process combines a heat-setting treatment with the application of finishing resins. The heat setting relaxes the fibers, permanently crimps the yarns, and sets the weave, giving the fabric a soft hand, good drape, and wrinkleproof qualities. The finishing resins provide abrasion resistance, launderability, and water repellency. Better color retention and the use of pastel shades is possible with the aid of this process.

Judging Fiberglas Fabrics. Most Fiberglas fabrics for consumer purposes are made of filament yarns. These fabrics are extremely smooth, almost slippery, lustrous, and heavy compared to other textiles.

• *Strength*. Fiberglas is the strongest of all textile fibers. Only high-tenacity nylon used for industrial purposes rivals the strength of Fiberglas. However, since glass cuts glass, as the yarns slide and rub over each other and are flexed, the filaments roughen and break, and the fabric becomes hairy. Coronizing will reduce this tendency considerably.

• *Elasticity*. Fiberglas is virtually inelastic. This property of being the least elastic of all textiles has obvious disadvantages for clothing. On the other hand, such fabrics when used for drapery and curtains will not stretch or sag out of shape.

This lack of elasticity has no effect on the flexibility and wrinkle resistance of Fiberglas fabrics. With the aid of certain finishes, Fiberglas fabrics have excellent draping and wrinkle-resistant qualities.

• *Heat Conductivity*. As with ordinary glass, Fiberglas yarns are good conductors of heat. Yet, when Fiberglas is in staple form, the thousands of fibers form cells of trapped air. These dead air spaces act as excellent insulation and make Fiberglas staple batting very effective as an interlining in jackets and coats. (The same principle is applied to insulate refrigerators and stoves.)

• *Absorbency*. For practical purposes, Fiberglas is not absorbent. This property represents both advantages and disadvantages. Being nonabsorbent, Fiberglas fabrics are water-repellent and, in general, unaffected by water. The disadvantage of no absorbency makes Fiberglas unsuitable for clothing to be worn next to the skin, because only the surface would get wet from perspiration and humid air, and the fabric would consequently be uncomfortable. This lack of absorbency makes dyeing by ordinary methods extremely difficult.

• *Cleanliness and Washability*. The smoothness of Fiberglas fabric makes it a clean fabric. Dirt and dust do not cling as readily to such fabrics as to rough materials.

Whenever necessary, the cleaning of Fiberglas fabrics is very simple and quick. They may be wiped clean with a damp cloth. If complete immersion in water is desired, the temperature of the water and the soap or detergent used is immaterial, since these factors will not affect Fiberglas fabrics. No strenuous agitation of the fabrics is necessary because the dirt comes off easily. The cloth will dry just as fast as the water will evaporate off the surface. If the fabrics are hung properly while wet, ironing is unnecessary.

• *Effect of Heat*. Fiberglas will not burn. It begins to lose strength at 600 degrees Fahrenheit and will begin to soften at about 1,500 degrees Fahrenheit. Fiberglas fabrics are highly resistant to heat, burning cigarettes, and the like.

• *Effect of Light*. Sunlight has no effect on Fiberglas fabrics. This makes them useful for outdoor purposes, such as awnings, as well as for such decorative fabrics as curtains and draperies.

• *Resistance to Mildew*. Fiberglas is unaffected by mildew. However, the binder or resin used to finish or size Fiberglas fabrics may be attacked by mildew.

• *Resistance to Moths.* Moths and other insects do not attack Fiberglas.

• *Reaction to Alkalies.* Fiberglas will be damaged by hot solutions of weak alkalies and cold solutions of strong alkalies.

• *Reaction to Acids.* Fiberglas is damaged only by hydrofluoric and hot phosphoric acids.

• *Affinity for Dyes.* Since Fiberglas is not absorbent, it cannot take dyes by ordinary methods. Special methods must be used to bind the color to the surface of the fabric. Another procedure is to add color to the molten glass before the fibers are formed, but this provides only a limited number of colors.

• *Resistance to Perspiration.* Fiberglas is unaffected by perspiration.

▶ TEST YOURSELF ON THIS CHAPTER

1. How are Fiberglas yarns made?
2. Discuss the strength and abrasion-resistant qualities of Fiberglas.
3. What desirable qualities does Coronizing give to Fiberglas fabrics?
4. Discuss the general care required for fabrics made of Fiberglas.
5. How does the elasticity and resilience of Fiberglas compare to other fibers?
6. What effect has sunlight on Fiberglas?
7. What effect have alkalies on Fiberglas? Acids? Perspiration?
8. What effect has heat on Fiberglas?
9. Does mildew attack Fiberglas?
10. What are some of the uses of Fiberglas filaments and of staple fibers?

21 | MINOR FIBERS

Useful and Economical

The textile industry uses other fibers in addition to those already studied. Each has its field of usefulness. Some have qualities that make them suitable for purposes that none of the fibers previously discussed could fulfill economically. Others can be used as acceptable substitutes or even adulterants, as long as the finished goods fulfill the purpose for which they are intended, and the selling price is in line with the value of the product.

Jute. Jute is a natural fiber obtained from a tall plant of the same name. It is grown throughout tropical Asia, chiefly in India, for commercial uses. The plant is easy to cultivate and harvest. The fiber is obtained by retting, similarly to flax. The fine, silklike fiber is easy to spin, but it is not durable, as it deteriorates rapidly when exposed to moisture.

Jute is the cheapest textile fiber and is used in great quantities. Because of its lack of strength, jute is difficult to bleach and can never be made pure white. It can be converted into a wool-like fiber by treatment with a strong caustic soda.

Though jute is often used as an adulterant with other fibers, it can be easily recognized when tested for its marked sensitivity to mineral acids. Concentrated mineral acids readily dissolve jute. Dilute mineral acids rot it quickly. It is especially weak in salt water.

Jute is used as a substitute for hemp, as binding threads for carpets and rugs, as rug cushions, as a filler with other fibers, and as a linoleum base. It is made into coarse, cheap fabrics, such as novelty dress goods and heavy cotton bagging.

Kapok. Kapok is a natural fine, white, hairlike fiber obtained from the seed capsules of plants and trees grown in Java, Borneo, Sumatra, and Central America. It is sometimes called "silk cotton" because its luster is almost equal to that of silk. Kapok resembles cotton in general appearance but, unlike cotton, is always of short staple—less than 1 inch.

288

The smooth, weak texture of kapok prevents its being spun into yarn, but it is felted for use in mattresses, cushions, upholstered furniture, and life preservers. Kapok is buoyant, but with continued use has a tendency to mat and become lumpy. This condition can be improved if bedding articles in which kapok has been used are aired and put in the sun at frequent intervals.

Kapok is resistant to vermin and is especially resistant to moisture, drying quickly when wet. It is adaptable for articles that are constantly exposed to moisture. Kapok is also used for soundproofing in airplanes and for insulating material in refrigerator cars and trucks.

Under the microscope, kapok can be easily distinguished from cotton, as it appears to be a hollow circular tube with very thin walls and frequent folds but no twist.

Ramie.   Ramie is a natural woody fiber resembling flax. It is obtained from a tall shrub grown in southeastern Asia, China, Japan, and southern Europe. Ramie is also known as rhea and as China grass.

The fiber is stiff, more brittle than linen, and highly lustrous. It can be bleached to extreme whiteness. Ramie lends itself to general processing for textile yarns, but its retting operation is difficult and costly, making the fiber unprofitable for general use. When combed, ramie is half the weight of linen, but much stronger, coarser, and more absorbent. It has permanent luster and good affinity for dyes; it is affected little by moisture.

Ramie is used as filling yarn in mixed woolen fabrics, as adulteration with silk fibers, and as a substitute for flax. The China-grass cloth used by the Chinese is made of ramie. This fiber is also useful for rope, twine, and nets.

Hemp.   Some thirty varieties of hemp, another tall plant with a natural woody fiber, are grown in nearly all the temperate and tropical countries of the world. All these varieties resemble one another in general appearance and properties; but the only kinds having commercial value are those having fibers of high tensile strength, fineness, and high luster. Hemp must pass through a retting process and subsequent manufacturing operations similar to those used for flax. It resembles flax closely, and its fiber is easily mistaken for linen.

Hemp is harsh and stiff, and cannot be bleached without harm to the fiber. As hemp is not pliable and elastic, it cannot be woven into fine fabrics. Manila hemp, which is very strong, fine, white, and lustrous, though brittle, is adaptable for the weaving of coarse fabrics.

Hemp is durable and is used in carpet and rug manufacturing. It is especially suitable for ship cordage and sailcloth as it is not weakened or rotted by water. Central American hemp is chiefly used for cordage.

Sisal. Sisal is a natural fiber obtained from the leaves of a plant that resembles cactus. It is grown in Central America, the West Indies, and Florida. The best supply is produced in Yucatan, where it is known as henequen. The smooth, straight fiber is light yellow in color.

Sisal is used for the better grades of rope, for twine, and for the bristles of inexpensive brushes. It is used as a substitute for horsehair in upholstering. Sisal may be mixed with hemp, but it should not be used for ship cordage because it disintegrates in salt water.

Coir. A natural coarse brown fiber called coir is obtained from the husk of the coconut. It is stiff but elastic. Because of its resemblance to horsehair, it is used for stuffing upholstered furniture. Coir is also suitable for cordage, sailcloth, and coarse mattings.

Pina. Pina, or pineapple fiber, is obtained from the large leaves of the pineapple plant grown in tropical countries. This natural fiber is white and especially soft and lustrous. In the Philippine Islands, it is woven into pina cloth, which is soft, durable, and resistant to moisture. Pina is also used in making coarse grass cloth and for mats, bags, and clothing.

Metal Threads and Tinsel. Any of the ductile metals, such as gold, silver, copper, and even the cheaper alloys, can be drawn out into fine filaments. These are used to ornament fabrics. Metallic threads are made round or flat and may be twisted with any of the major textile fibers. Sometimes, base metals are drawn out as fine wires and are covered with the more costly metals. Thus, silver thread may have a core of copper covered with a layer of silver; similarly, gold thread may consist of gold-plated copper wire.

When metal threads are elongated to an extremely fine diameter, they are usually known as tinsel; among the many types are fine tinsel lamé, tinsel laminette, tinsel bullion, and tinsel braid.

Metal threads are used in the millinery trade and as decoration in the form of fringe and braid, as well as for woven and embroidered patterns on tapestries, brocades, and upholstery fabrics. Fine tinsels are used in fabrics for evening dresses, handbags, and ecclesiastical robes.

Another type of such metal thread is Lurex, a thin, flat, narrow aluminum strip coated with a clear or colored acetate plastic. This thread may be of any color and have the desired metallic gleam. The plastic coating prevents the tarnishing that is so common with other metallic threads.

Asbestos. Asbestos is a natural fiber obtained from varieties of rocks found in Italy, South America, and Canada. It is a fibrous form of silicate of magnesium and calcium, containing iron, aluminum, and other minerals. The soft, long, glossy white fibers are pressed into sheets, and the best quality can be spun into yarn. Chrysolite asbestos is the most valuable for the latter purpose, as it has a fine, long staple that has strength and flexibility. Asbestos yarns are always made as ply yarns to increase their tensile strength.

Asbestos will not burn, but it will melt at a sufficiently high temperature. It is acidproof and rustproof. Asbestos is made into fireproof materials of many types—theater curtains, draperies, shingles, tiles, auto brake lining, andiron holders, and partitions. It is spun around copper wire and wrapped around pipes and joints of high-pressure steam engines. Inferior grades are used for soundproofing purposes.

Although asbestos has always been used when fighting fire, the challenging conditions of World War II greatly advanced the types of fire-fighting suits and fire-resistant fabrics for which this useful mineral fiber had already become noted.

Asbestos rock (at left) is manufactured into asbestos fiber (center). The magnified view at the right shows the similarity of asbestos fiber to a common fiber, such as cotton, for example.

Courtesy Johns-Manville Corp.

Slag Wool. Molten lead or iron can be processed into the form of fibers, which are used as felt and packing material for insulative purposes in the building trades. This by-product of the blast furnace is light in weight; it is fireproof, heatproof, soundproof, verminproof, moistureproof, and rotproof.

▶ TEST YOURSELF ON THIS CHAPTER

1. For what purposes are the minor natural fibers generally used?
2. Name five minor fibers, and give one use for each.
3. How are metal threads and tinsel made? For what purposes are they used?
4. Describe the qualities of asbestos and its uses.
5. What by-product of the steel industry is used as insulative material? Name four of its qualities.
6. Why is jute never available in a pure-white color?
7. Why is kapok always felted, never woven?
8. How does kapok differ from cotton?
9. Compare ramie with linen.
10. Why is hemp especially suitable for sailcloth?

& Minor Fabric Constructions

Up to this point, weaving is the only method of fabric construction that has been described. The drawing in Chapter 1, however, shows that fabric may be constructed by processes other than weaving; that is, by knitting, felting, braiding, and netting. Of these four, knitting comes second in importance to weaving. Although the knitting construction is not so widely used for general fabrics as weaving, it possesses qualities that make it preferable for certain garments—for instance, such important articles as hosiery, sweaters, and underwear.

History of Knitting. Hand knitting was probably an early invention of man, but the art seems to have been perfected in western Europe in the fifteenth century. The word "cnyttan" was first mentioned in English literature in 1492. Hand knitting spread rapidly throughout Europe within a few generations. Primitive needles of bone or wood were first used, producing a coarse mesh. The Spaniards began to use steel needles, which produced a closer mesh and a more evenly knit fabric.

In 1589, the Reverend William Lee, an Englishman, invented the first knitting machine, which knit 8 loops to 1 inch of width. As this construction was too coarse a mesh, he improved the machine so that it was possible to knit 20 loops to 1 inch. Today, the average is 28 loops, and the modern knitting machine still operates on the same general principles established by William Lee.

Knitted Construction Compared with Weaving. Knitted fabric is constructed with a single yarn that is formed into interlocking loops by the use of wires or needles. The loops may be either loosely or closely constructed, according to the purpose of the fabric. Crocheting is knitting in its simplest form. A chain of loops is produced from a single thread by means of a hook.

The interlocking loops of the knitted construction permit the fabric to stretch in any direction, even if low-grade yarn having little elasticity or yarn that lacks natural elasticity is used.

Woven fabrics are produced by the interlacing of two or more yarns; this method of construction does not allow the fabric to stretch to any marked degree. If a certain amount of stretching is necessary, woven fabric must be cut on the bias, that is, in a diagonal direction; but even then the fabric can be stretched only in the direction of the diagonal cutting.

This advantage of stretchability that knitted fabric possesses is an important consideration where fit and comfort are concerned. Knitted fabrics also give warmth because of the insulative air pockets contained in this type of construction. Knitted fabrics are very absorbent and light in weight, and do not wrinkle easily; it is not always necessary to iron them after washing. These qualities make the knitted construction desirable for underwear and especially for sportswear.

Certain kinds of knitted fabric have one serious disadvantage: if one of the loops breaks, a hole is made, which starts a run. This disadvantage can be eliminated by variation in the stitch, which protects the fabric from raveling if any single stitch is broken.

• *Evaluating Construction of Knitted Fabric.* It will be recalled that thread count (the number of threads per square inch) is used to evaluate the construction of woven fabrics. The construction of knitted fabrics is determined by the number of stitches or loops that can be counted in any square inch.

When the interlocking loops run lengthwise, each row is called a *wale*. A wale corresponds to the direction of the warp in woven fabrics. When the loops run across the fabric, each row is called a *course*. A course corresponds to the filling or weft. Thus, a knitted fabric having 40 loops or stitches in 1 inch of width, and 50 loops in 1 inch of length, is said to have 40 wales and 50 courses.

Classification of Knitted Fabrics.

Knitted fabrics are divided into two general types: (1) those produced by weft knitting, where one continuous yarn forms courses across the fabric; (2) those produced by warp knitting, where a series of yarns forms wales in the lengthwise direction of the fabric.

• *Weft Knitting.* There are three fundamental stitches in weft knitting: (1) plain knit stitch, (2) purl stitch, (3) rib stitch. Novelty stitches, such as the tuck, the cardigan, and the rack, are merely variations of these three. Weft knitting is the hand method of knitting.

The *plain knit stitch* can be produced flat knit or in tubular form according to the machine used, and therefore is sometimes known as the flat knit or jersey stitch. It is formed by the interlooping of one or more weft threads, and can be identified by *wales on the right side* of the fabric, or by *courses on the underside*. As the fabric will stretch more in width than in length, the plain knit stitch is used for underwear, sweaters, gloves, and especially hosiery.

The *purl stitch* shows *courses on both sides* of the fabric, and both sides are similar. This stitch produces greater lengthwise stretch. It is used for scarves and for various kinds of sweater suits.

The *rib stitch* is a combination of the plain and the purl stitches. It is a slower stitch to produce and requires more yarn. It is characterized by lengthwise rows and is identified by *wales on both sides* of the fabric. The construction makes the fabric more elastic and therefore appropriate for apparel where snugness of fit is essential. The rib stitch is used for knitting the wristbands of sleeves and the waistlines of knitted garments; and for bathing suits, men's undershirts, and men's and children's socks.

• *Warp Knitting.* Warp-knit fabrics are of only one type, the flat knit, which produces a flat piece of cloth. They are made on a machine called a chain loom. In warp knitting, a series of yarns is placed side by side on separate needles. Wales are produced in the lengthwise direction of the fabric, forming vertical rows of loops.

The most commonly used warp-knit fabrics are *tricot* and *milanese*; these are found in underwear, fabric gloves, scarves, and materials for foundation garments.

Warp-knit fabrics are less elastic than weft-knit, but they are stronger, firmer, and more resistant to snag. They do not run or ravel when a single stitch is broken.

FELTING

Felt differs from woven or knitted fabric in that it requires no interlacing or interlooping yarns. The fibers are interlocked by subjecting them to heat, moisture, and pressure. Felting is a relatively simple, and the least expensive, method of fabric construction. Felt is always made from short-staple fiber.

Wool fibers, hair fibers that have the same properties as wool, and the hair of fur-bearing animals all possess the cohesive or felting property that allows the fibers to be pressed into a compact fabric.

Felt has no warp, filling, or selvage. As it does not have a system of threads, it will not fray or ravel. Being made without twist, felt has little tensile strength and no elasticity. It cannot be draped, but it can be cut or blocked into any shape and will retain that shape unless subjected to undue tension.

Lack of strength limits the uses of felt as a general clothing fabric, but it is especially adaptable for hats. Felt is also suitable for such articles as slippers, shoe insoles, ear muffs, pennants, and table padding. It is used for insulative purposes and for noise absorption, and has various industrial uses.

Fur Felt. The short fibers of such fur-bearing animals as the rabbit, muskrat, nutria, and beaver are important in the manufacture of felt for hats. Felt is usually made from a mixture of fibers. The better grade of hat felt contains beaver fibers.

Wool Felt. In most satisfactory grades of wool felt, at least one-half of the fiber comprises wool, as the wool fiber surpasses all others in the physical quality of cohesiveness that makes this type of fabric construction possible. Short-staple wool fiber, or noil, is used for felt; but the finer the grade of staple used, the stronger the felt.

Some lower-priced grades of felt are also made chiefly from wool. Other felts are made by combining cotton, kapok, or rayon with wool. These felts may be easily distinguished from fur felt by the dull appearance, harder feel, and comparatively rougher texture.

The Felting Process. In the process of felting, two carding operations make the fibers parallel and of even thickness. At the end of the operations, the fibers are in the form of a fine web. Several webs may be built up until a sufficient amount of weight or thickness has accumulated. Timing is an important element during these processes, so that the web will not be broken or have weak areas.

The mass, or batt, may then be cut, and the edges trimmed to the desired width. Finished felt may vary in thickness from a few thousandths of an inch to 3 inches. Any thickness can be obtained by superimposing batts on one another and felting them together. Batts are usually about 40 yards long and 60 to 90 inches wide; their weights vary from 18 to 50 pounds.

The batts are evenly sprinkled with warm water, passed over a steambox to warm the fibers thoroughly, and then pressed between two rollers. The top roller rests on the batt and, with an oscillating motion, exerts the pressure that combined with moisture and heat produces the final felting action.

After the batts have been processed, they are allowed to drain and cool off for about twenty-four hours. The timing for each raw material or blend used in the felt is very important. The felt is then dampened with a suitable lubricant, such as a soap and soda combination, for the fulling process, by which it is subjected to a pounding action with hammers. The fulling time varies from five minutes to half an hour. The longer the felt is fulled, the firmer it will be; but this operation cannot be continued too long, or the quality of the felt would be spoiled.

Final operations include washing, stiffening, ironing, brushing to raise a nap, and shearing to produce a smooth even surface. Felt may be made water-repellent and may be flameproofed or mothproofed; it may be dyed against fading, perspiration, cleaning, and washing.

BRAIDING OR PLAITING

Another form of fabric construction is the diagonal or lengthwise interlacing that is most familiar as the method of braiding or plaiting long hair. Braid is formed on a braiding machine by interlacing three or more strands of yarn so that each strand passes over and under one or more of the others.

This principle of fabric construction is used for making shaped articles, such as straw hats and small rugs; narrow fabrics, such as ribbons and braids for millinery and accessory dress materials; cords and tapes, such as fishlines, shoelaces, wicks, parachute and glider cords, and elastic of various types; and cord coverings for tires, tubing, hose, wires, and cables.

Braids are divided into two types: (1) flat braids, in the form of strips or narrow flat tapes; (2) round braids, tubular in form, which may be hollow or have a center core of some material. Both types of braiding are produced from any of the textile fibers, as well as from metal threads, tinsel, straw, wire, or leather.

NETTING

Netting is an open-mesh form of fabric construction that is held together by knots at each point where the yarns cross one another. The mesh varies in size and type, and ranges from the very open fish net to the finest and most delicate lace designs.

The open-mesh construction is characteristic of both nets and laces. The true lace construction is always made with a design. Bobbinet, which is a machine-made net, does not have a design, and is therefore not a true lace.

Laces were first made only by hand, and hand laces have always been highly prized as trimming for apparel and as decorative pieces for the home.

Unusually beautiful and intricately designed laces are retained in families as heirlooms and are displayed in museums as representative of the handicraft of nations of the world. Real laces, such as needlepoint, bobbin, pillow, darned, and crocheted, are now duplicated so expertly by machine that the average consumer is not able to determine whether a lace is machine-made or handmade.

Linen yarns are generally used for expensive laces; but cotton, silk, rayon, and other yarns are used for various qualities and types. Lace may be made by knotting or by looping, braiding, stitching, or twisting.

► TEST YOURSELF ON THIS CHAPTER

1. How does the construction of knitted fabrics differ from that of woven fabrics?
2. What is the chief advantage gained by the knitted construction? For what types of clothing is it preferable?
3. Why is a knitted fabric always a warm fabric?
4. What is a disadvantage of the knitted construction? Can it be eliminated? If so, how?
5. How would you evaluate the construction of knitted fabrics?
6. Describe the two types of knitted fabrics. Name a finished product of each type.
7. Describe the felting process.
8. For what purposes is the braided construction used?
9. Why are at least three strands required in braiding?
10. Why is braiding confined to the production of shaped articles?
11. How does felt differ from other fabric construction?
12. Why is wool preferred in making felt fabric?
13. Why are fur fibers used in the production of expensive felt hats?
14. How is felt used for industrial purposes?
15. How does net differ from woven fabric?

A Major Product of Knitting

Before the sixteenth century, the Anglo-Saxon word *hosa* designated a woven cloth garment that covered the lower portion of the body as well as the legs. As knitting was popularized and practiced to a great extent throughout England and Scotland, it soon became customary to knit the leg coverings separately by hand. In the course of time, these garments became known as stockings.

Wool was used for such hand knitting. When William Lee invented the knitting machine, the English queen encouraged him to adapt it to the knitting of silk stockings rather than wool ones, as she feared that such a machine would take away the livelihood of the wool hand-knitters. But credit for the later development of machine-knit silk stockings must be given to France, as Lee was invited to that country to set up his machines there when the queen of England failed to grant him a patent. Misfortune still followed William Lee, and he died in France before the full value of his knitting machine became apparent.

Hosiery is an important knitted product, and its cost is often a large item in the clothing budget of the consumer. The construction of hosiery should be of interest because it has a bearing on the serviceability of the article. In most cases, the better-constructed hosiery is well worth its extra cost, provided it is given proper care in wearing as well as in laundering.

Yarns Used for Hosiery. Before World War II and before nylon was developed, *silk* had always been the most popular fiber for hosiery because of its strength, elasticity, and pleasing, soft, luxurious texture.

As silk strands are not of even diameter throughout their length, the use of one continuous yarn (which is typical of the knitted construction) had a tendency to develop noticeable rings at points where the diameter of the strand changes, though ever so slightly. A more even texture was obtained by knitting silk hosiery on a machine with a three-carrier attachment, so that three separate yarns are used instead of one continuous yarn. In this way, each yarn appears on every third row, and any irregularities of size are scattered over a large area and are not readily discernible. Silk stockings knit by this method are called three-carrier construction or *ringless* hose.

• *Cotton* is suitable for hosiery as it is soft and absorbent and dries quickly. It has less tendency to run when a thread is broken.

• *Wool* is adaptable to hosiery chiefly for warmth. The high absorbency of wool is another good feature. Of course, the grade of the wool yarns used has an important bearing on the quality and price of woolen hose.

• *Rayon* was the first of the man-made or synthetic fibers to be used for hosiery. But it does not possess the elasticity nor strength necessary to produce good-looking, fine hosiery for women.

• *Nylon* has proved to be the outstanding fiber for hosiery. Nylon filament yarn is stronger and more elastic than silk, and it became the first yarn that was acceptable for fine hosiery in place of silk. Nylon has a greater resistance to abrasion and outlasts silk in the heels and toes of stockings. It lacks the absorbent quality of silk, however. Once a thread is broken, a nylon stocking runs fast, and it snags easily.

Nylon yarn can be spun into fine deniers, so that a large variety of styles, types, and weights of women's nylon hosiery can be made. At first, the full-fashioned construction was used, but the use of the circular-knit construction on high-count needle machines has increased because nylon can be preset by heat. A preboarding operation stabilizes the nylon stocking fabric against distortion of stitch by subjecting it to conditions higher in temperature than those that will be subsequently encountered.

The nylon staple can be spun into wool-like yarns, which are usually knitted into men's hosiery. Spun nylon hosiery is soft and warm, and the yarn is even more abrasion-resistant than nylon filament yarn. Therefore, spun nylon hosiery is very durable and will wear for a very long time, in fact, outwearing all other hosiery. Spun nylon hosiery launders easily and does not shrink. The one big disadvantage of this type of hosiery is its tendency to cause the feet to perspire.

• *Spun Orlon, spun Dacron,* and *Vicara* yarns are also being made into men's hosiery. None of these fibers have the abrasion resistance and wearing qualities of spun nylon. Both Orlon and Dacron have low absorbency, although they make warm socks. Vicara has high absorbency and a cashmerelike feel but will not produce durable hosiery.

Types of Hosiery Construction.   There are four types of hosiery construction: (1) full-fashioned; (2) circular, or seamless; (3) fashioned seamless; (4) cut and tailored.

• *Full-fashioned Hosiery.* Full-fashioned hosiery receives its name from the narrowing process performed during the knitting operation to shape the hose to fit the leg. The fabric is knitted flat on two separate machines called the *legger* and the *footer.*

The legger knits the leg of the stocking as well as the heel. It drops loops at appropriate points between the knee and the ankle, thus tapering the width of the stocking. Stitches are also dropped to shape the instep and the heel. The leg is then transferred to the footer, and the foot is knit to the leg. Both operations have been combined on one machine, called a *single unit.*

When the selvages are joined together, the stocking is fully shaped. The joining produces a noticeable seam on the back of full-fashioned hosiery.

Compare the foot of a full-fashioned stocking (at left) with the foot of a circular-knit stocking (at right).

Courtesy U.S. Department of Agriculture

Compare the detailed construction of the well-shaped toe of a full-fashioned stocking (at left) with the toe of a circular-knit stocking (at right).

Small dots, called *fashion marks,* appear on both sides of the seam indicating where the stitches were decreased during the narrowing process. Lines or wales radiate from these fashion marks.

Because full-fashioned hosiery is shaped in the knitting operation, its fit is assured and its shape is retained after wearing and washing. On all parts of full-fashioned stockings, there are the same number of loops to the inch.

Detailed construction of the leg of a full-fash-
ioned stocking, shaped in the knitting, is shown
at the left. The mock seam and simulated fashion
marks of one type of circular-knit stocking are
shown at the right.

The well-shaped construction of a full-fashioned
heel can be seen at the left. At the right is the
heel of a circular-knit stocking.

Courtesy U.S. Department of Agriculture

• *Circular-knit, or Seamless, Hosiery.* Circular hose is knit from hem to toe on a circular machine and is therefore seamless. There are the same number of stitches in the width of circular-knit hosiery from top to toe, making the hose of even width throughout its length. Therefore, certain areas must stretch to fit the leg and foot and will eventually show signs of strain. After wear and laundering, circular-knit hose returns to its original tubular shape.

Circular-knit hosiery can be made to simulate full-fashioned hosiery by using the more expensive yarns that ordinarily go into the manufacture of better-quality hose and by using mock seams with tuck stitches to resemble fashion marks. The tuck stitches can be recognized as such by noting whether or not the number of wales is the same above and below the fashion marks. Also, in circular-knit hose, the wales run parallel with the fashion marks; in full-fashioned hose, the wales radiate from the fashion marks.

The application of a seam on the back of circular-knit hosiery simulates the true seam of the full-fashioned construction. This type of circular-knit hose is also known as *mock-seam hosiery.*

• *Fashioned Seamless Hosiery.* Fashioned seamless hosiery is knit on a special flat machine. The hose is started at the toe, where only a small number of needles is used. As the stocking is widened from ankle to calf and finally to hem, one needle at a time is added to obtain the full-fashioned effect. The added stitches form a V at the back of the leg. This V identifies fashioned seamless hose.

The fashioned seamless construction makes a comfortable stocking because the seam in the foot is eliminated. Seams are associated with the more popular full-fashioned construction, however, and fashioned seamless hosiery is generally given a seam down the back of the leg. Fashioned seamless hose is usually made from cotton, wool, and the coarser rayon yarns.

• *Cut and Tailored Hosiery.* Cut and tailored hosiery is an inexpensive type of hose. In this construction, circular hose is cut up the back of the leg, and the hose is seamed to fit. This method makes it possible to cut stockings from plain or lace fabrics and to seam them after conforming the fabric to the shape of the leg.

Women's Nylon Hosiery.

Nylon is the most popular textile for hosiery among women. Nevertheless, many women find fault with the durability of their nylon hosiery. For greater service, the following factors should be considered when purchasing nylon hosiery.

• *Types of Stocking Fabric.* The manner in which hosiery is knit has a

The first four of the eight steps in making nylon stockings are shown here. (1) knitting, (2) seaming, (3) inspection, and (4) preboarding for shaping. Testing and dyeing follow; then the stockings are boarded again for final shaping and are paired for packaging.

great deal to do with its durability, appearance, and fit. There are two main types of knit: plain and mesh.

The *plain knit,* of which most hosiery is made, has several advantages. It stretches in both directions, has a smooth clear texture, and provides unequaled sheerness. The outstanding disadvantage of the plain knit is that a break in any loop can cause a run.

The *mesh knit* can be produced in a variety of patterns. Usually, the fabric is of a "run-resistant" construction. As in the plain knit, the yarn can snag, but this will develop only a hole in the fabric rather than a run because the loops are interlocked. Since most mesh-knit fabrics are less stretchable than plain-knit, special attention should be given to proper fit to avoid unnecessary strain on any part of the stocking. A half-size larger stocking is recommended to make up for this lack of stretch. Mesh-knit hosiery is not as smooth or as sheer and flattering to the leg as plain-knit, but it tends to be more serviceable.

• *Hosiery Sheerness.* The sheerness of nylon hosiery is dependent on the fineness (denier) of the yarn used and the closeness (gauge, for full-fashioned, and needles, for seamless hosiery) of the stitches or loops.

The term *denier* indicates the weight of the nylon yarn used in a stocking. Therefore, the higher the denier, the heavier or thicker the yarn. Conversely, the lower the denier, the finer the yarn. Nylon deniers most commonly range from 12, which is the finest yarn used, through 15, 20, 30, 40, 50, 60, and 70.

The term *gauge* refers to the closeness or fineness of the loops across the width of the full-fashioned stocking. Technically, the gauge indicates the number of stitches or loops per $1\frac{1}{2}$ inches across a knitted row in a stocking. Each needle makes a loop; the more needles used, the more loops, and the finer the gauge. Since a high gauge uses more and finer stitches, it uses more nylon yarn and gives greater strength to the stocking. Consequently, the higher the gauge, the finer the stitch, the greater the wearing quality and snag resistance. The gauges of hosiery range from a low of 39 through 42, 45, 48, 51, 54, 57, 60, and 66.

In seamless hosiery, the closeness of the loops is measured in terms of *needles,* which refers to the number of needles on the circular stocking knitting machine. The needle count ranges from 260 to 432. Like gauge, the higher the number of needles, the closer and finer the knit. Sometimes, a seamless stocking is also referred to by its equivalent gauge count—that is, 432 needle count is as closely knit as 54 gauge, and 400 needle count is similar to 51 gauge.

Gauge affects the appearance and durability of hosiery, but it is the combination of denier and gauge that determines the sheerness of the hose. For example, 45 gauge, 15 denier hosiery is sheerer than 51 gauge, 15 denier hosiery, but the 45 gauge stocking will probably not wear as well because it is not so closely knitted. Likewise, 54 gauge, 15 denier hosiery should wear even better because of the greater number of stitches to each $1\frac{1}{2}$ inches of the stocking. In any event, when comparing hosiery deniers and gauges, similar qualities must be used. Each stocking is a combination of the quality of knitting, the quality of the yarn, the denier of the yarn, the gauge, and the construction features.

The following facts are helpful when purchasing hosiery.

15 denier, 51 gauge—filmy and supersheer, for evening wear
20 denier, 51 gauge—sheer weight, desirable for evening wear
30 denier, 51 gauge—average weight, for afternoon or business
40 denier, 45 gauge—duty weight, often preferred for daytime wear at home

60 to 70 denier, 45 gauge—service weight, best for outdoors and for extra long wear

• *Construction of Hosiery.* For hosiery to wear well, it must be properly constructed. The fact that strong nylon yarn is used, or that a high gauge is employed in knitting the stocking, does not automatically insure long-wearing hosiery.

The *seams* in full-fashioned hosiery should be straight, sturdy, narrow, and trim, with no raw fabric edges showing. Nylon thread should be used because it assures long-wearing and fast-drying fine seams. When correctly sewed, the heel reinforcing, welt, and fashion marks will match on both sides of the seam.

The *welt* or hem should be 3 to 4 inches long to permit firm anchoring of the garter. The welt should be sufficiently wide and elastic to fit the thigh without binding. It should measure 7 or 8 inches when flat and should stretch to about 12 or 13 inches to be comfortable on the average leg.

There should be a well-constructed *shadow welt,* or *afterwelt,* directly below the welt. It gives added strength to the upper part of the hosiery by taking up the garter strain.

Just below the welt or the shadow welt, there should be a row of *"run-stop" stitching* around the stocking, which discourages runs, starting in the welt, from running into the body of the stocking. This stitching can be made in several ways, such as by interlocking the loops during the knitting process.

Construction of full-fashioned hosiery.

Welt

Shadow welt

Run-stop stitching

Leg

Seam

Fashion marks

Splice

Heel

Reinforcement

WOMEN'S HOSIERY SIZE CHART

Shoe Width	AAA	AA	A or B	C or D	E or EE
Shoe Size	**Stocking Foot Size**				
2½	8	8	8	8½	8½
3	8½	8½	8½	8½	8½
3½	8½	8½	8½	8½	8½
4	8½	8½	8½	9	9
4½	8½	8½	9	9	9½
5	9	9	9	9	9½
5½	9	9	9½	9½	9½
6	9½	9½	9½	9½	10
6½	9½	9½	9½	10	10
7	9½	9½	10	10	10½
7½	10	10	10	10½	10½
8	10	10	10½	10½	10½
8½	10½	10½	10½	10½	11
9	10½	10½	11	11	11
9½	11	11	11	11	11

LEG LENGTH CHART

When stocking foot size is	8, 8½, 9	9½	10	10½, 11
and stocking is marked	**Lengths available are**			
"Short"	28"	28"	—	—
"Medium"	30"	31"	31"	32"
"Long"	—	34"	34"	34"

This is a typical leg length chart. There is some variation of length in inches of hosiery produced by different manufacturers. The salesperson should have accurate information about the brands of hosiery sold in the store.

Reinforcement in the toe, heel, and sole is desirable for greater durability, and should be in proportion to the weight and style of the hosiery. Some styles of sheer hosiery are made with little or no reinforcement. Fortunately, nylon is strong and can withstand unusual rubbing and abrading before it will wear through.

The *volume* of the stocking is another important consideration. Since nylon hosiery has unusual two-way stretch, flat measurement alone is not sufficient to assure that the stocking is correctly sized. Good construction requires that stockings should conform to standard leg-form sizes. This volume should not be skimpy but rather should be adequate in both girth and length of the foot, leg, and thigh.

Regardless of the quality of construction, no hosiery will give proper service unless the wearer selects the correct foot size in accordance with the width and size of her shoe, and the correct leg length.

Cause and Correction of Hosiery Runs and Breaks

Cause of Break	Possible Correction
Too much pull from garters. Lack of elasticity of garter or sharp edge on garter clasp.	Wear longer stockings. Have elastic and garters in good condition.
A skimpy welt or not enough elasticity in welt.	Buy stockings with plenty of stretch in the hem or those with a special stretch-top feature.
Stocking is either too tight or too long.	Buy stockings with more ample tops and of correct length. Garters should never be put into sheer leg fabric or shadow welt.
Too sheer a stocking for the occasion.	Wear stockings of heavier denier yarn or higher gauge knit.
Improper fastening of garter.	Always fasten garters into hem of stockings. Garters fastened into sheer leg fabric, shadow welt, or on the seams frequently result in tears and runs. Handle hose carefully.
Snags or pulled threads.	Avoid contact with sharp or rough objects, as broken or rough fingernails or toenails, zippers, crinoline skirts, and the like. Buy stockings that fit the leg more snugly. Loose, poorly fitting stockings are more readily snagged.
Strain at knee due to too-tight or too-short stocking.	Buy longer stockings.
Too-small foot size causing excessive wear above heel reinforcement.	Buy larger foot size.

Reinforcement is too thin.	Buy hosiery with heavier reinforcements. Use lightly reinforced hosiery or sandal foot types only for more dressy occasions.
Stocking snagging on rough shoe lining.	Have shoe lining repaired. Wear shoes with snug-fitting heels.
Stocking too short in foot causing runs in toe reinforcing.	Buy larger-sized stockings.
Runs above toe reinforcing when too-long stocking is folded under.	Buy smaller-sized stockings.
Worn lining in shoe.	Have shoe lining repaired.
Insufficient reinforcement.	Buy hose of heavier denier or more heavily reinforced in toe.
Reinforcement worn through.	Buy stockings more heavily reinforced or of heavier denier for the occasion. Check rough shoe linings.
Friction from bunions, callouses, or similar abrasion.	Take proper care of feet.
Friction from arch supports.	Buy hose with heavier foot reinforcements.

Men's, Children's, and Infants' Hosiery. Men's, children's, and infants' hosiery, with minor exceptions, is circular-knit and is made of any of the various kinds and combinations of yarns, in many styles and in color effects.

Dyeing of Hosiery. Most stockings are dip-dyed or piece-dyed. This method is satisfactory if proper care is taken to insure evenness of color, for the flesh background quickly reveals inadequately dyed hosiery. By stretching the seamed part of the stocking, the consumer can tell whether the dyeing was well done. Unevenness of color indicates poor or incomplete penetration of the dye.

Hosiery is sometimes yarn-dyed. Ingrain stockings are made from yarns that were dyed before knitting. The amount of ingrain hosiery produced today is very small. A richer color results, but the hosiery is not as durable as when piece-dyed.

MEN'S AND CHILDREN'S
HOSIERY SIZE CHART[1]

Size of Shoe	Men's Hosiery	Children's and Infants' Hosiery
1	..	4
1½	..	4
2	..	4
2½	..	4
3	..	4½
3½	..	4½
4	..	4½
4½	..	4½
5	9	5
5½	9½	5
6	9½	5½
6½	10	5½
7	10	6
7½	10½	6
8	10½	6½
8½	11	6½
9	11	7
9½	11	7
10	11½	7
10½	11½	7½
11	12	7½
11½	12	7½
12	..	7½
12½	..	8
13	..	8

[1] Courtesy National Association of Hosiery Manufacturers.

Care of Hosiery. Hosiery should be washed after each wearing, as perspiration weakens the fiber. Unusual care is necessary in washing, as rough skin or sharp fingernails cause snags, which eventually result in runs. Obviously, rings should be removed from the hands when hosiery is being handled.

Lukewarm water with suds made from mild soap or soap flakes should be used, and the suds squeezed through the hose. Stockings should never be wrung or twisted. When drying, they should not be exposed to the direct heat of the sun nor hung near a hot radiator or stove.

These precautions apply to all types of hosiery. For wool stockings, the additional precautions for washing any wool fabric should be observed.

In addition to careful washing, the following suggestions will also help lengthen the wear of hosiery.

1. Strain on stockings, which tends to break the thread and produce runs, can be avoided by the proper distribution of garter support. Also, garters should be fastened to the hem of the stocking while the knee is bent.

2. At least two pairs of stockings of the same color should be purchased at one time. This makes it possible to match pairs when a single stocking has been damaged.

3. Examine shoe linings frequently to detect development of roughness that may cause undue wear on stockings.

4. Keep stockings in a separate box, when not in use, to prevent contact with anything that may mar their texture.

5. Select the proper size of hose according to well-fitted shoes. The stocking should be at least a half inch longer than the wearer's foot. The accompanying charts are an aid to such selection.

▶ TEST YOURSELF ON THIS CHAPTER

1. What are the types of hosiery construction? Which is preferable, and why?
2. How would you judge a pair of women's stockings that you consider purchasing?
3. What is meant by gauge of hosiery? What is meant by denier?
4. How will the gauge and denier of nylon hosiery influence the consumer's choice when purchasing hosiery?
5. How will the fit of shoes affect the wear of hosiery?
6. Why is it important to examine the reinforcements of hosiery?
7. What are the average lengths of hosiery for women?
8. What considerations should be given to the care of hosiery?
9. Compare cotton, wool, silk, rayon, nylon, Orlon, Dacron, and Vicara for use in men's hosiery.
10. How are stockings dyed?

24 | TEXTILE FLOOR COVERINGS

Floor coverings have been made from textile fibers for more than 5,000 years. Throughout civilization, the production of rugs and carpets has formed a part of the history and culture of races and nations. Early kings and conquerors included valuable rugs among their treasures and trophies, and many of these famous pieces have retained values that in some cases are inestimable. Priceless handmade carpets and rugs woven hundreds of years ago in the Far East are exhibited today in museums as representative of the patient labor and creative art of weavers whose skills have been passed on through many generations.

Well-chosen rugs or carpets serve as a colorful foundation for the decorative plan and color scheme of all rooms in the modern home. As floor coverings are among the most expensive items in the consumer's house-furnishings budget, careful consideration must be given to fiber, color, decorative character and design, size, and construction to obtain the best value for any price level.

Rug Construction. The terms *rug* and *carpet* are used synonymously, but the form or the size in which these coverings are manufactured differs. Rugs may vary in shape as well as in width and length; in general, certain size standards are maintained that have been adapted, in the larger rugs, to standard sizes of rooms.

Floor coverings are made from various kinds of fibers—cotton, silk, wool, rayon, acetate, nylon, and blends of these fibers, and from mohair, jute, hemp, or grass straw. The wool fiber is most popular because wool offers the advantages of extreme softness, resiliency, absorbency to shock and noise, and, particularly, resistance to long wear when the right fibers and construction are used.

Construction factors explain differences in quality and price: for example, the quality and quantity of wool used, the length of staple, the amount of twist, and the number of ply in the yarns. Each factor has a definite bearing on the final price of the finished product.

The term *broadloom* does not refer to quality but describes a type of carpet that is woven on a loom wide enough to produce the width desired. The carpet is woven all in one piece—not formed by stitching narrow widths together.

Terms Used in Carpet Industry. Judging a rug for quality of construction requires some understanding of certain terms used in the carpet industry.

Tufts are the cut loops of surface yarns held in the small squares that are discernible on the reverse side of the rug. *Pitch* expresses the number of warp threads crosswise of the loom to each 27 inches of width. *Wires* refer to the number of tufts to the inch in the warp or lengthwise direction.

The construction of the rug is indicated by the closeness of the tufts in each direction—that is, by the pitch and wires. The number can usually be determined by counting the rows of fiber on the back of the rug.

Compact construction of the tufts, represented by a high number of pitch and wires, indicates a dense pile, showing that a greater quantity of wool has been used, with a resulting more durable product. Density of weave is considered the most important factor for determining the durability of floor coverings.

Additional crosswise yarns are used to bind the pile to the backing of the rug. The number of yarns used for this purpose is indicated by the term *shot*. In a two-shot construction, for example, one crosswise yarn can be seen between each row of tufts; the other crosswise yarn is behind the row. In the three-shot construction, there are two crosswise yarns between each row of tufts, and a third yarn is in back. As the three-shot construction requires additional yarn and more loom operations, it is more expensive; but it increases durability.

Classification by Weave. Rugs and carpets may be classified according to weave, of which there are three general types.

1. Cut pile. Examples are Oriental, chenille, Wilton, Axminster, and velvet.
2. Uncut pile. Examples are tapestry and Brussels.
3. Flat weaves. Represented in novelty and special-purpose rugs made from miscellaneous fibers. Such rugs ordinarily can be used on either side.

DOMESTIC RUGS

In the United States, floor coverings are often classified as domestic and imported. The *domestic* group includes all kinds of rugs made in this country regardless of the source of their raw materials. The *imported* group includes Oriental, Chinese, Indian, and other foreign products. Today, these divisions and even specific types of rugs do not tell the consumer all that should be known because both good and poor qualities are found in all weaves.

Chenille.   Chenille is the most expensive of the domestic types, and it offers the widest range of possibilities with respect to depth of pile, design, colorings, and width. Chenille may be woven even as wide as 30 feet without a seam, and can be made as a single unit to fit irregularly shaped areas. It can be produced with a pile up to a full inch in height. This height, when supported by a heavy wool cushion back, gives a luxuriously soft and resilient quality and remarkable durability.

The chenille construction requires two separate loom operations. First, woolen or worsted yarns are woven into a blanket containing cotton warp threads. Actually, this blanket is composed of vertical woolen or worsted yarns bound together by the cotton warp.

Another machine cuts the woolen filling halfway, producing furry strips, which are held together by the cotton yarns in the center. This strip, which resembles a caterpillar, is pressed into V-shaped form, and the separate ends are tied together, forming a continuous chain. This chain is subsequently used on the second loom as a filling for the final weaving of the chenille rug. A well-constructed chenille uses a fine quality of wool and a densely packed high pile, which results in the durability characteristic of this weave.

Smyrna rugs resemble chenille, as they are made with a chenille fur; but the fur is twisted into a round yarn instead of the V shape of the chenille type. Also, a shot of fiber filling makes the Smyrna rug reversible—the pattern and pile are alike on both sides. It has a shorter pile than the chenille.

Wilton.   Wilton is an expensive weave to manufacture, ranking next to chenille. It is always woven on a Jacquard loom and is considered one of the best of all machine-made rugs.

In weaving the Wilton, the surface yarn is held in trays called frames. Each frame holds spools wound with yarn of the same color. If there are six full colors in the pattern of a Wilton, there must be six frames. In a six-frame Wilton, only one of the six pile yarns appears on the surface at a time. The other five lie underneath, constituting hidden value in the form of added resiliency and quality. The number of frames in a Wilton varies from two to six, indicating the thickness of its wool cushion and the number of sepa-

Hand tufting in chenille weaving. A steel comb is used to bring the surface yarn in the fur up through strong cotton catcher warp threads, as four motions of a shuttle weave the heavy backing yarn to the base of the fabric.

Courtesy Mohawk Carpet Mills, Inc.

Woolen blanket cloth from which chenille fur, or hairy caterpillar, is made. The cloth is shown partly cut so that the warp of the caterpillar may be seen.

The weft blanket cloth before being cut

The chenille fur or furry caterpillar

The warp of the chenille fur

Courtesy Mohawk Carpet Mills, Inc.

Chenille construction shown in detail.

rate colors in its design. A method known as *planting* makes it possible to add, in small areas, more colors than are indicated by the number of frames.

The pile effect of the Wilton is produced by looping the surface yarns over wires that have razor-sharp knives at the ends. When the wires are withdrawn, the knives cut the pile.

The Wilton is made with worsted or with woolen yarns. When closely woven, the worsted Wilton offers maximum durability together with fineness of texture and delicacy of design even though it has a short pile. The finest grade of worsted Wilton is woven with six frames, with a three-ply yarn. It has 13 wires to the inch, a three-shot construction, and about 115 tufts to the square inch. Lower grades are woven with a smaller number of frames, have 10 wires to the inch, a two-shot construction, and as few as 60 tufts to the square inch.

The woolen Wilton has a more luxurious feel than the worsted Wilton because of its greater softness and depth of pile. It is made with at least two and a half frames and has 7½ to 9½ wires to the inch and a pitch of 214.

Courtesy Mohawk Carpet Mills, Inc.

Worsted Wilton construction shown in detail.

Courtesy Mohawk Carpet Mills, Inc.

Woolen Wilton construction shown in detail.

• *Saxony.* Saxony is the name given to a better grade of woolen Wilton made from unusually heavily twisted woolen yarns with large and firm tufts. These yarns produce a luxurious depth of pile with large, loose tufts and a coarse design. The rug is especially durable in spite of its extreme softness of texture.

Brussels. The Brussels was the first type of carpet to be woven on a Jacquard loom. It is woven like a Wilton except that the wires used to make the surface loops do not have any cutting ends. As the wires are withdrawn, the pile is left as upright loops instead of cut pile. Worsted yarns are used for the pile, the worsted producing a very durable product. The best quality of Brussels is usually woven with five frames and has 9 wires to the inch and a pitch of 256.

Axminster. The Axminster rug has been the most popular type of carpet. There is no limit to the number of colors that may be used in its design. The colored yarns are wound on separate loom spools in the weft direction. The spools are fitted in an overhead roller and produce an endless supply of surface yarn. Weeks are required to set the yarns for an Axminster design; but,

Axminster construction shown in detail.

Courtesy Mohawk Carpet Mills, Inc.

once arranged, the 9 by 12 size may be woven in only an hour or two. Only woolen yarn is used for the Axminster, as the weave is not tight enough to permit the use of hard-surfaced worsted yarn.

The surface of the Axminster closely resembles hand-knotted carpet, but the Axminster can be easily distinguished from any other type of carpet because it can be rolled only in its lengthwise direction. The stiff jute fibers used in the backing form pronounced ridges on the reverse side.

The better-quality Axminster has a deep pile, some flexibility in its backing, and as many as 70 tufts to the square inch. The less expensive grades have fewer tufts, a low pile, and a very rigid back.

Velvet.   The velvet construction is the simplest pile weave. Its pile is woven over wires having cutting ends that produce the cut tufts as the wires are withdrawn. All the wool lies on the surface of velvet carpet, with no buried yarns in the backing. Only one yarn is used, and it must be uniform and of good quality throughout to absorb the dye evenly when printed. The common method of producing a pattern on velvet rugs is by printing the design after the rug has been constructed. Sometimes, yarns that have been printed before weaving are used.

The velvet rug is inexpensive, as it is the fastest type to weave. It is made on an ordinary loom, with worsted or woolen yarns. Twisted yarns are used to produce what is known in the trade as hard-twisted velvets. For firmness, jute yarns, sized with glue, are used as stuffing warp yarns. The better-quality velvet rug has a deeper pile; its density should range from 56 to 80 tufts to the square inch.

Sheen-Type or American Oriental.   The name "American Oriental" is frequently used for the sheen-type or luster-type domestic rugs that are produced by the Wilton, Axminster, or velvet weave. The sheen in the domestic product is obtained by washing or brushing the rugs in a chlorine solution,

Velvet construction shown in detail.

Courtesy Mohawk Carpet Mills, Inc.

which imparts the characteristic luster of the imported Oriental rug. The patterns are faithful reproductions and in many cases are woven through to the back, as in the genuine Oriental. When made of good-quality yarns, the American Oriental gives satisfactory wear and has steadily grown in popularity.

Tapestry. The construction of the tapestry rug is similar to that of the velvet except that the wires used to form the pile do not have any cutting ends. Thus an uncut pile is left when the wires are withdrawn. Because of its resemblance to the Brussels type, the tapestry rug is sometimes termed "tapestry Brussels." This is a misnomer. The term attempts to attribute to the tapestry rug the superior construction of the Brussels, which is made on a Jacquard loom with a two- to five-frame construction. The tapestry rug is made on an ordinary loom and requires only one warp yarn.

Tapestry offers the consumer an inexpensive and sturdy product. A good grade should have 8 wires and a pitch of 8. The tapestry rug is not intended for heavy or long wear. It does not have the softness of other rugs, nor does it have delicate or distinct designs. It is intended to satisfy the demand for a low-priced rug.

Patent-Back Rugs. In patent-back rugs, each tuft is locked into its place by applying a plastic binder to the back of the rug, or by vulcanizing a solution of rubber cement to the back. Patent-back rugs can be cut in any direction without danger of having frayed edges or raveled yarns; the edges do not require binding. This feature permits the patent-back broadloom to be fitted easily to irregularly shaped areas. Also, holes caused by damage or wear can be cut out and matched pieces put in their places.

Punched Felt Rugs. Punched felt rugs have a heavy burlap base reinforced with jute. Over this base is spread a fine-quality wool, which is punched through to the back. Rubber composition is then spread on the back to lock the fibers. This coating gives the rug a cushioned effect and prevents it from slipping.

Hooked Rugs. Hooked rugs from the southern and New England states and from Canada are popular as throw rugs for bedrooms and halls. These are handmade of rags and usually reproduce Colonial patterns. They are now produced commercially in room and small sizes in cotton and in wool.

Grass Rugs. A wirelike grass that grows wild in the northeastern section of the United States is used for grass rugs. They are woven with a plain weave that shows on one side; a pattern applied by stencil appears on the other side. Colored warp threads can be used to form geometric designs. Grass rugs are always varnished to preserve their surface.

Sisal Rugs. Sisal fiber imported from Central America and the West Indies can be made into rugs. The chief use of this fiber is for twine and rope, but its durability makes it adaptable for floor coverings. Sisal fiber is obtained from the leaf of a plant. It is twisted into strands and woven similarly to any of the fiber rugs.

IMPORTED RUGS

Oriental. Very few of the Oriental rugs produced before 1795 are on the commercial market today, but many are displayed in museums. These older Orientals are valuable because of their age, beauty, and intricacy of design. Those made in the last seventy years are accepted as "old Orientals," and although scarce, are still obtainable.

Oriental rugs are classified according to the country and the section from which they originated. They are divided into six groups: Persian, Turkish, Caucasian, Turkoman, Indian, and Chinese. These groups can be subclassified according to their weave, and also by the method of looping or knot tying that is characteristic of Oriental rug construction.

Only two kinds of knots are used for the many kinds of Oriental rugs made throughout Europe and Asia. The Persian or Senna knot is more of a twist or wrapping; the Turkish or Ghiordes knot is a real knot as understood today.

The largest class of Oriental rugs has a pile surface composed of tufts. Each tuft is made separately by means of the knot formed by strands looped around the warp yarns. When the quality of an Oriental rug is being judged, consideration should be given to coloring, design, depth of pile, quality of the yarn, age, condition, and fineness of texture. The number of knots to the square inch may vary from 50 to 500.

The consumer may find it difficult to distinguish between the imported Oriental and the machine-made domestic product. It may be helpful to remember that the reverse side of the Oriental always shows the entire pattern in detail and that the pile is produced by rows of knots, which can be easily seen by separating the pile. The back should also be examined to see whether the entire pattern has the same colors on the reverse side as are on the face of the rug, and to check the number of knots to the square inch.

In the genuine Oriental, the fringe of the rug is never sewed on; it is always an extension of the warp threads. In proportion to size the Oriental is always heavier than the domestic. Experienced rug merchants distinguish the two by examining the dyed portion of the pile nearest the knot. Oriental rugs use natural dyes, which usually fade to a lighter shade of the original color. The domestic rug uses aniline dyes, which fade to different hues.

Chinese. Antique Chinese rugs were made with the Persian or Senna knot, making possible a large number of knots to the inch and a close shearing of the pile. Later, rugs were made with large coarse designs and a deep pile. In more recent years, Chinese rugs have been made in plain colors as well as in the floral and dragon patterns characteristic of Chinese design. The pile is unusually deep, making these rugs remarkably durable.

Indian. Small-sized rugs imported from India are made from felted goat's hair and embroidered by hand with bright wool threads similar to the work found in crewel fabrics. They are known as Numdah rugs. They are inexpensive and adaptable for general household use as they can be easily washed.

Another rug imported from India is woven with the wool of wire-haired sheep; jute is used in its backing. This rug is called a *drugget*. It is usually highly colored and therefore should be dry-cleaned instead of washed.

CARE OF RUGS

The appearance and the life of a rug depend on the amount and kind of attention it receives. Dirt and grit must be removed frequently; otherwise, dirt works into the recesses of the pile and into the backing, soon cutting the yarn fibers and finally producing worn areas. A broom, carpet sweeper, or electric cleaner should be used on carpets for a few minutes every day, surely twice a week. All cleaning of this kind should be done in the direction of the pile, not against it.

When sweeping or brushing a new pile-surfaced rug, loose pieces of the pile, or fuzz, are likely to come off. This is caused by the excess short wool fibers worked in during manufacturing operations; it does not necessarily indicate defects. When ends of tufts appear above the surface of a new rug, they should never be pulled out; they should be clipped level with the general surface of the rug.

A new rug or one recently returned from storage should always be swept and brushed gently because the wool in the rug is in a dry condition, not having had sufficient opportunity to absorb its natural intake of moisture. The constant absorption of moisture from the atmosphere, so important for the healthful condition of a rug, keeps it resilient and resistant to wear. Plenty of water should be kept in a room; it may be in fish bowls or in metal containers on the radiators.

A rug should never be shampooed while it is on the floor. It is impossible to clean the pile thoroughly and to rinse out the soap and dirt completely when the rug remains on the floor. A pile rug made with highly twisted yarns should be dry-cleaned; washing or shampooing may untwist the yarns.

Often, constant pressure on certain parts of a rug flattens the tufts or slants them in one direction. The position of the rug should be changed so that the wear may be distributed instead of concentrated in a particular area, and so that the uneven shading that occurs when sections of a rug show localized wear may be prevented.

Any stains should be removed promptly. Many spots can be easily removed when they are fresh, whereas removal is difficult when the stain has set. The rules for the removal of spots and stains from general textile fabrics apply as well to textile floor coverings. (See Chapter 25.)

Damage from moths may be expected in rugs as in any wool material, but keeping the rug clean and providing a healthful circulation of air reduces the danger. For this reason, some persons do not put their rugs away during the summer months, but let them remain on the floor to give them the frequent cleanings so essential for long and serviceable wear. Rugs that are cleaned frequently with a vacuum cleaner are never attacked by moths.

If a damaged area is regular in form, this is an indication that the attacking insect is not the moth but the tow bug, which is likely to be found in overstuffed upholstered furniture. Moths usually show preference for one grade of wool or for a particular color.

Curling of the corner of a rug can be remedied by applying a hot iron on a damp cloth to both face and back of the corner. The curling is usually caused by constant tripping or by some similar unusual strain.

An important safeguard in the care of a rug is to place a cushion backing under it to absorb the constant impact.

► TEST YOURSELF ON THIS CHAPTER

1. What basic properties of textile fibers are required for floor coverings?
2. What are the two main classifications of floor coverings?
3. What materials are used in making real Oriental rugs?
4. What identifying characteristics distinguish Oriental and Chinese rugs?
5. How does the Brussels carpet differ from broadloom?
6. Describe the Wilton construction. How does a worsted Wilton differ from a woolen Wilton?
7. How can humidity affect floor coverings? How is this indicated to the owner? What remedy is available?
8. Describe the Axminster carpet, showing how the consumer may distinguish it from other carpets.
9. What are the advantages of a chenille carpet? The disadvantages?
10. Compare the imported Oriental with the domestic product.
11. Why is the patent-back construction an important development in carpet production?
12. What are some precautions that a consumer should take in caring for floor coverings?
13. Under what conditions may a wool rug be left on the floor during summer months?

Not only should fabrics be carefully selected but they should be given proper care throughout their lives. This care includes: (1) frequent brushing and airing of garments, (2) clean storage when not in use, (3) immediate mending when damaged by tearing, (4) stain removal before washing or further use, (5) intelligent choice of method of cleaning—washing or dry cleaning, (6) frequent laundering when the fabric is washable, (7) use of laundering method proper for the type of fabric, (8) proper pressing and ironing.

Brushing and Airing. The frequent brushing of garments, especially those having napped surfaces, removes the kind of dirt that starts as dust. The accumulation of dust particles not only soils the fabric, even though the soil is not readily discernible, but eventually causes deterioration.

When a garment is not washable, and does not require frequent dry cleaning, very often its life can be prolonged and its appearance kept bright and attractive by brushing. To offset the absorption of perspiration in such garments, they should be frequently aired, outdoors if possible. If outdoor airing is not possible, hanging clothes for a time outside the closet, in a well-aired room, is helpful.

Frequent brushing with a clothesbrush that has soft but firm bristles is necessary to keep wool garments in good condition. Such garments should be hung on wide-shouldered hangers in a closet where clothes are not packed tightly together. Occasional airing is also necessary to prolong the life of wool fiber. Clothes hanging in a closet should always be buttoned, and zippers should be closed.

Clean Storage. Clothing that is not in daily use should be protected from deterioration by storage in dustproof containers in which some kind of moth preventive is used. No useful purpose is served if the garment is stored without careful brushing and airing, for accumulated dirt works damage on such stored articles. For long storage, garments should be washed or dry-cleaned and then properly stored immediately, preferably in sealed containers.

If newly purchased linens are to be stored for a while, they should be washed to remove any possible sizing. There should be no residue of starch in new or used stored linens as it will cause mildew. If white linens are wrapped in blue paper, and the ends of the package are sealed to exclude light and air, the linens will not turn yellow during storage.

Mending. A torn fabric should be mended before further use. Makeshift repair by means of a pin, besides being unattractive, tends to cause a longer tear or fraying, which will be still more difficult to mend. The mended portion will naturally be less noticeable if it is repaired before the surrounding yarns are further damaged.

Methods of Stain Removal. Successful removal of stains from fabrics depends on the basic principle of not allowing the spot or stain to become set. A stain should be removed at the first possible opportunity because it may be more easily dissolved when fresh.

Different fibers require different methods and different stain removers. Use of an incorrect remover may damage or even destroy the fiber content of a fabric.

Knowledge of the nature of the stain makes possible the immediate use of the appropriate method and removal agent, and prevents resorting to experimental procedure. Hot water should never be used on an unknown stain; the heat will set the stain, making it more difficult to remove. If the stain is known to be of a nongreasy nature, sponging with cold water may be all that is necessary. On the other hand, a greasy stain requires the use of carbon tetrachloride or some other dry cleaner, such as benzine, gasoline, turpentine, or denatured alcohol.

There are four effective methods for removing spots and stains.

• *Dipping*. When the entire fabric can be immersed in the stain remover, the method is called *dipping*. This is the most convenient method if the spot is large or if there are many spots on an all-cotton or all-linen fabric.

• *Steaming*. Stains on wool, silk, or any colored fabric may be removed by steaming. The stained area is saturated with steam by spreading the cloth over a bowl partly filled with hot water into which a small amount of the appropriate removal agent has been placed.

• *Drop Method*. Small drops of a removal agent can be applied by means of a medicine dropper, glass rod, or orange stick.

The dipping method may be used for some fabrics.

The drop method requires a medicine dropper, glass rod, or orange stick.

Sponging must be done with care.

• *Sponging.* Sponging is the most frequently used method of stain removal, but if it is not done with care, it will not be effective. An absorbent cloth or a blotter should be placed underneath the stain to absorb the removal agent as well as the stain. The blotter also prevents further spreading of the wet area. Both the sponging cloth and the absorbent material should be renewed whenever they show the slightest tinge of the stain.

The stained portion of the fabric must not be soaked with the cleaning fluid, and the fabric must not be harshly rubbed. To be effective, small quantities of the fluid must be applied with a soft cloth by light strokes in a circular direction from the outer rim of the stain toward its center. The edges of the stain should be feathered to prevent formation of a ring.

The appearance of a ring indicates an improper method of brushing, an excessive amount of cleaning fluid, or lack of sufficiently quick evaporation. Rapid evaporation can be obtained by blowing on the fabric or by placing it in front of an electric fan. A ring can be eliminated by holding the fabric over the spout of a steaming kettle until the area is damp; then ironing immediately.

Stain Removers.   Acids, alkalies, and water are the three types of removal agents. No single chemical can be used to remove all spots from the many different kinds of fibers. For example, acids destroy cotton and linen, and therefore cannot be used to remove stains from these fibers. Similarly, alkalies cannot be used on silk and wool.

Either of the rayons, viscose or cuprammonium, can be treated like cotton; but acetate requires special care as it dissolves in acetone, acetic acid, and chloroform, or when it is exposed to a hot iron.

Acids and alkalies should be used only as mild solutions. When an acid solution is necessary, any possible damage that might occur to the fabric must be counteracted by applying a weak alkali, such as a solution of bicarbonate of soda or ammonia water to neutralize the acid. The fabric should be thoroughly rinsed in clear water.

If an alkali solution is necessary, it should be followed immediately with a mild acid solution, such as lemon juice, vinegar, or a dilute solution of acetic acid, to neutralize the action of the alkali. The fabric should be well rinsed.

Bleaching Agents as Stain Removers. Various bleaching chemicals are commonly used to remove stains, but such chemicals must be used carefully because they extract color and weaken the cloth. Javelle water and other chlorine solutions (sodium hypochlorite) should be used only on cottons, linens, and rayons—never on silk or wool.

If a stain is to be removed with a bleaching chemical, the fabric should be stretched over a bowl of hot water and fastened around the edge of the bowl. The bleaching agent should be dropped on the stained area with a medicine dropper. This application must be followed immediately with a thorough rinsing. The entire procedure must be done quickly so that the bleaching agent will not remain too long on the material and cause undue weakening of the fabric.

When Javelle water is used, a few drops of oxalic acid or sodium thiosulphate (photographer's hypo) will neutralize the action of any chlorine bleach that may remain in the fabric. If a bleaching agent is used on a colored fabric, the dipping method is advisable to avoid unequal distribution of any subsequent loss of color.

Sodium perborate and oxalic acid are effective in removing iron rust, metal stains, and some ink stains from all types of fabrics. These chemicals are the least harmful of all bleaches, but they must be used quickly to prevent abstraction of the dye. For white woolens, sodium perborate is particularly effective and harmless.

For the removal of mildew, ink, iron rust, dye stains, iodine, grass stains, and fruit stains, a solution of one teaspoon of sodium hydrosulphite in a glass of water is one of the most effective bleaches. But the liquid must be used quickly, and the fabric rinsed well; otherwise, the color will be destroyed, and the fabric weakened.

Hydrogen peroxide may be used on all kinds of fabrics. It is a mild bleach, but it can be made more effective by the addition of a little ammonia. Oxalic acid and sodium hydrosulphite cannot be used on weighted silk.

Oxalic acid is poisonous if taken internally. It should be labeled, so that it will not be mistaken for anything else, and placed out of reach.

Solvents. Where a stain is known to be of a greasy nature, the use of a solvent alone is sufficient. Grease stains are easily removed by the application of any of the following solvents: carbon tetrachloride, benzine, turpentine, Stoddard solvent, gasoline, ether, acetone, alcohol. With the exception of ether, acetone, alcohol, and colored gasoline, these solvents will not change the color of the material.

Sponging is generally most effective. The solvent should be applied on the wrong side of the fabric. The absorbent cloth underneath the stain will draw the dissolved grease and solvent from the fabric.

For fresh grease spots or slight oil stains, a sprinkling of talcum, powdered chalk, or magnesium carbonate (magnesite), rubbed into the stained area and left for a while, will absorb the grease. When the absorbent powder is subsequently brushed off, the stain will be entirely removed. Butter stains can be removed in this manner, but they must first be heated to melt the butter before they can be fully absorbed.

Removal of Specific Stains. Many of the synthetic fibers, such as Orlon, Acrilan, Dynel, X–51, and Dacron, are not very absorbent. Therefore, fabrics made of such fibers do not readily stain. The removal of stains generally requires merely wiping with a damp cloth or washing with a mild soap in warm water.

Removal of Stains from Fabrics Made of Natural Fibers

Kind of Stain	Type of Fabric	Procedure and Remover
Acid	All	Neutralize with ammonia.
Alkali	All	Neutralize with vinegar.
Blood	Cotton, linen	Soak in cold water, then in dilute ammonia. Wash.
Blood	Silk, wool	Sponge with cold water.
Butter	All	Sponge with naphtha or with carbon tetrachloride.
Candle wax	All	Scrape away, then sponge with benzine.
Chewing gum	All	Carbon tetrachloride or ether.
Coffee or chocolate	{ Cotton, linen	Sponge with cold water.
	{ Silk, wool	Glycerin, then hydrogen peroxide.
Fruit	Cotton, linen	If fresh, pour boiling water through stain. If stubborn, bleach with Javelle water.
Grass	All	Sponge with alcohol, then with soap and water.
Ice cream	All	Sponge with gasoline or with carbon tetrachloride.
Iodine	All	Soak in alcohol, or boil in solution of sodium thiosulphate.
Ink	Cotton, linen	If fresh, soap and water. If dried, use bleach, then oxalic acid, then wash; or put in sweet milk, and let turn sour.
Ink	Silk, wool	Sponge with hydrogen peroxide, then with oxalic acid or skim milk.
Iron rust	Cotton, linen	Oxalic acid, rinse well. Or spread with salt, moisten with lemon juice, and place in sun.

Kind of Stain	Type of Fabric	Procedure and Remover
Lipstick	Cotton, linen	Rub with lard until stain is soft. Scrape off grease, and wash in hot suds.
Mildew	Cotton, linen	Sponge with Javelle water.
Milk or cream	All	Sponge with benzine or with carbon tetrachloride.
Oil	All	Soap and water or carbon tetrachloride.
Paint	All	Soap and water, sponge with carbon tetrachloride or with turpentine on wrong side of stain.
Perspiration	All	Sponge with peroxide and ammonia.
Rubber	All	Sponge with carbon tetrachloride.
Rust	All	Sponge with lemon, vinegar, or oxalic acid.
Shellac	All	Sponge with denatured alcohol.
Scorch	All	If light, dampen and place in sunlight, or sponge with hydrogen peroxide.
Sugar	All	Sponge with hot water.
Tar	All	Moisten with carbon tetrachloride or with benzine. Scrape off, then sponge residue with same solvent.
Tea	Cotton, linen	Soak in borax solution, rinse. Or keep stain moist with lemon juice, then expose to sun for day or two.
Varnish	All	Sponge with equal parts of alcohol and benzine.
Vaseline	All	Sponge fresh stains with carbon tetrachloride, or spread talcum. Let stand. Then brush.
Water spot	Silk, wool	Hold in steam until damp. Iron damp.

Dry Cleaning. Many consumers make serious mistakes when deciding whether to wash or to dry-clean a fabric. In general, it is best to abide by the advice of the salesperson who sold the material or by the information concerning cleaning that is sometimes attached by label to a garment or fabric. Though dry cleaning is more expensive than washing, it pays to have a garment dry-cleaned rather than take a chance on washing and, as a result, ruin the garment.

If acetate fabric is dry-cleaned at home, the cleaning fluid must not contain alcohol, chloroform, strong acetic acid, or acetone. Any of these destroy acetate—particularly acetone, which is the solvent used in the acetate process. The commercial dry cleaner identifies acetate by moistening a finger with acetone and rubbing it on some unexposed portion of the fabric. If the threads become hard and feel soaplike, the fabric is acetate.

Laundering Methods. When a fabric is known to be washable, frequent and prompt washing is desirable, particularly of clothing worn next the skin. If such garments are not washed after each use, they are more difficult to clean, and the body perspiration that they have absorbed causes the fabric to deteriorate while awaiting cleaning.

In general, fine underwear and attractive, brightly colored outer garments and household linens should be laundered at home. Knowledge of how to wash fragile and dainty white garments as well as dyed fabrics is most essential for good results.

Just knowing that a fabric is washable is not enough information for obtaining good results in laundering. The consumer must be acquainted with the proper method for washing each type of garment and fabric. Some fabrics may be subjected to what is termed "hard" laundering without too great a strain on their durability. This type of laundering includes boiling and the use of strong soaps. It may be done at home as well as in commercial laundries, where it is customary to use strong substances for bleaching purposes and for sanitary reasons.

Before any attempt is made to wash clothes, colored fabrics should be separated from white ones, and heavy work clothes from fine and delicate pieces, as different washing methods are necessary.

If bad stains have not been removed, they must be removed before the fabrics are immersed in the hot water that is generally used for washing. Slightly soiled clothes that do not require soaking should be washed in water not over 115 degrees Fahrenheit. Extremely hot water tends to set dirt spots and minor spots or stains that may not have needed special treatment. Clothes that are very soiled should be soaked in warm, soapy water for about ten minutes.

A good quality of household soap should be dissolved in a washing machine or in a tub of hot water. Soft water will lather quickly, resulting in a more thorough cleaning. If the water is hard, the soap tends to curd because there is a high concentration of iron, calcium, magnesium, and aluminum salts in hard water. Any of the good commercial water softeners may be used to precipitate these soap-destroying metals in the water. Hard water can be softened by the use of washing soda, or sal soda (hydrated sodium carbonate).

▶ TEST YOURSELF ON THIS CHAPTER

1. In what way does the label on a garment help in caring for the garment?
2. Why should all clothes be placed on hangers when not in use? Why are

knitted garments an exception to this rule? Where should knitted clothes be kept?

3. Why is a firm brush recommended for brushing clothing?

4. Why should garments not be crowded in a clothes closet? Why should white garments be kept separate from colored ones?

5. Give illustrations of what is meant by "needed repairs." Give reasons for attending to these without delay.

6. Why should clothes be given a rest? How does this apply particularly to wool clothes?

7. Why should a stain or a spot be removed as soon as it is discovered?

8. For your next buying trip to a retail store, prepare a list of questions that you consider important enough to ask the salesperson to make certain that your selection of the clothing item is a prudent one.

9. Cut six advertisements from a newspaper, and circle all the textile terms that have taken on new meaning for you since studying textiles. Explain how familiarity with these textile terms has proved helpful to you recently.

BIBLIOGRAPHY

Bendure, Z., and G. Pfeiffer. *America's Fabrics*. New York: Macmillan Company, 1951.

Bray, H. A. *Textile Fibers, Yarns, and Fabrics*. New York: Appleton-Century-Crofts, Inc., 1929.

Caplin, J. *Knit Fabrics*. St. Paul, Minn.: Riverside Press, Inc., 1940.

———. *Lace Book*. New York: Macmillan Company, 1932.

———. *Linen Fabrics*. St. Paul, Minn.: Riverside Press, Inc., 1939.

Denny, G. G. *Fabrics*, Sixth Edition. Philadelphia: J. B. Lippincott Company, 1947.

Dooley, W. H. *Textiles*. Boston: D. C. Heath & Company, 1943.

Dyer, E. *Textile Fabrics*. Boston: Houghton Mifflin Company, 1927.

Evans, M. *Fundamentals of Clothing and Textiles*. New York: Prentice-Hall, Inc., 1949.

———, and E. A. B. McGowan. *A Guide to Textiles*. New York: John Wiley & Sons, Inc., 1939.

Hall, A. J. *Standard Handbook of Textiles*. New York: D. Van Nostrand Company, 1947.

Hartsuch, B. E. *Introduction to Textile Chemistry*. New York: John Wiley & Sons, Inc., 1950.

Hess, K. P. *Textile Fibers and Their Use*, Fourth Edition. Philadelphia: J. B. Lippincott Company, 1948.

Hollen, N., and J. Saddler. *Modern Textiles*. Minneapolis, Minn.: Burgess Publishing Company, 1952.

Hoye, J. *Staple Cotton Fabrics*. New York: McGraw-Hill Book Company, Inc., 1942.

Matthews, J. M. *Application of Dyestuffs to Textiles*. New York: John Wiley & Sons, Inc., 1920.

———. *Textile Fibers; Their Physical, Microscopical and Chemical Properties*, Fifth Edition. New York: John Wiley & Sons, Inc., 1947.

Mauersberger, H. R., and others. *American Handbook of Synthetic Textiles*. New York: Textile Book Publishers, 1952.

McGowan, E. A. B., and C. A. Waite. *Textiles and Clothing*, Revised Edition. New York: Macmillan Company, 1931.

Merrill, G. R., A. R. Macormac, and H. R. Mauersberger. *American Cotton Handbook*. New York: Textile Book Publishers, 1941.

Miller, M. C. *Principles of Knitting*. New York: McGraw-Hill Book Company, Inc., 1931.

Moncrieff, R. W. *Artificial Fibers*. New York: John Wiley & Sons, Inc., 1951.

Moore, A. S. *Linen*. New York: Macmillan Company, 1922.

Nystrom, P. H. *Textiles*. New York: Appleton-Century-Crofts, Inc., 1916.

Page, E. *Lace Making; the Home Craft of All Ages*. New York: Pitman Publishing Company, 1930.

Pellew, C. E. *Dyes and Dyeing*, Revised Edition. New York: Medill McBride Company, 1927.

Schenke, E. M. *Manufacture of Hosiery and Its Problems*. New York: National Association of Hosiery Manufacturers, 1935.

Schwarz, E. R. *Textiles and the Microscope*. New York: McGraw-Hill Book Company, Inc., 1934.

Sherman, J. V., and S. L. Sherman. *New Fibers*. New York: D. Van Nostrand Company, 1946.

Small, C. P. *How to Know Textiles*. Boston: Ginn and Company, 1932.

Staples, M. C. *Essentials of Textiles; a Notebook*. Minneapolis, Minn.: Burgess Publishing Company, 1946.

Taylor, L. *Know Your Fabrics*. New York: John Wiley & Sons, Inc., 1951.

Von Bergen, W., and H. R. Mauersberger. *American Wool Handbook*. New York: Textile Book Publishers, 1948.

Watson, W. *Textile Design and Color; Elementary Weaves and Figured Fabrics*, Fifth Edition. New York: Longmans, Green & Co., Inc., 1946.

Wingate, I. B. *Textile Fabrics and Their Selection*, Third Edition. New York: Prentice-Hall, Inc., 1952.

Woolman, M. S., and E. A. B. McGowan. *Textiles: A Handbook for the Student and the Consumer*, Third Edition. New York: Macmillan Company, 1943.

MAGAZINES AND PAMPHLETS

Monthly and weekly magazines are published that cover single or combined textile industries. Examples of these are the *Du Pont Magazine, American Fabrics, American Textile Reporter,* and *Rayon Organon.* There are many others.

Pamphlets, reprints of articles, and a variety of information in similar form can be obtained from the public relations department or the advertising department of the large manufacturers of textile fibers and fabrics throughout the United States. Those mentioned below are only typical and may not be available over a long period. But new and up-to-date articles and pamphlets are constantly being published and distributed by manufacturing companies.

Celanese Corporation of America, *Acetate, the Beauty Fiber.*

Chemstrand Corporation (The), *Acrilan "Created by Man."*

Du Pont de Nemours (E. I.) & Company, *About Du Pont Nylon, Close-up of Nylon, Nylon and You, Nylon Textile Fibers in Industry, Orlon Acrylic Fiber, Dacron Polyester Fiber.*

Household Finance Corporation, *Hosiery* (and other helpful pamphlets).

Owens-Corning Fiberglas Corporation, *Fiberglas Yarns for the Textile Industry.*

Virginia Carolina Chemical Corporation, *Vicara Textile Fiber.*

United States Department of Agriculture issues at small cost pamphlets on such subjects as textile fibers and fabrics, hosiery, clothing, rugs, their composition and care, and stain removal.

INDEX

Silk (*Continued*)
 effect on,
  of acids and alkalies, 28, 211; *table,*
   30–31
  of heat and light, 25, 26, 30–31, 211
  of mildew and moths, 26, 30–31, 211
  of perspiration, 211
  elasticity and crease resistance of, 18, 210;
   table, 30
  fabrics, 210–213
  finishing processes for, 210
  heat conductivity of, 20, 210; *table,* 30
  length of fiber, 14; *table,* 30
  luster of, 15; *table,* 30
  pure-dye, 37–38, 208, 210, 211
  shrinkage of, 211
  spun, 208–209
  strength of, 16, 210; *table,* 30
  structure of, 7; *table,* 30
  tests for, 35, 37–38, 42, 44; *illus.,* 36
  throwing, 203–204
  weighted, 37–38, 100, 207–208, 210–211
  wild, or tussah, 7, 209–211
  yarn count, 206–207
Singeing, 90–91, 187
Singles, 204; *illus.,* 205
Sisal, 290
Sisal rugs, 320
Sizing, 55, 98–100, 169, 170
Skein dyeing, 119
Slag wool, 292
Slashing, 54, 55; *table,* 125
Slip resistance, 111
Sliver, 49–51
Slub yarns, 59–60
Smallen, L. C., 270
Smyrna rugs, 314
Snow cloth, 198
Solution pigmenting, 122
Souple silk, 213
Spinneret, 202; *illus.,* 217
Spinning, 48–63, 53–54, 167, 182–183, 217–
   220, 238–239
Sponging, 187, 327; *illus.,* 326
Spray painting, 136; *table,* 135
Spun rayon, 221–222
  elasticity and crease resistance of, 19, 225
  heat conductivity of, 226
  shrinkage of, 226
  tests for, 35, 43
Spun yarns, 240, 249, 260, 265
Squeezing test, 46
Stabilized finish, 100
Stain removal, 325–331
Staple-fiber process, 284–285
Staze-Right, 100

Steaming, 123, 187, 325
Stencil printing, 132; *table,* 134
Stock dyeing, 119; *illus.,* 118
Suede cloth, 160, 198
Sulphur dyes, 116; *table,* 125
Surah, 74, 213, 233
Swivel weave, 81–82

Taffeta, 69, 71, 213, 233
Taglocks, 177
Taking up, 65, 66–67
Tapestry fabric, 85, 160
Tapestry rugs, 313, 319
Tartan, 233
Tearing test, 46
Teasel, 103
Teg wool, 176
Tentering, 97–98
Terry cloth, 79, 160; *illus.,* 150
Terry towels, 149–151
Tests, 34–47
Thread count, 60–62
  of sheets, 146–148
Three-shaft twill, 74; *illus.,* 72
Throwing, silk, 203–204
Thrown silk threads, 204–206
Tickings, 74, 77, 78, 160
Tie dyeing, 134–136
Tinsel, 290–291
Tobacco cloths, 153
Tow, 166, 265, 270–271
Toweling, 172
Tram, 204; *illus.,* 205
Tricot, 233
Tricotine, 233
Triple sheer, 233
Tropical weights, 198
Trubenizing, 100
Tweed, 69, 74, 198, 233; *illus.,* 60
Twill weave, 71–74
Twills, 160, 228
Twist, amount of, 55–56, 203–206
Twisting, 48–50; *illus.,* 51
Two by two, 206; *illus.,* 205
Typewriter ribbon cloth, 160

Uncut pile, 313; *illus.,* 79, 150
Unfinished worsted, 186–187
Unidure finish, 106

Vat dyes, 116–117; *table,* 125
Velour, 79, 198, 233
Velvet, 79, 213, 233–234